A Twentieth-Century Odyssey

Psalms and Songs is both a record and an assessment of one of the most remarkable human journeys of our century. It was an outward journey that began early, when Malcolm Lowry left school in England to sail to China, commencing a life of ceaseless wandering and searching. It was an inward journey that led him into the depths of a private hell and to the heights of creative genius. It was an artistic journey that led from his early stories and autobiographical first novel, *Ultramarine*, to his masterpiece, *Under the Volcano*, and the late, great novels and stories which have appeared since his death, including *Lunar Caustic*.

Now, under the editorship of his wife Margerie Bonner Lowry, we are given a realistic portrait of Malcolm Lowry— the artist and the man.

Malcolm Lowry: Psalms and Songs

EDITED BY

Margerie Lowry

A MERIDIAN BOOK

NEW AMERICAN LIBRARY

TIMES MIRROR

NEW YORK AND SCARBOROUGH, ONTARIO

ACKNOWLEDGMENTS

STORIES

"China," first published by Aloe Editions, 1974. Used by permission of Margerie Lowry.

"Enter One in Sumptuous Armour," printed here for the first time from manuscript by permission of Margerie Lowry.

"Ghostkeeper," published in the Spring, 1973, issue of *American Review* #17, Spring, 1973. Used by permission of Margerie Lowry.

"Hotel Room in Chartres," first published in *Story Magazine*, October, 1933. Used by permission of Margerie Lowry.

(The following page constitutes an extension of this copyright page.)

"June the 30th, 1934," printed here for the first time from manuscript by permission of Margerie Lowry.

"Kristbjorg's Story: In the Black Hills," first published by Aloe Editions, 1974. Used by permission of Margerie Lowry.

"Lunar Caustic," first published in *Paris Review* #29, Spring, 1963, and in England by Jonathan Cape, 1968. Used by permission of Margerie Lowry.

"On Board the *West Hardaway*," first published in *Story Magazine,* October, 1933. Used by permission of Margerie Lowry.

"Seductio ad Absurdum," first appeared in *Best Short Stories of 1931,* ed. by Edward J. O'Brien, published by Jonathan Cape. Copyright 1931 by Malcolm Lowry. Used by permission of Margerie Lowry.

"Under the Volcano," first appeared in *Prairie Schooner,* Winter 1963/64, Malcolm Lowry issue. Used by permission of Margerie Lowry.

ARTICLES

"Malcolm Lowry: A Note," by Conrad Aiken. From *Canadian Literature* No. 8, Spring, 1961. Used by permission of Conrad Aiken.

"My Friend Malcolm," by Clarisse Francillon. From *Les Lettres Nouvelles,* November, 1957. Translated by Susan Kim. Used by permission of Clarisse Francillon.

"More Than Music: Glimpses of Malcolm Lowry," by Downie Kirk. From *Canadian Literature* No. 8, Spring, 1961. Used by permission of Downie Kirk.

"Malcolm Lowry and the Outer Circle of Hell," by Conrad Knickerbocker. From *Paris Review,* Winter/Spring 1963 issue. Used by permission of the Estate of Conrad Knickerbocker.

"Call It Misadventure," by Clarissa Lorenz. From *The Atlantic Monthly,* June, 1970. Used by permission of Clarissa Lorenz and The Atlantic Monthly Co.

"Recollections of Malcolm Lowry," by William McConnell. From *Canadian Literature* No. 6, Autumn, 1960. Used by permission of William McConnell.

"Malcolm Lowry Visits the Doctor," by Dr. C. G. McNeill. From *American Review* #17, Spring, 1973. Used by permission of Dr. C. G. McNeill.

"Malcolm Lowry: A Reminiscence," by David Markson. From *The Nation,* February 7, 1966. Used by permission of David Markson.

"Second Encounter," by Norman Matson. Printed here for the first time from manuscript by permission of Peter Matson.

"Malcolm Lowry: 1930," by Gerald Noxon. From *Prairie Schooner,* Winter 1963/64, Malcolm Lowry issue. Used by permission of Gerald Noxon.

"Malcolm Lowry: The Writer," from a thesis on Malcolm Lowry by Dr. A. C. Nyland. Printed from manuscript and used by permission of Dr. A. C. Nyland.

"Malcolm Lowry: A First Impression," by James Stern. From *Encounter,* September, 1967. Used by permission of James Stern.

MERIDIAN TRADEMARK REG. U.S. PAT. OFF. AND FOREIGN COUNTRIES
REGISTERED TRADEMARK—MARCA REGISTRADA
HECHO EN CLINTON, MASS., U.S.A.

SIGNET, SIGNET CLASSICS, MENTOR, PLUME and MERIDIAN BOOKS
are published *in the United States* by The New American Library, Inc.,
1301 Avenue of the Americas, New York, New York 10019,
in Canada by The New American Library of Canada Limited,
81 Mack Avenue, Scarborough, 704, Ontario

First Printing, October, 1975

1 2 3 4 5 6 7 8 9

PRINTED IN THE UNITED STATES OF AMERICA

Contents

IV. *Some of the Last Stories*   185

V. *Lunar Caustic*   255

Preface

MALCOLM LOWRY: PSALMS AND SONGS. The title was given to me by William McConnell, a lawyer of Vancouver, Canada, an old friend from the days when we lived on the beach of Burrard Inlet, B.C. The Psalms I think of as the short stories; the Songs, recollections of Malcolm by people who knew him. There is also included here part of a thesis written by Dr. A. C. Nyland for the University of Ottawa, Ontario, Canada, in 1967. Dr. Nyland is a nun, Sister Agnes Cecelia of the Order of St. Ann, and she teaches English Literature at the University of Ottawa. The whole thesis (for which she received her doctorate), entitled *The Luminous Wheel: The Evolution of Malcolm Lowry's Style,* has never been printed.

The early short stories were written when Malcolm was young and were published in various English literary magazines. Although they do not have the depth of his later work, these stories are all valuable for their portraits of time and place, and for the glimpses they give of Malcolm's earlier vision. "Seductio ad Absurdum" was actually a chapter of the novel *Ultramarine,* first published by Jonathan Cape in 1933, when Malcolm was twenty-four years old. But the story was previously published and chosen by O'Brien for his volume *Best English Short Stories of 1931.*

Of the later stories, three were published prior to this volume: "China" and "Kristjorg's Story: In the Black Hills" were published by Aloe Editions in 1974, and "Ghostkeeper" was published in the Spring, 1973, issue of *American Review*. The novella, *Lunar Caustic,* was published in the Spring, 1963, issue of *Paris Review* and in England by Jonathan Cape, 1968.

The recollections of Malcolm were mostly published by various magazines I have credited, except for Dr. McNeill's story, and all were voluntarily written since his death, by friends who loved him and thought him an extraordinary person. I hope this medley will further advance his reputation as an artist and give, to some degree, a picture of the man, though it is not, to me, an entirely accurate picture: writers naturally are inclined to dwell on the sensational aspects, rather than on the dedicated and hard-working writer.

MARGERIE LOWRY

Biographical Note

Malcolm was born July 28, 1909, in Cheshire, England. His father was Arthur O. Lowry, a wealthy cotton broker who also owned oil and cotton in Egypt, Peru, Texas, and elsewhere. His mother was Evelyn Boden, daughter of a Norwegian, the skipper of the *Scottish Isles,* a famous sailing ship.

Malcolm was sent to a boarding school when he was seven, and later to a prep school, The Leys. He was interested in sports and was the junior champion golfer of England when he was fifteen years old.

After leaving The Leys, Malcolm went to sea as a cabin boy. His father had entered him for Christ College, Cambridge, and there was much discussion before he was permitted to sail, Malcolm promising to return, go to Cambridge, and get an honors degree, which he eventually did. While at sea he kept a journal which eventually became the novel *Ultramarine* and also served as his thesis for his B.A.

In 1933 or '34 he went to Spain with Conrad Aiken, and it was there he met his first wife, Jan Gabriel. They were married in Paris, but shortly afterward Jan returned to the United States. In about 1934 or '35 Malcolm came to New York. Later, his old friend from Cambridge, John Davenport, was hired by Hollywood to write the script of one of Faulkner's novels. John wrote Malcolm, asking him to join him there and help him, which Malcolm did for a short time; but he did not like Hollywood nor could he work well there. However, he had rejoined Jan, and they left together for Mexico. The reconciliation did not last. She returned to Hollywood while he stayed on in Mexico, now working on his great novel *Under the Volcano.* Later, he returned to Hollywood, where he and Jan were divorced. I met him in the summer of 1939, but he had to leave the States and affect a reentry as his visa had expired.

He expected to return to Hollywood, but the war broke out and he could not get back from Canada. I joined him in Vancouver, and we were married in 1940. Malcolm was turned down by the armed forces because of a bad injury to his knee caused by a bullet wound, suffered on his earlier trip to China. He was working on the second draft of the *Volcano* and on various poems at this time.

In the autumn of 1945 we went to Mexico to do some research on this book. We returned to our house on the beach in late May, but in the winter of 1946 or '47 we went to Haiti, and then to New York when *Under the Volcano* was published. In the autumn of 1947 we sailed for France in a cargo boat going down the west coast and through the Panama Canal. We spent the following year traveling through Europe and returned in 1949 to our beach home, where we remained until August, 1954. We flew to New York, then sailed for Genoa on an Italian cargo boat. From there we went to Sicily, where we finally settled in Taormina until summer, 1955, when we flew to London. Later we moved to a tiny Sussex village, Ripe, where we lived until Malcolm Lowry's death in June, 1957.

PART ONE

Some of the Early Stories

Seductio ad Absurdum

"I ain't telling you the word of a lie but this yankee fellow came up to me and e sez steyord e sez fond of cigars so I sez yes I am fond of cigars—like who wouldn't be on this here fore and aft sea-crane. Wall e says ketch hold of these—plenty of these where they come from. And he give me a great box of cigars. Yes."

"Yes, but that's only cigars. This bird was a journalist or something of that on a paper in Australia. He's travelling round the world for it and singing at the piano. He says if you talk to me—"

"Lorlumme days. Talk to you. Do you mean he stood you that feed just for talking to him?"

"Certainly he did. He kept saying, now say that again. And all the while he was writing in a little black notebook."

"Well what did you tell im?"

"Ave you heard about Hilliot chaps? Andy nearly crowned im this morning with a frying pan. The seven bell dinner watch sent im up to the galley to tell him the sea-pie was lousy."

"—guano—"

"Well, so it was, lousy."

"—Pass—"

"I don't like im; serves im right; he's what you call a no-classer that feller."

"Where is he now?"

"—one no trump—"

"Oh dreaming about on the poop, he always gets up there during the lunch hour."

"—Gang—"

"He's probably listening at the skylight to all we say."

"Three hearts."

"Probably—"

"Romeo: wherefore art thou Romey bloody O—"

3

"But I didn't know there was a seven bell dinner today—not on Sunday."

"That's not your ruddy heart! It's my ruddy heart!"

"Yes. We're sailing this evening. The mate came down and served out a lot of bull about getting in more mail. So Mister Hilliot had to get a seven bell dinner in."

"And Andy nearly crowned him for telling im it was lousy. Well let me tell you that that's the lad's job. The sailors' peggy always has orders from the bosun to complain about the food; you know, if it's rotten—"

"Yes. But the silly twirp went about it in the wrong way. You know the way he'd go up. Not going straight to the point like. You know the way e does. . . . Well, it's no business of mine sort of thing but these fellers—these damned sailormen say your food's rotten. No wonder that Andy got on his ear."

"Well for heavens' sake. But Andy's all right, eh?"

"Yes, Andy's all right, fellers."

"Guano gang—"

"Well, wot did Hilliot do?"

"Hey, you didn't shuffle up these cards right and all."

"Damn all. He didn't do a darn thing. A good thing for Andy, I reckon, but anyway Hilliot just said well, just as long as you know, Andy. And walked out."

"Oh wot a twirp."

"Hullo, ere's the second steward."

"Ow go second?"

"My trick—"

"Second, while you're about it, you might give this god-awful peggy of ours a clean dishcloth. He never washes the thing es got: and it's about as white as a gyppo's—"

"Are you still abusing that boy? I like him for myself like. He's got pluck that Hilliot. I seen him aloft too right on the foretopmast there swinging on the ladder and laughing like a son of a bitch—"

"And the bosun bawling him out from below."

"Guano—"

"Yes, Mister!"

"One club—"

"Well, what about that dishcloth, second!"

"Pass."

"Reminds me of the story of the nigger fireman on one of

Lamport and Holt's. Ah doan min dirty hands: ah doan min dirty face: but ah du like clean-food!"

"Ha ha ha!"

"Pass—"

"Well, well, so do we—"

"Go on and get your bloody club—"

"But Andy doesn't like im second."

"Gang, guano—"

"No my gosh."

"Andy crowned im this morning with a frying pan. Or would have done if Hilliot hadn't got out of the road."

"So I heard."

"It was pretty good I thought. It'll teach im that not every little Christ Jesus in the temple can come running around cargo steamers."

"My trick!—"

"Well, no. But what he done in coming to sea at all shows the right spirit—"

"My trick!—"

"He came up to the ship in a car didn't he—no—I dunno—but the Chinese storekeeper tell me."

"Well boys, he didn't come up to the ship in any car last night: as a matter of fact, he got on to the wrong ship."

"The wrong ship. Second, how come?"

"The *Hyannis.* Sister ship to this one came in late last night. He was tight as a tick so couldn't tell the difference."

"—my trick—"

"But the *Hyannis,* her foc'sles forward ain't it? Like it should be on my ruddy boat, instead of being stuck under here like a lot of bloody ventilator covers."

"Yes. That was the joke. He went right down aft looking for the forecastle and, of course, couldn't find it; so being very drunk he slept on the poop."

"Well, wot did he do in the morning?"

"—my trick—"

"He just got up and walked off. Nobody said a word to him."

"—for Jesus sake—"

"—for Jesus sake—"

"—told me so himself this morning when he came aboard. I was standing on the gangway—"

"The silly twit—eh? That's why he's on the poop now. Afraid the Captain'll tell his Mama."

(But, tut-tut, a pipe must be filled to contemplate this scene with more penetrating intelligence, and a thick dirty hand inserted into my right dungaree pocket in search of the tobacco-pouch, the last birthday present you gave me, Janet . . . do you remember? It was in Central Park, a year ago tomorrow, when we paused to watch the children playing on the swings, and then, "Look, would that be any good to you, dear? Many happy returns of the day . . ." Loew's Orpheum. Ruby fisheries. Do you remember going there to get the cod-steaks for your mother? Well, I have my pouch now, which I have drawn out, crackling and yellow, sprinkling crumbs of tobacco around me. And now I have my pipe well alight. The day? What of the day? Well, the sky has that sort of blackness which in February, in England, would presage thunder. There was wind last night; and moreover, I slept on the wrong ship. But there is a feeling of approaching disaster, of terrible storm, and my own mood, one of hilarious morbidity, conceals also just such a thing. It is useless for me to tell you of it. Instead—what shall I tell you? Of the junk that is standing out to sea? Of the Japanese destroyer that came in this morning? Or merely of the crew, of those at any rate whom I see through the skylight. McGoff, for instance, down there, filling his pipe too, the old devil, with hasty trembling fingers. Ted, taking the scurf out of his fingernails, ha! a touch, a visible touch! Horsey: lying across the table with his face on his arm. The second steward's broad back, and the patch on his trousers. . . . But the joke's on me. I have to admit that of these men who become day by day intricately and more intensely part of me I know nothing. Nothing at all! Even of Andy, who is more part of me than the rest of them, I know nothing. That awful incident in the galley, everybody is talking about it. Why do I not fight Andy, then? To know a thing is to kill it, a post-mortem process? Why won't I? Undignified? too Richard Barthelmess? . . . Perhaps, but I might lose, and I know less than nothing. But there is no reason to fight, even about last night? Bad, dreadfully bad, as that was. . . . My fault. Love makes tradesmen of us all. But how can I stand for it, how can I suffer on top of last night's usurpation, when I was beaten out by that simpering chinless applesquire, this further petty insult added, in the galley, to an injury of which he was not aware? I won't stand for it by god. Jimminy christmas no, as Taff would say! But perhaps Andy won't want to fight, even if he has invited it plainly enough. Then this is not heroic, and there's the humour of it. To fear the foe, since fear oppresseth strength, gives in his weakness, strength unto his foe, and so his follies fight against himself. Argal. Let us take refuge in the sailor's coil, contemplate a world of winches as a world of machine guns: let there be a sabbath of earthworms, a symphony of scorpions, a procession of flying grand pianos and cathedrals, and the idea, the absolute, is fly-blown. Tucket within, and a flourish of strumpets. Beware Andy! I move like a ghost towards my design, with Tarquin's ravishing strides. . . . Nevertheless, I fear too greatly decisive action in an emotional crisis of this calibre; nor do I wish to admit to myself that I consider Andy sufficiently important; but this, as you say, is clearly enough a case of self-defence—)

"—one club—"

"—one heart—"

"—one diamond—"

"—one no trump—"

"Well . . . !"

"Lorlumme bloody days eh."

"I don't care if he do mate."

"Lorlumme bloody days eh."

"This first mate's a man; he's got me weighed up; like that."

"—dishcloth—"

"—here you're cheating!—"

"No, I'm not."

"Yes, you are."

"Yes, I am too."

"He had the ace in his Shanghai jacket."

"No, I tell you, the poor twot didn't say a thing. He just said well as long as you know, Andy."

"All these bloody no-classers are the same."

"You can bet your boots. We had a feller once—been in the Royal Air Force he says during the war as a capting. Capting hell. First time he goes aloft he nearly throws a fit."

"I wonder wot made that bird Illiot come to sea; doing a good lad out of is job that's wot I say—"

"That's what Andy says."

"That's what we all says, I reckon."

"No. You've got the lad in wrong there. You can't get him on that at all. It's up to the man himself to get the job. If he don't why then, I guess he don't."

"That sucker's got influence at the office."

"He came to the ship in a car. Do you know that?"

"Oh, watch it! Let's talk of something else."

"—and listen here this mate, he, he, says—air-force officer or no perishing air-force officer you're not nut—"

"Go on, you ain't got hiccups, ave you mate?"

"Not going up to that nest again or I'll lose my bonus. So no more painting for you, Mister Officer he says: the next job of painting you'll do will be—"

"Aw shag off second, you'll be in the boy's bunk next."

"This air-force officer I was telling you about was always falling off derricks. Hullo Andy."

"Hullo there."

"I ain't telling you the word of a lie but this yankee feller come up to me and e sez steyord e says fond of cigars so I sez yes I am fond of cigars—like who wouldn't be on this fore and aft sea-crane. Waal he says ketch hold of these—plenty of these where they come from—"

"Hullo Andy. Ow go?"

"Hullo there . . . hullo second; hullo McGoff."

"What about last night Andy—we saw you."

"Oh, you did: you may've seen me at arf past nine—but you didn't see me at arf past two this morning. Or if you did you oughtn't to have done."

"No—and you didn't see me either at half past two in the morning."

"No—nor me."

"Nor me."

"Nor my ruddy self."

"Well, what were you doing, Lofty?"

"What do you think? I didn't go ashore at all. I'm a god-fearing man and I don't go running after women."

"Aw watch it. Well anyhow, it's Sunday today."

"I don't care if he do, mate. That's wot I always says. I'm a feller like this, I don't mind. . . . Always willing to do a good turn for anybody, that's me. I don't care if he do."

"Russian eh?"

"Second—can we have another pack of cards—the King, Queen and Ace are all bollocksed up in this pack and you can spot em, you know."

"A change for last night eh? Won't your usual Jane get jealous?"

"Sure. There's a pack in the linen locker. Here are the keys."

"A fine woman."

"Well, before I was in the guano gang, I was only an apprentice lad for myself like, apprentice, and we was going out to Walfish Bay the whole gang of us with a cargo of lighters in sections although at Cape Cross they had to load from surf boats because the lighters got all broke up—"

"Six pounds a month mate, and all found."

"Carbeerian sea, a guinea note—"

"Well, I don't care if e do mate—"

"Six months or so I suppose we was there under canvas like and I'll tell you it was a rum shop. There was one chap we had and we called him Deaffy—"

"Wot do you think of that for a cockroach?"

"—this is better eh? you shuffle them—"

"—king of the steamflies eh—"

"Everything in white, you know, lovely buildings, very nice indeed."

"And one night this chap Deaffy come into wot you might call the messroom, you know. And e sez look ere fellers come along with me there's a bloody big barrel of wine oooooh eh?—Just been washed up on the shore. So we get our cups and a corkscrew and followed him along—it was pitch dark outside—and we came to where the barrel was—and one chap had brought a basin—"

"—your deal!—"

"Can't you see the water boiling I sez; and this bloody old skipper turns round to me and he says, 'Lamptrimmer,' e says, 'we always speak the King's English on this ship—' "

"And it wasn't wine at all but Cape Dopp, wot we call Cape Dopp—raw spirit Gawd blimey. Why do you know we all went mad, mad and they had to tie Deaffy up to the bullock post."

"—two diamonds my bloody foot!—"

"—two diamonds my bloody foot!—"

"Yes. And the joke about it all was that it hadn't been washed up on the shore at all but Deaffy had pinched it, see, from the stores."

"Good god!"

"And there we all bloody were doing time and building breakwaters round the magistrate's house."

"Fancy that now."

"That reminds me of the time in—"

"Chamaeleons. Fellers used to keep em as pets and make em drunk on Cape Dopp. They were as long as that, you know. Beautiful pretty things. They used to roll about and change into all sorts of colours, it was like being at masculine and debutante, you know, and then I had a pet one and one day a silly bastard fed it on nuts and bolts. Nuts and bolts, yes. Oh, we had a rare time there, I can tell you . . . didn't wear no shoes! Oh no, no shoes, walking on the salt plain, we wore what we called veldshols. One day coming back from the West Indie feller's tent—I'd had one or two, you know—I got lost in the salt plains all night and there were jackals and scorpions, bags of the bounders—"

"Scorpions. You ain't heard nothing yet. Let me tell you this when I was in Belawandelli, it was on a Norwegian bastard out of Trondjhem, the *Hilda*—"

"—herons, vodka distillery—"

"Your trick, Ted."

"We had one fellow there in the guano gang, not a surf boat man, but loading the bags. He used to work from five in the morning till about nine, he was a sneak, a proper sneak, and a religious bounder too, you know . . . and he was always going to the boss with complaints! We got no money ourselves, we used to gamble with sticks of tobacco and you know how expensive clothes are out there— well he used to get clothes sent from home and sell to us at a much increased price like, the bounder. So one day we kidded him along that there was going to be an attack by the Vompas—a tribe—wot we call the Vompas, yes—they come from Vompaland, and we kidded him along and kidded him along and one night, see, he was in his tent—"

"—she's only got one titty but she's all the world to me—"

"One titty—"

"But she's all the world to me."

"—one heart!—"

"—two diamonds!—"

"And you know how cold it is at night there and the tents were stretched tight as a drum; and there we all were outside firing off rifles into the air; and throwing haricot beans into the tent and of course he thought they were bullets and then we went into the tent with assegais—there were always plenty of those knocking about— and some of us pretended to be wounded and one thing and the other and there this bounder was all the time underneath the bed, praying for Christ sake!—"

"—fer Christ sake—

—praying!"

"Niggers. Yes. Fuzzy wuzzy niggers there used to be there, curly-headed. Dirty? My god, I've seen them cooking the entrails of a sheep and squeezing the stuff out of them like putting your mouth under a tap and eating it, and if you asked them they say: 'Wo! auh. Wolla wolla! Very good! Very good!' "

"—yes?—"

"—yes?—"

"But in the end Deaffy went mad with the loneliness; and it took nine or ten strong men to hold him; and he used to lie down on the ground with his eyes wide open and let the flies crawl over his eye-balls . . . yes, and one day he was in charge of a donkey waggon with guano; and the donkey died; and he lay down beside the donkey and died too; and in the morning when we found them, the jackals had scooped them both out—"

"Gawdblimey eh!"

"Well, talking of niggers, there was two whacking bull niggers in the Miki too, last night: firemen they were, and when I told Olga—"

"No you don't say for gosh sake, Andy."

"For gosh sake."

"And do you know what she said. He he."

(. . . If I could shut my ears to this, and my eyes, and not have the whole sordid matter set forth in all its startling vividness; if I could drown or fly away; if I could only be walking down Plympton Street, Cambridge, Mass., again that day in late February with spring approaching and the grey birds sweeping and dipping in curves and spirals about the singing tele-graph wires—or weren't there any?—and later the two Sophomores fighting outside the Waldorf. And the brown street cars Harvard-Dudley, which always darted so surprisingly from behind corners as though they had some important message to deliver! . . . This is only a nightmare, of course. I am not on a ship. I am not a seaman. The ship is not alongside the wharf in Dairen. I lie in my bed at home, a cold dry bath of sheets! Beside me, the reading lamp with the scarlet shade. For a moment, think of the book I have been reading, Kipling's *Captains Courageous,* and fall asleep, easily as a child gliding down a steep incline into slumber. I dream a dream. In this dream there is Andy—but who is Andy?—singing as he rolls aimfully down the Kuan Tsien Road; Andy fumbling with his entrance ticket to the Miki dancing saloon; Andy dancing lumberingly and possessively with Olga—but who is Olga?—like a chinless orangoutang in the forest with his human captive; Andy leaving his shoes outside the door. And later, after the second bottle, shifting his shoes outside the second door. There is Andy leaning out of the window in his shirt sleeves, singing to the moon—)

"I don't care if e do mate."

"No well, that what I sez anyhow Andy: I see a look in his eye which means trouble."

"Trouble. Yes. It will be trouble too if I have anything to do with it. Trouble! You're right."

"—three no trumps. Jesus Christ Almighty!"

"I'm damned if I see what you've got against the boy all the same."

"Well, you'll see right enough, once the fun begins. What you do with a chap like him, stamp on his foot, and—whup!—like that. Uppercut. That's what he wants, the Glasgow punch."

"Ah, that's a deadly one that is—"

"Shut up for Christ's sake, we're playing bridge."

"He pinches my steam covers too—"

"Ah, come now, what would he want to do that for anyway?"

"Gawd knows, I don't. But I saw him with my own eyes or rather, no I didn't, but the Chief Steward did and he says that he took it to keep extra soda for scrubbing out! . . . And he pinches soft soap off me. He'd pinch the milk out of my tea, that boy, and that's the sort of thing that comes out of your public schools. Well I don't ruddy know. I don't really. Honest."

"What Hilliot wants is a good strong woman!"

"Ha ha ha!"

"He went ashore last night."

"Yes, and you all know what happened, don't you."

"He went and slept on the *Hyannis.*"

"Because he couldn't find his way here."

"—is that so?—"

"—is that so?—"

"What was the name of the place?"

"Sapporo Café and Bar. Here, I've got the card. Listen to this. Nice and clean accommodation. Quick Service. Sapporo Café and Bar, No. 157, Yamagata-Dori, Tel. No. 6705. Soft and hard drinks. Mariners are all welcome. Here is a place you must not fail to visit, everything at very moderate charges."

"Hullo Sculls."

"Ow go?"

"All right."

"I ain't telling you the word of a lie about this yankee fellow came up to me and e sez steyord e sez fond of cigars so I sez yes I am fond of cigars—like who wouldn't be on this here fore and aft dung-barge. Waal he says ketch hold of these—plenty of these where they come from. And he gave me a great box of cigars. Yes."

"I had an experience like that on the *Plato*—in Manila—last voyage . . ."

"Last game—"

"Listen to this, just listen to this. Here you will find every comfort and equipment that is sure to please you. Here you will find also best foreign wines and liquors of well known brands only. Sold by retail or by bottle. Don't forget to drop in on your way to or from wharf. He he, just listen to this little lot. A variety of magazines and newspapers are kept in our hall for your free inspection."

"Ha ha ha ha!"

"Hullo Lamps boy, how are yer doin?"

"Hullo Jim boy."

"All right there Jock?"

"All right eh?"

"All right."

"That's right."

"Me nice girl very nice very clean very sweet very sanitary."

(Why not, Janet? I put it to you; I mean really kill Andy. Who was it, the chief cook, said the other day that Andy couldn't swim? And we're going to sea tonight. That habit he has in port of sitting on the starboard rail on the poop! It will be dark before he has knocked off and washed, which makes it all the simpler. At sea, tonight perhaps. Murder at sea! A murderer in thought, a murderer in deed. Now I see it all plainly; I can do it pat. Norman, whose duty it is to arouse Andy, upon being called by the quartermaster tomorrow at four bells, slides his hand with its broken blackened nails under his slip pillow case to bring out half a crumpled cigarette, Gold Flake, charred and uneven at the end where it has been smoked before turning in. He jumps up and sits on the edge of his bunk, the lower one, with his legs swinging and his feet poised to drop into his size seven unlaced white sandshoes; he looks around the room, noticing particularly Ginger, the pantry boy, lying on his bunk with his mouth open and his underpants, which are all he wears at night, vibrating evenly with the thrumming of the engine.

He will remark for the hundredth time the photographs on the wall. Tallulah Bankhead—or is it Bulkhead? Ginger's mother with an armful of horrible children. Joe Ward taken at the police house, Flint, with his twin brother. Monozygotic twins. Taff standing on Bull Bay sands, Amlwch, swinging a mashie-niblick. He wishes profoundly and for the hundredth-thousandth time that he may grow that extra inch, praying sofly: "Our father, which art in heaven, may I grow another inch and become a policeman of the Lord." He pulls his check trousers on over his sandshoes, and pays attention to his chainbreaker singlet. He brushes his hair,—and oh, how yellow it is!—and cleans his teeth, spitting into a bucket. Now he is walking along the well-deck, his bucket on his arm, scarcely pausing as he spits resonantly into the scuppers; now he is hoisting himself up the galley-companion-steps. He enters the galley (where a quartermaster's singlet is drying), and rakes out the fires. Four bells strike, he throws his cigarette to leeward, and goes to call Andy. The white cabin door, brass-silled, windily creaking on the prehensile hook. Everything the same as the chief cook left it when he had turned in, according to his custom, just as eight bells-all-hands-pipe-down had finished striking. The chief cook snoring peacefully—let him lie in till a quarter of six. Andy—where is Andy? His razor strop is stirring in a breath of wind through the open port; the canary in its brightly bordered cage is already chirruping with joy, its little heart almost breaking with anxiety to see the blue sea morning. The slim parcel of blankets, embroidered with the company's crests, undisturbed. Andy! Andy! Anybody here seen Andy? Was he sleeping out on deck do you know? No, not bloody likely, too damp, not a worth while thing to do when the tropics were lousy with malaria! Too damp, Norman, yes, that's it, too damp. No good worrying any more about Andy, think of yourself, of your mickey, take the cover off his cage as though you should hope to find Andy there, and see—how knowingly and sagaciously the pigeon eyes you! The adoring eye of God's dog. He knows. Think always of that extra inch, get the potatoes from the potato locker and proceed with your work as scullion. For the sea is picking Andy's bones in whispers. Yes, yes, yes, sculls. Oh you who throw the peel to starboard, acuerdate de Flebas, que una vez fue bello y robusto como tu—)

"Hullo Joe."

"How go?"

"Not bad."

"Not bad."

"How are you doing, McGoff?"

"Ah Joe, I've got a little story to tell you. Now I ain't telling you the word of a lie, mind you, but this yankee feller, you know that chap, you was there—you saw him didn't you?—well he comes right up to me and e sez steyord fond of cigars. Straight he did. So I sez yes sir, I am right fond of cigars—"

"Skipper. Old fellow. I knew years and years ago it will be now—"

"Well, of course, it was his business to find faults. When he does that he's pleased and lights a cigar. When he ain't got no faults to find no cigars for the skipper that day, savvy. Well I reckon it's the same on this God damn dugout—"

"Plenty of these where they come from, ha ha!"

"Well, I always believes in writing, so as a chap can read because he might owe me something—"

"Ha ha ha!"

"—naval relics.

"Chatham—"

"Heard the bosun getting at Hilliot the first day. Well, he was only telling him what to do like—"

"—one more game, come on now, boys—"

"What's that, Andy?"

"I says, the bosun, the first day, telling Hilliot what to do. I expect this room to be speckless, e said. Well, look at it—I bet the bilges are kept cleaner than this and e pinches enough soft soap from me to keep the whole ship clean Gawd blimey—and that ain't all. You've got my room, the carpenters', and the lamptrimmers' rooms to do—e said our washbasins to clean—and the brass to do in there as well, and everything got to be scrubbed out white every day. If you don't do it, I'll hit you till you do, you've got all the meals to get in, and you've got your washing to do as well as the washing up and you've got to keep yourself clean. It's my business to see you do that. Sailors aren't dirty. You ruddy farmers think they are. But they're not. Muck in. . . . Well, look at the boy now, he never washes himself, this room's like a pigsty, Gawd blimey eh—"

West Hardaway—Portland, Ore.

Seamen.

Certified for use as sailors' messroom. Tin.

Murder, with his silent bloody feet—

"Why, here he is!

"Hullo Lovey, what've you been doin?"

"How go Hilliot?"

"Andy. I'm going to speak to you. Listen everybody while I speak to Andy. It's for you too. Now then it's about time I had this out with you. I don't deny I've been listening to what you've been saying from the poop. And you can't deny that you've been doing your level best to make life a misery for me since we left home. And what's more, you've been telling a lot of damned lies about me! You say I pinch your steamcovers, and your soft soap—well, let me tell you I don't. I've never pinched anything of anybody's. You've said that I've made a mess of my job. Well, I don't think that's true—this room's not too bad. It's as good as you could make it yourself. Anyone could see that. And I'd like to know how you make out that I'm doing another lad out of a job: god damn it man, it's surely up to the lad himself to get the job. But, wait a minute, I've got something more to say, I haven't wanted to fight before —but to be frank with you that wasn't because I'm afraid of you and your Glasgow punches—no, simply because I didn't want to hurt you. . . . You weak-chinned son of a Singapore sea-lion. You cringing skulker. You've got a face just like a filthy jackal, all nose and no chin. . . . What a spiteful cunning dirty wreck of the *Hesperus* you are! That's just it, your face. I've just been afraid for you, that's all. Why by Christ if you'd got a chin you little bastard, I'd hit you on it."

"Here, go easy Hilliot."

"Why should I go easy?"

"Come on, you ship's cook, you chinless wonder, you—Put them up. Up I say."

Tin.

"Here . . . Go easy, Hilliot."

"What the hell? What've I got to go easy for?"

"Well—listen—it's like this—"

"Sit down Andy: don't be a bloody fool. Sit down! Sit down!"

"Like what? What's wrong with you all? You know I'm in the right."

"Now then, Hilliot, don't you be a bloody fool either and go shooting your face off about Andy. He's an older and better man than you."

"Yis. He's knocked seven bells out of harder cases than you in his time!"

"Yes, go easy boy. . . . We all know, you see, Andy lost his chin in the war and he's had plates in it, and all, and if you hit him on it he might croak. You mustn't talk like that. We know it's your first voyage and you just get the same as any one of us got on his first voyage. Andy and I've been shipmates for ten years. You mustn't talk like that. Go easy, man."

"Three times torpedoed!"

"No you mustn't talk like that sonny."

Tin.

"Oh Andy!"

"—Well I'm going to work in a bathing costume and a sweat rag this afternoon."

"Me too."

"Where was it you bought those bloody things—Cebu?"

"Yes, that's right. . . . Well, I dunno what sort of ship this is at all!"

"Aw she's just a laundry boat, that's what, going round picking up washing."

"Laundry boat? Huh. She's an orange box, a balloon boat, a haystack—"

"—Mate says we're getting a lot of animals in this afternoon, elephants, tigers, and I dunno what all. I suppose that'll mean the watch on deck. I suppose that's what he meant by more mail, Gawd blimey. I dunno when we'll be away tonight I don't really. One of the elephants for Rome, we'll get her off at Port Said for Brindisi; oh, they've all sorts of bloody things all going to the Dublin zoo eh, and a special keeper fellow's coming on board with them, prize snakes and Java sparrows for gosh sake—I suppose to feed the snakes. I dunno what sort of ship this is at all with a lot of pouncing serpints aboard her. Well, I certainly don't know when we'll be away tonight."

"Yes, I says, I certainly am fond of cigars."

"—pass—"

"—pass—"

"—pass—"

"—one spade—"

> (And Samson tol' her cut off-a ma hair
> If yo' shave ma hade

Jes as clean as yo hair
Ma strength-a will become-a like a natch-erl man
For Gawd's a-gwine t'move all de troubles away
For Gawd's a-gwine t'move all de troubles away. . . .)

Hotel Room in Chartres

The Paris spring morning with wavering clouds of rain, like smoke, and with the smoke itself, from the chimneys, grimed smokestacks —he told himself—seemed to him looking out of the window over Alesia, to be a sea morning, a desolate sea morning of fog and rain; the Eiffel Tower, like a lighthouse shadowed behind the rain and the murk, and everywhere the smoke, smoke from factory chimneys, blown and torn by the wind, awakened no feeling of growth, but revived only within him the forlorn pain of the sea.

"I wish I was back again," he said.

"In Chartres?" his young wife asked.

"No. At sea."

They had been quarreling since dawn; perhaps, he felt, he had been forcing the quarrel, since the day before they had planned to go to Chartres and once more the melancholy of the rain, preventing their journey, dividing their minds, had opened in him the wound of an old parting, many years ago, with her.

The gulls flew over the river, the freighter severed its cord and slipped from the quay's gray womb, the channel between them grew wider, handkerchiefs fluttered; the ship swung around and steamed for the open sea.

He had been a bosun then, a very young bosun; but that had been his last voyage. He returned to his girl, and to translate into music a suffering which was in excess of his strength; he had left the sea, no longer able to endure the pain of its reality, as now without the presence of that reality he could no longer endure the pain of its illusion.

Ah, the sweetness of that farewell, the sweetness of the memories, of her bright laughter, of her lips, the sweetness of looking forward, and of the looking back, if only farewells were not so sweet!

19

"I'm going to Chartres this afternoon," he said suddenly. "Are you coming?"

"You must learn not to be headstrong with me, like that," she replied. "Anyway, what's the good of going to Chartres now? It's too late and it's still raining. We couldn't get anywhere."

"Headstrong or not, I'm going to Chartres now, this afternoon. Are you coming?"

"No."

"All right then. Goodbye."

"Goodbye."

He went down into the Avenue de Chatillon with a determined, sullen countenance, he thought, catching sight of his rain-scarred reflection carrying a small suitcase, coming towards him from a shop window; but by the time he reached the Alesia metro, his footsteps were faltering, and he was looking around. His wife was not following. By the time he had stripped his ticket from his metro carnet, he was feeling already bereaved. As the train, Direction Porte de Clignancourt, was some minutes in arriving, he watched the people passing through the barrier, eagerly hoping that she would come. But she did not.

On the metro he asked himself why he should want to go to Chartres, of all places, alone, when Chartres was where their own life had really come into being. They both knew that. Chartres was his wife, his very blood, to him. Compassion for her flowed through him like fire; he could not go alone to the Ruelle de la Demi-Lune, not to that street, it was their hotel, their room. The mornings they spent wandering in the cathedral, St. Piat at the south door, that time they lit a candle to their love; and the droning nights which by the planes from the neighboring airport were turned into a world of moving green and gold stars. Even the absurd Grotte Luminaire, and the Café Jacques Restaurant Bar du Cinéma were theirs. And the strange station which was being repaired and of which their French friend had said: It might be a lunatic asylum, it might be a church, but a station. . . . No, all these somehow belonged to them, and it was a treachery to deny it.

At Montparnasse he got out and went up and into the concourse. He searched the lists: Brest, Le Mans, Passy, Versailles. Ah, the 17:03 train for Brest stopped at Chartres. He had half an hour to wait.

He sat down where even though it was daylight an electric notice flickered: Sandwiches, Paniers Repas, Provisions. He ordered a beer, and watched the crowd; they drifted slowly past, like shadows in a black mist, porters, lovers, nurses, cripples. Another advertisement flickered: Passez vos vacances à la mer. The rain drummed on the station roof, his torture smouldered on, but at intervals all thought would be blasted away by the terrible screech of a starting train, like a ship letting off steam in her winches. The noise of shouting, the smell of wet iron, it might have been sea wet iron, freshly red-leaded. He felt old and sick.

He watched the clock on the wall above the tracks, its silver finger creeping towards five. Fuir-là-bas, fuir. . . .

It was now time, but at the moment he made up his mind to leave, he saw his wife coming swiftly towards him, and felt instantly a tenderness for her and relief that she had come; but when he moved towards her to speak, found himself suddenly fighting down a desire to hurt, a brute within him that surprised even himself. And when he finally did speak, it was non-committally, as if to a stranger.

"So you did come after all."

"Yes."

"Are you going to Chartres?"

"I meant to."

"Well, come on then, we'll have to hurry."

He saw that she had expected a reconciliation, that she had carefully planned her arrival, and that his indifference hurt her bitterly. But he could not merely be kind to her at that moment, his conflict was buried too deeply, and he loved her too much to insult her with sympathy. He bought another ticket, and they were carried with the crowd beyond the wicket, to the platform.

In the compartment he sat resolutely, his lips firmly shut, his eyes focused above his wife's head, on nothing, occasionally directing at her a look intended to punish; while she sat equally resolute, determined not to give way.

So, he thought, is a sailing ship, in the doldrums or in irons, in her relationship with the sea. Then the sea storm breaks, the ship is driven, is broken, in the howling tempest, on treacherous rocks, not the province of the sea. But the sea will never quite break her; however long he may rock his nauseous belly, he will never wholly lap her away. For in his senseless fury he has succeeded only in quite losing her—

Oh, if they could only be again like the sea and the tide, with the cool moon summoning them over the sand, when either was disconsolate or forsaken, they would soon be again so happy in each other! Why aren't you more like Father Neptune? he was asking himself—when the four sailors who had been in the corridor entered the compartment. He gave his wife a triumphant look: See how the word is a forest of symbols—

> Ohe Kalo
> Ohe O he O
> Ohe Kalo les matelots
> Les matelots
> Ohe O he O

"I suppose you wish you were with them," she said.

"You mean, you wish you were a man," he replied quickly. "As you're always saying, so that it could be you yourself with them. But the moment I want to be with them, to be myself, not only with sailors, but with anybody, you hate me."

> O he Kalo
> O he O he O

He looked at the sailors, and guessed they were bosun, lamptrimmer, carpenter and one able seaman. Perhaps that last one was an ordinary or a fireman, or even a donkeyman, but he seemed to be an able seaman. The bosun had smashed a window in the corridor, they sang, passed the bottle around, pulled each other's hair, stamped on each other's feet, but they were discreet and looked around courteously to see that they had not embarrassed his wife. They stopped singing, fearing that they were being impolite. One of them read aloud, instead, from *Seduction,* while the others crowded around the journal, evidently sure that his woman would not be offended by this.

"Flower of April," the bosun read, "20 years, blonde, distinguished, seeks correspondent to alleviate the sadness of living in a little town in the provinces . . ."

The others huddled around and read together with childish delight: "Velvet Eye wishes to be godmother to a little blue solider." "Velvet eye," he laughed to his wife. The other sailors were also laughing.

"Butterfly with wings of blue wishes to exchange thoughts and dreams, 30 years; pretty; cultivated."

As he watched them, as the train thundered through Maintenon on its way to the sea, he was joining all his ships once more, going

from Exchange to Prester to join the *Suley*, to Birkenhead to join
the *Mentor*, to Oslo to join the *King Haakon*, and all the others.
He saw a ship silent at dawn, as they approached the port: at the
deskboy's knock crawling fuddled with sleep from his bunk: then
stumbling, feeling his way to the bridge for the orders of the day.
You don't want to bother with a wash-down today, the mate would
say, just square up the after deck, bose, and get them derricks up.

"Modern Eve. 23. Sportive. Seeks good comrade for automobiling
and true friendship."

At that he looked at his wife savagely: "That's what you wanted,
isn't it, and got? To read à deux: 300 histoires pépères. . . . Eve
ressuscitée, ou la belle sans chemise," he added brutally. "Yes, I
do wish I were back, I wish I were among them. Don't you see, they
restrain themselves when you're here."

His wife left the compartment. She was crying.

When she returned, her husband was waving the bottle and singing with the other sailors:

> Ohe Kalo
> Ohe O he O
> Ohe Kalo les matelots
> Les matelots
> Ohe O he O

But the moment she entered the compartment they stopped singing, nervously bridled, blushed like school-children, were resolved
into their own community; and, by her entrance, he, similarly, became separated into his world and hers. He passed the bottle back.

The train was passing St. Prest, Preston, Prester he thought with
sudden terror, and saw the ship, sea-weary, lying against the wharf,
and the stacks of timber from Archangel beside her. A dark skeleton
of iron stood over that damned ship, from which the coal was pouring, clattering into the bunkers endlessly; and he lost six years of
his life seeing himself once more, not as a bosun, but as a fireman,
a fyrbotere, one of the black gang, his hair blowing in the wind,
standing outside the engine room entrance after his watch.

"Yes," he said suddenly to his wife. "I wish I were back, that I
were going with them to join some lousy old ship. It's a rotten life
reeling from filthy port to filthy port, perhaps, but it's better than
this ceaseless quarreling, this dissension. There, at any rate, our
lives were sometimes in danger."

"Isn't our life in danger now?"

He saw now the rain had stopped, and he watched the train's shadow drifting beside them along the fields, over the apple blossoms, and the flowering spring hawthorn, keeping pace with them, and all this loveliness he noted with anger. Now they were at Chartres.

He saw one of the sailors standing out in the corridor; saw him move the heat indicator from chaud to froid, backwards and forwards; full speed, half speed, astern, until his mates pulled him away for a drink.

As his wife and he made their way to the barrier, the sailors circled round them as though they would assist them. At the barrier itself, he turned to them and said,

"Bonne chance. Good luck. A good voyage. And give my love to Malay Street."

"We're not going to sea, we're going home," said one of the sailors.

"Yes, now we're going home," said another. "We signed off at Bremen and now we're going home to Brest."

"Oh, you're going home," he found himself laughing. "Why, so are we." And his wife laughed with him.

"Yes, we're going home."

Then the sailors had to make a rush for their carriage, grabbing a bottle on the way from the buvette.

"O he O les matelots," they shouted, leaning out of the windows as the train left the station.

Turning around, the station seemed to him like a huge ship being dismantled. Coming out they saw the cathedral, its roof the configuration of a green wave, falling along the tall rock of the spire, the blue and white sea of the cool sky rushing behind—Grotte Luminaire, Café Jacques Restaurant Bar du Cinéma, Ruelle de la Demi-Lune—

The aeroplanes droned over them: the world was turning to an evening land of apple blossoms and stars. The moon drew softly the outgoing tide of the woman towards the calming sea of the man.

And up in the only room in the world they were folded together in each other's arms crying with joy that they had found each other once more.

On Board
the West Hardaway

And they removed from Ezron-Gaber and pitched in the wilderness of Zui, which is Kadesh. And they removed from Kadesh and pitched in Hor, in the edge of the land of Edom.

And they departed from Mount Hor and pitched in Zalmonah. And they departed from Zalmonah, and pitched in Punon. And they departed from Punon and pitched in Oboth. . . . And they departed from Almondiblathaim and pitched in the mountains, before Nebo—

Dana, a deck-boy who had just finished chipping a samson post, looked down into the engine-room. So this was what they called going to sea.

He was tired. Sweat had glued his dungarees to his thighs. His temples were bursting, and the rust had worked its way into the pores of his skin.

Now his hours were his own. He had only to run in the crowd's chow at two bells—and he was knocked off until the morning.

He was supping the wind that blew into the fiddley, and he felt the wind to be like a cold clean scourge. This was what they called going to sea—and he knew that what Nikolai had said was true, a man was a scaler these days, not a sailor!

Down below the shovels scraped and the engines pounded: cloom-cloom-cloom.

He liked to stand there watching the engines, marvelling at the nicety with which lever weight and fulcrum worked, opening and closing their hidden mechanisms, and always functioning with such an exactness. And he thought of the cranks holding in their nerveless grip the shaft that turned the screws—that dynamic thing, the life of the ship.

An engineer understood these things, but to be that was not only outside his own sphere but demanded an intelligence which he could not even apprehend.

If the samson posts had not to be chipped, or the deck, then it was the hold. And that was all that seemed to happen on the *West Hardaway*.

But there was a drowsy calm in the forecastle during the time they might spend between being roused from their bunks and being turned out on deck. The coffee pot was brought from the galley and placed on the cold stove; on the curve of the chimney (which led up to the forecastle head through the division of two skylights) a pair of dungarees would be hanging. Hear how Horsey's limbs crack in the last sleepy stretch!

Yet when four bells had gone on the bridge, they stood by the paint-locker, they felt their blood streaming red and cheerful in the fresh morning breeze, and Dana felt almost joyful with his chipping hammer and scraper. They would follow him like friends through the endless day.

Cleats were knocked out, hatches and tarpaulins were pulled away by brisk hands, and they went down the ladder deep into the hold's night, clambered along the ship's side where plank ends bristled, and sat down and turned to wildly.

Hammers clapped nimbly against the iron, the hold quivered, howled, crashed, the speed increased; their scrapers flashed and became lightning in their hands. The rust spurted from the side in a hail of sharp flakes always right in front of their eyes, and they raved, but went on.

But all at once the pace slackened, and the avalanche of hewing became a firm, measured beat of an even deliberate force, their arms swung like rocking machines, their fists lost their grip on the slim haft.

Why had he come to sea at all? he asked himself then. Yes, why? The whole thing seemed to be a jest in terms of rust and sweat.

Yet he knew why; and because he knew it he felt that in order to justify this cause, both to himself and to Janet, he must prove to somebody, anybody, that here was a man, a real man with hair on his chest. As for Janet, she seemed to him at this moment to be a white dream that must have been dreamed by somebody else—

He knew himself to be afraid of life, and that satisfied him as an explanation.

He rose and stepped over the sill onto the boatswain's alleyway.

Then he went down towards the forecastle. Outside it he paused for a time, gazing up at seagulls high in sunlight who were screaming and mewing around the funnel, blowing down a gust. His eyes wandered to the maintruck and as he watched the topmost ladder shook gently in the breeze.

There was something up there—a bird perched there like a finial! The smoke from the funnel suddenly obscured it, and he lost interest. The black shadow of the smoke stretched back from the ship almost to the horizon. He went into the forecastle.

After supper his thoughts returned to the mainmast.

Some day somebody would be up there beyond the ladder (which did not reach the entire distance between the main cross-trees and the maintruck) and lose his nerve. He, Dana Hall, would bring him down. The old man would call him and congratulate him: "My boy, I'm proud of you. You're a credit to the ship—"

He swung his legs over into his bunk, narrow as a baby's coffin, and lay down on his Board of Trade blankets. He was still dreaming of the mast and his gallant rescue, only now he permitted the captain a greater familiarity with him. First a steward would be sent down to call him. "The old man wants to see you on the bridge."

And then the old man himself, in his white uniform and speckless shoes, putting his hands on Dana's shoulder: "You're a credit to the ship."

His heart was beating with the pulse of fate: it beat in his left ear—and far below the great engines kept time; cloom-cloom-cloom. He could see the captain standing there now, a little gray-haired, grizzled man, but with what dignity! Then somewhere iron started to sing and the symphony of the engine began to mock him, like furies singing over a victim—driving him mad.

The next day some of the crew decided that there must be something queer about the bird perched on top of the mainmast. It was certainly not a seagull, not a dung-hawk; what was it?

Dana ventured that it would be an idea to go up and get it. He was looking on in his shuddering dungarees in the dinner-hour; while some of the firemen off watch from the adjoining forecastle had mixed in the group.

"Aw you, you'd pass out before you got up to the table, you would," blustered a stoker in a chain-breaker singlet, eyeing Dana's frail figure with contempt, his tattooed arms folded on his chest.

And Dana was surprised to find himself laughing in acquiescence.

But before he could make up his mind one way or the other everybody saw that Norman, the Norwegian galley-boy, who had been taking a spell, was climbing up the mast.

"That's the boy, Norman," they shouted. " 'Urry up or it'll fly away, that's the stuff, Sculls, good, fine—there now, come to Daddy." And both seamen and firemen were immensely pleased with their new hero.

It was a tricky job at the top, for as everybody knew, beyond the ladder a man had to scramble up as best he could and the mast was so thick it was impossible for Norman to get his arm around it properly. There was a moment when it seemed he couldn't do it, reason stood still, the men below held their breaths, but he accomplished the task at last and returned to the deck with the bird securely captured. Norman was quite covered with soot and grime from the smoke, which had been blowing directly on the mast from the funnel. The bird was a gray carrier pigeon, tired and hungry. It had round its leg a message from a Swansea jail, of a reprieve.

There was a queer elation in the eyes of the Liverpool men as they shuffled into the forecastle. Something had happened at any rate, a tender voice from home had whispered for a moment to those in exile, a mystery had shown its face among the solitudes. Dana stood apart from the others, leaning on the rail. After all, what was the good of understanding?

The pigeon might be the very messenger of love itself, but nothing would alter the fact that he had failed. He would hide his face forever, and walk in darkness for the rest of his days. Yet if he could only see Janet at that moment, she would give him another chance, she would be so gentle and companionable and tender. Her hands were like sun, gently brushing away the pain. His whole being was drowning in memories, the smells of Birkenhead and Liverpool were again heavily about him, there was a coarse glitter in the cinema fronts, children were huddled in the porches of public houses, a gas jet in the market steadily whirred—

In a day or two Norman had clipped the pigeon's wings and made it a cage which he placed on top of the bread locker outside the gallery, so that he could watch while peeling onions.

When he had dumped his last mess down the ash-shoot, hung up his dish-cloths and made up the gallery fires for the quarter-master, he would share his own supper with it, then turn in himself. He gave it as much freedom as he could during the daytime by letting it out on number four hatch. When it wandered about there Norman had always tied it by the leg with a strand of heaving line attached to a cleat.

When Dana saw Mickey, as everybody called it, it used to give him a queer nostalgic feeling in his throat. It was such an innocent and helpless creature there in the moonlight, he thought. On the *West Hardaway* it seemed to be actually a mystery of birth, a miracle on board a ship that could slay like a lion. In Dana's affection now was a feeling of his own destiny, a comprehension of the dark forces which had driven him to sea, which had poised him in space for an instant and then closed their dark impenetrable features around him, and out of this blossomed strangely the really happy memories of his life. He dreamed back along a chain of days— dark blue pools of magic—years and years and years ago—a late tea in the nursery, the turf crisp with the summer heat, and the lazy tennis players below him as he lay on the bank—shadows on walls and towers that suddenly galloped. . . .

Janet had been so white that day when the train left; and both of them knew that that last moment was the last in their lives. It was as if they had died that evening, both could write: but in spite of the dying and the farewell, they were both alive.

The deep wound had healed again, the heart slept. Oh, no sorrow is as bad as that which quite goes by!

The *West Hardaway* reached the Straits Settlements and unloaded some of her cargo in Penang, leaning with a quiet gratitude against the wharf, sea-weary after her long journey.

The loneliness struck up from the wharf, never before so painfully new, footsteps, shadows, arc-lamps, the hum from the dark town. There man was met by man with a call, a glance, a smile. . . . But Dana stayed aboard at first; never before had his heart loved in that solitude!

His yearnings sailed over sea and evenings and dawn. Vast teeming cities and palaces and prairies rose out of his imaginings, and he captured them, and made them his.

Then one night he and Norman went ashore together—

Now in the phosphorescent light there rolls a dark and seething burning, the eternal vortex of youth along the cold coast of the houses. It is as if the air quivers with an electric tension, with hesitating, anxious desire, with derision and petrified delight.

O, here is our street, whose lights intoxicate and torment, whose hearts spin towards the light and burn themselves in its fire, whose nerves are played to death and sing like violins in defiance and painful exultation because we still exist!

But the ship moved on, as always, to another port, and then anchored in another, yet even more obscure and fever-ridden than the first.

It was Saturday afternoon, and Dana had strapped up in the messroom—the ship was to sail that afternoon.

He did his dhoby. God brought a wind, and the sun and wind danced through his clothes, hung on the line. All around was the afternoon's blue crystal: the sun sparkled with a thousand flashes on the waves' gentle fall. The sun shone on deck as he washed and scrubbed his coal-black dungarees, stiff from dust and ashes, red lead and rust and grease.

In the forecastle also the washing dangled along a line in the alleyway, so that it was quite dark.

But the wind dropped and the heat increased. The sun spun like a great catharine-wheel. Dana put his clothespegs away, and went amidships to have a yarn with Norman.

As he approached the galley he almost ran into Andy the cook, who was just coming out, carrying his mess-kit. Andy asked Dana if while he was there he would give Norman's Mickey a drink of water, because Norman was down in the refrigerator and the Mickey would be thirsty.

"Norman and his Mickey," laughed the cook. "He loves that thing like a brother. He's going to paint its cage this evening when he's knocked off. I seen him just now bumming paint off the lamp-trimmer."

Norman's real ambition was to grow another inch and become a policeman, but now he was a galley-boy working down the refrigerator.

Dana came to give Mickey a drink, but it was not in its cage, which was open. He looked on number four hatch. It was not there. Up above, on a line strung between the rail aft of the wireless room and the bottom of the galley chimney, a quartermaster's dungarees flapped themselves dry; but there was no Mickey. Dana called Andy. They searched everywhere—down the bosun's alley, on the boat deck, in the galley—the Mickey seemed to have disappeared.

"It couldn't have flown," said Andy, bewildered. "Norman clipped its wings. We must find it, or it'll break his heart."

In a few minutes they had looked over the side. There, not twenty fathoms from the boat, the Mickey was swimming. Its clipped wings pathetically flapped in the water. It was gradually sinking as it became more and more sodden. There was not one chance in a thousand that it would ever reach the bank, and even if it did—Andy and Dana looked at each other. Dana was quite a good swimmer, but as he did not want at this moment consciously to appear braver or wiser than his friend, he said nothing. Andy was an old seaman, homo sapiens. Andy knew a thing or two. And now he was shaking his head.

"Crocodiles, sharks, water snakes—you dunno what things are in this damned place. I'd go in, but I think more of my missus than of a pigeon," he said. The bosun and the carpenter came up.

"Gawd blimey!" said the bosun, rolling a cigarette. "The Mickey got loose? I always said it would. Sculls doesn't know how to look after it. By crimes, the bastard's swimming, ain't it, Chips?"

"Well, it's the last time that bird will ever swim!"

"Yes? All Lombard Street to a Tahiti orange on that, mate. I'm afraid he'll make a nice little bit of supper for one of them sharks, eh?"

"Thirsty, I suppose," said Andy moodily. "It's this lousy heat, you see—I was just telling Dan here to give him a drink—thirsty it must have been, and seeing the water like this—"

Ah yes, they nodded their heads sagely. Thirsty, they hadn't thought of that—

Dana tried to stifle a mean feeling which swept over him. This serves Norman right for going up that mast, he was telling himself against his will; that'll teach him. Anyhow, the bird was happier dead. He felt both sick and astonishingly elated, watching intently —nothing must be missed. Good Lord, he must, he would jump in after it. His bowels weakened at the thought. But it would be sheer bravado in front of all these more capable men, he reassured himself. He did nothing about it.

Two quartermasters came up, and an A.B. from the forecastle with a bucket full of his Saturday's washing.

"What's up, Bose?"

"Sculls' Mickey. 'Avin' a ruddy barf!"

"Aw, that thing. Norman shouldn't let it out on that bastard string!"

"Wot's to do there?"

" 'Ere, wot's all the crowd about? Is there a Jane in the water or summat?"

"Damn all Janes in Swettenham. It's only Norman's Mickey—"

"Aw, wot a ruddy shame!"

"I was only tellin' 'im about that string yesterday. 'E didn't know 'ow to keep the bird."

"Fed it wrong, too—"

"Where is Norman anyway, for heaven's sake?"

"In the frige."

"He was going to paint its cage this evening," said the cook. "I saw him getting paint off the lamp-trimmer. He loved that bird like a brother."

"Never got a chance to let my brother out on a string."

"It's not my pigeon," put in a Q.M.

Two firemen who had been hoisting coal to the galley, two ordinary seamen (resplendent in gay bathing costumes they had bought in Cebu the last trip, in which they now often slept), the chief steward, and the purser joined the crowd. The firemen, covered in coal, said nothing, but stood there quietly watching.

"Lor' lumme days, it's Sculls' Mickey," said an O.S. "Sheer killing himself, though, it would be to go in after it in this place."

"Yes."

"It's a ruddy shame, though, I reckon—"

"Here," said the chief steward, "we must get a sampan. We can't let the bloody bird drown like that."

"No sampan within a couple of miles, sir."

"Hullo," said the purser, "there's a motor-boat."

"Where?"

They looked where a little white motor-boat was coquettishly skidding along the waters, and then, turning almost in its own length, retracing its course looking more foolish than ever. The crowd yelled at it—all hooting and trumpeting at once—but its engine was making too much noise and its only occupant was dividing his attention between the wheel and the spurting exhaust which he seemed to be admiring from time to time by looking over the side at it. The chief steward spread out his hands helplessly. Near the number four hatch one of the agents for the company stood, talking to the first mate. They did not know what was going on.

"Look here," said the chief steward. "We must get a sampan. We can't let the bloody bird drown like that."

The mate and the agent went on talking.

Dana thought, but said nothing.

"I suppose it would be sheer suicide to go in," ventured the purser.

"You'd get eaten. And if you were rescued you'd get logged," said the chief steward, doing nothing about the sampan. "There, I always said he was going to lose the thing."

The Mickey struggled on bravely, half submerged.

"Poor little bastard," said Andy.

Suddenly it disappeared.

"Mr. Croc, eh?" winked the bosun wisely, spitting out a brown stream.

"For heaven's sake!" said Andy. "He probably couldn't go any further."

Norman came out of the refrigerator, slipping off an extra jacket. He felt quite contented. He had a few more onions to peel, and then he was free for the rest of the evening, to paint the cage. He came over to the crowd who were looking over the rail. The situation was explained to him. He flushed up.

"What's the big idea not telling me, eh? What's the big idea, I'd like to know. You knew I was down the refrigerator, Andy, what's the big idea? You mean you stood there and watched that Mickey drown? What's the big idea?"

"Well, you couldn't go in, Norman," explained Dana, distressed for him. "This harbor's full of sharks and crocodiles."

"Yes—and I'll tell you something—you're full of prunes, that's what, yes! Full of prunes that's what you are. What do you think I am, eh? You think that I'd let that Mickey drown do you—whatever the harbor's full of—eh? Yes, well, you're ruddy wrong."

But his anger collapsed. He suddenly turned white as chalk and went slowly down to the forecastle.

The motor-boat was still playing about; it was as carefree and as jolly as a little frisky terrier. Quickly its occupant was spinning the easy wheel while it circled the ship gaily and with incredible speed, then turned on itself and rolled in its swell. All at once it was away as inconsequentially as it had arrived, keeping a straight course for the shore and leaving a scar of foam behind it. Its white segment of stern—*Mabel* Penang—soon dissolved into the blue of the harbor.

The crowd remained there for some time talking, and after a few moments the agent, whom the first mate had by now left, came over

to them. He was smoking a cigar and in a jolly mood. He was a
jolly agent, familiar and affable with all men, whatever their station.
He remarked upon the ordinary seamen's Cebu bathing costumes.
They were very nice, very nice texture, he said.

"If any of you want to bathe," he puffed, blowing out a flood of
grey air, "it's all right this time of the year, I've been in myself
several times. It's really quite safe. You could get the pilot ladder
put down, Chief—it would really be very nice."

The group dispersed, wavered, and broke and flowed. They went
about their businesses. Andy sat on a butter-tub in the galley, yawning at a three weeks old Singapore *Free Press*, fascinated by a
heading: "Murder of Brother-in-law's Concubine." After a while
he rose, cursing his luck, to finish the dishing-up. Norman sat on a
little stool gloomily peeling onions; once he stole a glance at the
cage on the break locker and wondered if he would ever grow
another inch and become a policeman: the bosun and the carpenter
padded up and down the deck in carpet-slippers. The ether seemed
to be tingling; sunlight above them roared like a cauldron.

Dana sat on a hatch outside the forecastle washing a singlet in a
bucket. The hours folded their wings beneath the sky.

Frequently the yellow soap slipped from his hands and he stooped
to pick it up. There was a sudden hush, as the tide turned, as
though the jungle had caught its breath. The ship swung right round
with the tide and was soon facing a different part of the harbor.
The deep day was ending; shadows stole silently round bulkheads.
From where he sat the bars of the galley were like the bars of a
penitentiary and the cook's hands moved slowly and remorsefully
behind them. Let me get out—

Dana put his bucket under his bunk, hung his singlet out to dry,
and walked amidships. On number four hatch he found a length of
heaving line attached to a cleat. He listened to some of the quartermasters talking.

"—these mozzies are artists—"

"—yes?"

"At night it's an awful thing when you're lying on your bunk,
you know, and you hear one and you can't make out whether it's
inside your net or not. I can never figure out whether it is a mos-
quito or a dog barking, far off—"

"Ha ha ha!"

"—breakfast this time tomorrow. Yis."

"—from Dublin to 'Olyhead you can get it very very severe. During the war it was full of troops and all—"

"Newfoundland is where I want to go again, boy. Tor Bay, eh, and eat codfish tongues up there, eh!"

"This afternoon it was Norman's Mickey, yis. Well I ain't telling you the word of a lie but that's what the agent said—"

"—bacon and eggs, you know, and one bloody little piece of toast."

"—is that so?"

"—is that so?"

Tin-tin: tin-tin: tin-tin. Night had fallen, the bosun took a few men on the forecastle head, the carpenter was at the windlass. The engine began to pound like a great heart, the telegrapth rang furiously. Suddenly the siren boomed, swallowing all other noises with its terrific volume: it echoed back and forth across the harbor, it was the cry of an imprisoned animal thrilling to the prospect of release. Again the siren lanyard was jerked and the noise rang forth this time even more devastatingly till all the ship's old plates were dithering and quivering with the delight of it. Its echoes seemed to hover uncertainly in the air for fully half a minute, mingled with distant alien sounds which it seemed to have aroused.

The *West Hardaway* was steaming out of the river towards the open sea, gliding calmly among the solitudes as though nothing had happened—cloom-cloom-cloom-cloom.

Soon there was a sense everywhere of peace and languid discussion among those off watch as the *West Hardaway* settled down to be a ship once more.

Then most of them turned in.

Dana looked up for an instant at the mast before ducking into the black cavern of the forecastle entrance.

Once there, he immediately crawled up into his bunk. Around him the watch below and the day workers snored as one man.

Outside was the roar of the sea and the darkness.

June the 30th, 1934

Silently the train for Boulogne drew out of the Gare de l'Est.

This was surprising. One had expected an excruciating din, a series of spastic propulsions, to be thrown from one's feet. The Reverend Bill Goodyear, of West Kirby, Cheshire, England, threw his suitcase on the rack and sat down behind *L'Oeuvre*. But there was nothing comprehensible in The Work so he looked out of the window.

Advertisements swam past, for Oxygènée, for Pernod Fils, for Jean Cocteau's *Machine Infernale*, at the Theatre des Champs Elysées, for Charles Boyer in *La Bataille*, playing at the Rex.

He gazed out beyond the hoardings, perforated to counterset wind pressure, over the leaden acres of rooftops with their aerials and lines of washing dancing in the sun, to see if he could catch sight of his favorite church, at Alesia. But obviously, it was too far away. He returned to his paper in which he tried to follow an article devoted to the Stavisky case. He did not understand it at all. And what were those references to the great riots in the Place de la Concorde, and elsewhere, in February? His dog collar, glimpsed in the window, seemed like a disguise, so that he felt a bit like Stavisky himself. It appeared that nothing less than another French Revolution had recently taken place without his knowing it. Nor did he quite understand why in order to promote peace it should be necessary for the French inner market to be stimulated by closer contact with the German steel cartels. But his French was bad and perhaps the writer was trying to convey something quite different.

After a while Bill Goodyear realised that he was not reading, so much as hiding himself, behind the paper. Ah, what a nuisance it was always to be so ill at ease in trains, on ships, in drawing rooms! Just as in the pulpit it took him such a long time to reestablish himself, to be aware of a new community. Perhaps it was because, believing passionately in mankind, he was afraid of superficial contacts, of the mere brushing of wings with a fellow creature. He folded his paper and looked out of the window again.

The signals saluted like clockwork, a wooden man in a box marked Paris 5 hauled on a lever and a score of rails rippled away and became one; and as if brushing away trucks bearing old wartime inscriptions, 40 hommes, 8 chevaux, buildings, elevated railways, even the Eiffel Tower itself, from its course, the train, free of the ambiguity of suburbs and junctions, swerved ahead whistling towards Boulogne and England. The black powerful engine, the determination of the thing, pleased him.

Goodyear produced his pipe and some hateful Scarfelati tobacco he had bought in Chartres. But the pipe too might at least conceal his uneasiness, which was now more like panic, a fear that at any moment the summons would come from the dark of things and his little universe be overthrown. Soon he was hidden behind a flood of vile grey air, a smoke-screen between himself and a toppling world.

But the Scarfelati was mere tinder, the pipe grew uncomfortably hot and the man opposite him proffered Goodyear his pouch.

In the pouch were little yellow ringlets of aromatic English tobacco.

While Goodyear was relighting his pipe he looked at his companion out of the corner of his eye. He was a short, bronzed man a good deal older than himself, he thought, badly but expensively dressed, with a jutting chin and steady grey eyes. He held one leg out stiffly.

But more than of any physical impression Goodyear was strikingly aware of a feeling of kinship, even in the other's silence. His uneasiness fell away.

"Thanks," he said. "This is a good deal better."

"Name's Firmin. Been in France long?"

"Goodyear. No. I was just visiting a confrère of mine at the American church in Paris. On the Quai d'Orsay."

"I don't like the French," said the other. "Too vindictive. Not enough sincerity."

"I wouldn't like to say that. I like them; a great people."

"Too much bureaucracy."

The men did not speak again until they reached Amiens, then he said:

"This was a very busy place during the war. You'd scarcely

recognize it." He paused. "But you were too young for the war, I suppose."

Goodyear said nothing, ashamed that he had been too young.

"Well, how do you do."

"How do you do."

The two men shook hands. Firmin looked out.

"This is the Somme," he said.

They were silent until they had passed Etaples, when Firmin said: "There was a lot of fighting here."

The train hurled swiftly on through peace; fields of campion, or cornflowers. The haystacks stood together in the meekness of love, like loaves. Now a boy and a girl were fishing in a canal.

Goodyear produced a notecase, from which he withdrew a photograph. He handed it to Firmin. In the photograph three children grouped themselves in a garden about a herbaceous border.

"That's Dick, there. He'll be twelve next July."

"Fine looking children. I'll bet you're anxious to see them again."

The man handed back the photograph which Goodyear replaced in his notecase. As he pocketed it he said:

"Ah well, I'm being returned empty anyhow."

Firmin nodded. Not seeming to have noticed the other's last words, he remarked:

"I once thought of marrying. But I smashed my hip to hell in the war. Doesn't interfere with my walking any longer. Still, in my job, I mustn't let it interfere . . ."

The two men sat smoking, looking out of the window. There were more boys fishing.

"Fishing," Firmin said. "You cast all round the fish. Sometimes after you've followed them a long way you find it's no good."

Goodyear chuckled. "That last goes for the fish too."

"There was a lot of fighting here," repeated Firmin.

Suddenly and embarrassingly Goodyear felt one of the fits of hysteria coming on which had been tormenting him on the voyage home. His lips trembled around the pipe stem. Turning his face further to the window so that Firmin would not see, he forced his eyelids against his quickening tear ducts. With his eyes queerly screwed up he was watching a labourer straightening his back as he gazed up at the roaring passage of the express. Next Goodyear tried to fix his eyes on the telegraph wires, undulating and diving after the train. This did not succeed either and he was about to give in to his emotion when he saw, among the woods they were passing, a bare-legged boy. He was running furiously and the curious thing about this boy was that he seemed to be keeping up with the train. Goodyear was so astonished that he quite forgot his embarrassment. Now the boy had fallen down. Extraordinary! He turned away and turned his thoughts away from the delusion, only for them to fasten on Firmin. He looked out of the window and there was the boy, but now—could it be? Good Lord no, impossible—there was no mistaking him, the boy *was* Dick.

It was preposterous. They were passing a river and it was Dick and no other who plunged into it joyously. And it was Dick, unmistakeably Dick, who was swimming that river. And Dick too who was scrambling up the opposite bank and running on faster than ever.

He did not say anything about it but every time he looked out of the window there was the boy.

"There was a place here called the bullring," Firmin was saying, "All sand—that was why they called it the bullring. You wouldn't think sand gets frozen. But my word, it was cold in winter."

Goodyear only looked out twice more but both times he saw his boy charging along, keeping up with the train.

Villages and war cemeteries plunged past them and were gone. They made conversation but the swaying of the train dragged their sentences apart. The wheels cried out against the iron.

Passing Neufchatel the track became smoother. Firmin said:

"This was a very busy place in the war. You'd scarcely think it now. Whew!"

Goodyear watched the sunset. A solitary street lamp was alight. A far plane flew over high-banked clouds. It looked like rain. Smoke was curling gently from peaked houses. There was a strange sadness about this journey in the train through the sunset, and a longing for comfort.

Now they were getting into Boulogne.

"The train goes right over the main street," said Firmin. As they slowed down the character of their motion altered, the train was becoming the appurtenance of a wharf, of the sea.

"That place was a terrible place over there during the war," said Firmin. "The Café Cristol."

And Goodyear peered out into the rain, which had just started to fall, over towards the once notorious café. Then they were at the wharf.

They were changing elements, but the idea struck him; no, it is more than this, something greater is being changed—

Shortly after the ship was clear of the quays the two Englishmen stood together at the rail looking into the wilderness of clay and rain which was France disappearing.

Presently there was nothing but darkness and the roar of the sea.

"It's desolate, desolate," said Goodyear.

"Ugly, ugly."

"I never felt so desolate. I don't know why," Goodyear laughed.

"Come on and have a drink, man, and cheer yourself up."

"A sound scheme."

Firmin limped before Goodyear down to the bar. It was heavy smelling and warm; the thrum of the engine was loud. They decided on Bass.

"Every time I have a few drinks I imagine I'm getting demobbed again," said Firmin, drinking.

Goodyear drank, then for some reason said a peculiar thing.

"So do I!"

This was, by implication, a flat lie and he was astonished at himself.

"What! Were you in the war? Why didn't you tell me? Here I've been talking as though I fought the whole war by myself."

"I don't know. As a matter of fact I had an only brother killed." Goodyear was lying again. "We used to like to think that he's buried in France. His body was never identified and we don't care to speak of it."

Firmin was silent. Goodyear's heart beat with the beating of the engine. He wondered what had made him tell this curious falsehood. Of course he had no brother at all. Could this be himself talking? And had that been himself before who had seen the boy running? And now, coming on top of it, was this stupid lie about an imaginary brother.

He took another drink and saw, in his mind's eye, the boy running again, but now the boy was Firmin. Firmin as he had been some years before the last war, when he was about the same age that Dick was now.

But Goodyear didn't understand why he had told his untruth. Had he wanted to be this man's comrade; to make up to him somehow, for his wounds, and had thought by his falsehood about the war, to bring himself nearer to him, and so to humanity, towards which was his responsibility, and in whose eyes—and were not these also Firmin's eyes?—his failure would seem the more excusable?

And with another part of his mind Goodyear was uneasily anticipating the questions Firmin might ask. What regiment? what platoon? do you remember Captain so and so? which he would never be able to answer.

But Firmin changed the subject.

"Mean, did I call them, the French? Perhaps I did them an injustice. They had to battle to get the crops out, they say. And for poor prices. A country of hard bargains."

"My American friend at the Quai d'Orsay was talking this morning about his country. All around them is electricity and they can't use it. Wheat fields, but nobody has bread. Clothing everywhere, they can't buy it. A terrible situation."

Through the porthole Goodyear watched the moving sea which close in under the glare of the lights was as green and fluctuant as the landscape from the train window.

"Fruit rotting, can't eat it. What they want they can't have."

"What can they do?"

"What can any of us do?"

After a pause Firmin said, "A ship's bar always reminds me of a play called *Outward Bound*. If I'm not mistaken there was a chap like you in it."

Goodyear checked himself from replying.

"I remember the play very well indeed," Firmin went on. "All the charcaters were supposed to be dead. It took place in a ship without a crew but it had a bar. Oh yes, it had a *bar!* I even remember the barman's name: Scrubby. The characters were dead, were voyaging out to what you might call their Last Judgement. It wasn't the sort of play you forget in a hurry. Saw it done in Singapore by an amateur company."

"Singapore, did you say?"

"Yes, Singapore."

"Was it in July, 1927?"

"Yes, it would be, July, 1927."

"Then I produced the play," Goodyear said.

"You produced it? That's funny. Seven years ago. Let me see, now, would that be after Lindbergh had flown the Atlantic?"

The two men stood looking at each other. Strange, Goodyear was thinking: the lie had begotten the truth.

"I may have met you then."

"I was doing mission work."

"I was a prospector out there."

"We may have met."

"Well, that's funny. Well, we'd better have another drink on it. No bird ever flew with one wing."

Goodyear ordered another Bass. "This one on me," he said.

"Here's," said Firmin.

"Good health."

"Ah, but the world isn't what it used to be," said Firmin. "Don't you feel something in the air yourself. If you don't mind my saying so, don't you find it difficult to keep your faith? Of course I'm not a religious man myself, but isn't it difficult?"

"I must admit," said Goodyear, "I *have* to admit that the Church has failed in many important respects." He looked helpless, obviously speaking about himself. "But it is difficult to start again."

"Yes, I know it is. Before the war I was training to be an engineer at Bradford Tech. After the war, after I'd got out of the hospital, I found I couldn't work at the Tech any more. In the first place we weren't allowed to smoke. Wasn't that funny? After the trenches— Good God! We complained to the Principal and he said, 'Well, as a matter of fact, I find it damned difficult too.' Then I absolutely broke away from it, became a prospector."

"You're on leave now: didn't you get very homesick? I did."

"That's what you read in books. No. Only the youngsters really felt that way." Firmin covered this by adding, "Anyway, I'll be glad to get back out East again. Can't stand the traffic here. It take me ten minutes to cross a street."

"Only the youngsters, eh? What about me? I'll be glad enough to get home," said Goodyear. He looked at his Bass. "And that is a fact."

"I work for a German company," said Firmin. "I'm going to London first, then to Hamburg for instructions. Then out East again. Yes, prospecting's meat and drink to me. Metal. All sorts of metal, every sort. Well, it's like fishing. You cast all round the place. Sometimes you may find it after you've followed it a long way and it's no good. It may be only a hundred yards. The great thing is you have to sell your dud ground."

From the other's words a sermon was forming itself in Goodyear's mind. 'Brethren, aren't we all prospectors in life? You find the vein, you cast all round it. The fishermen among you will know what I mean.' He would pause here for *smiling* . . .'Follow me,' he said, 'and I will make you fishers of men.'

Still only half aware of what Firmin was saying but catching a familiar word here and there, Goodyear watched the pendulum of the clock over the bar above the bottle of Bass, Worthington, Johnny Walker; the pendulum that swung enormously over the world, that was swinging him back to West Kirby, Cheshire, and Firmin out again to Ambat and Batu, to Changkat and Jelapang, to Kuala Langkat, or to the Klang River. Changkat . . . Jelapang . . . Kampong . . . *Klang*, the engines said. Metal. Metal that streamed through land and sea: metal from the earth, moulded in fire, conqueror of air and water.

"Then of course they salt it," Firmin was concluding. "Three pickle earth. Why sometimes you can go on walking until you're dead. Well, I'm happy. I've been places you can't go without a gun, it isn't safe. And I've shot all sorts of animals. After you've been out there a while, you forget there ever was a place called England. But I daresay you've done all this sort of thing yourself?"

Goodyear watched the pendulum and now he thought of the restless moving finger of God. Systems were formed, were destroyed. At one moment a creature was set on earth to become self-evolving, at another wars were written of, and wars took place. Here a people were created, there erased.

Was there really a sort of determinism about the fate of nations? Could it be true that, in the end, they got what too they deserved? What had a given people done or not done that they should be obliterated? It struck Goodyear as odd at that moment that while he and Firmin had patronized France, while they had been dismayed over America, while they had 'handed' it, sportingly, to the defeated nation, Germany, they had not said one word about England. What about England? They had not asked each other that. Nor had they considered openly that there might be anything wrong with themselves. What is wrong with *us*? They had been virtually silent on that point. And what is wrong with me? He had not asked Firmin that, and even while Goodyear put the question half-heartedly to himself he was being bothered by a sinister contradiction in Firmin's existence. Wasn't it a little ominous that Firmin, badly wounded in the war, should spend the rest of his life searching for the very metals with which Man *might* indeed construct a new world, a stellite paradise of inconceivable strength and delicacy, that would enable him, through vast windows of new alloys, to let the light of the future pour in, but with which, or so *L'Oeuvre* had assured him, Man was doing nothing of the sort, but on the contrary, with diabolical genius, merely using to prepare the subtler weapons of his own destruction? He imagined their quarreling about this obviousness and Firmin's inevitable answer, that religion had been the origin of numerous wars, and that when it was not, in some particular case, the war always masqueraded as a crusade, with God, or the Right, firmly supporting both sides, and so forth— all the wooled, unreal but inescapable facts that by repetition and repetition and repetition were enough to create a chaos in themselves—and all this while the two men stood facing each other still as death, as though an actual quarrel had taken place between them.

"I stopped for a while at Crete on the way home," Goodyear said at length, thoughtfully. "A fascinating island! Many thousands of years ago they had a civilization strikingly like our own. A sporting people, but not religious. At Cnossos, which might be compared to London, they'd reached a position where they thought the human intellect, by itself, could solve all their problems. Perhaps Adam made the same mistake! Anyhow, the barbarians came, who really had a God—an evil God but still one which was unanimously worshipped, the God of War that is—who was all their culture rolled into one, and it was all up with the Cretans! But not," he added earnestly, "with the Cretan spirit, that is, the human spirit, of which one assumes the intellect is only a part. And I believe that when that spirit, in spite of all its setbacks, has reached a point of development in its understanding and humility where the real God, the God of Life, be he ever so patient, doesn't have to feel sick at the very thought of it, then it will have already largely triumphed over the greater obstacles and we shall have a real world."

"I don't believe that bit about the development of the intellect applies to you and me though, eh," chuckled Firmin. "Eh?"

Goodyear, privately injured by this, said nothing.

The clangor of the engines filled the silence: from down below leverweight and fulcrum jangled their gongs: further away the turbines screamed in a whirlwind as the water was driven violently against the curved vanes of the wheel rims: and a hissing tangle of sound was weaving itself thickly through the low tunnel of the alleyway to the bar.

Metal . . .

"Well, it's a funny old world," Firmin said.

The men laughed.

"Have a drink. That's the best thing. I like to see a clergyman take a drink."

"Many of them feel like taking to it," said Goodyear.

The drinks were brought.

"Well," Goodyear sighed, "once more, I say it. I'm being returned empty. Yes, and you're right, it seems that there *is* a great change taking place, but you can't put your finger on it."

"But you're only a young man yet."

"Thirty-four."

"You wouldn't think it, but I'm only thirty-nine. Five years can make a difference."

They drank.

"Seven years ago I thought that a missionary's was the life for me," Goodyear said, breathing the hot smells of the ship, that distilled memories of parting, "after two years I went home and married. This time I came out and I've only stuck it six months. Did you ever read a story called 'The Country of the Blind,' by Wells, I think? It's about a mountaineer who fell down the crater of a volcano to find himself unhurt but in a country where everyone was blind. The refrain 'the one eyed man is king in the country of the blind' sang in his head. He wanted to give the people sight. Then he discovered that they were happy to be blind, and so he climbed up out of the crater again before it was too late. The trouble was, they wanted to blind him too."

He watched the pendulum.

"Well, here's how," said Firmin.

"Yes, how."

Folkestone was now alongside. They climbed up on deck into the wild weather. A freighter was passing, outward bound, its siren sounding hoarse and sorrowful. The gangway fell spastically, yawning, then banged into place.

"Clickety click," said Firmin.

Their ship, in turn, had now ceased to be a ship and had become a huge station. The passengers stood in droves, their scarves close over their mouths, passports ready, lining up for their landing cards. It had almost stopped raining, but wild drops still fell. Wet light picked out familiar advertisements; nostalgic: Carter's Little Liver Pills, Players Cigarettes, Bovril: a weeping bull looking, ironically, he thought, into a bottle of meat extract: 'Alas, my poor brother!'

Built on an incline above them a cinema was showing Chaliapin and George Robey in Pabst's *Don Quixote*; Walt Disney's *Three Little Pigs*.

This time, as Goodyear stepped on to the wharf, he had a curious apprehension—he couldn't say where it came from—that he was not so much changing elements as changing worlds. He passed without difficulty through the customs and then wandered, pipe in mouth, down the platform, where everyone seemed to be reading newspapers. The newsboys were shouting and Goodyear bought a *Star* from a boy who wore this announcement like an apron: *Hitler Atrocities. Germany Under Arms.*

What did all this mean? Was another war really starting already? No. Impossible. And Goodyear was reassured too by the paper, which, in spite of the headlines, merely gave a gentlemanly account of a revolt in this chap Hitler's army, in which a few brownshirts or blackshirts—or were those Mussolini's gang?—had been shot. Poor fellows. Nevertheless, he couldn't rid himself of the feeling that this was only confirmation of what he'd suspected; that a new cycle was beginning, that the face of the world was changing . . .

The long London boat train lay curved to the platform and already trembling to be gone. A horrible fancy struck Goodyear: the 7:30 to Cnossos—

He met Firmin in the Pullman and they sat down opposite each other.

"They're at it again," Firmin said, opening his paper. "There's something radically wrong somewhere."

"Yes, they're at it again."

"They're forcing another one on us now."

Firmin appeared ill at ease. Doubt and vexation showed in his face as he shook out the newspaper. They had a long wait for the last passengers to get through the customs.

"I never lie about what I've got," Firmin shifted irritably in his seat. "I always declare it."

"War: what price war? What's the prospect now? But I don't really think that this means war," said Goodyear, reading his paper.

"War," said Firmin unpleasantly, "there isn't enough money for war—yet."

"And every prospect pleases."

"There never is enough money, but they always find it," said Firmin.

Goodyear wondered: am I lying to myself as well? Deceiving

myself, smuggling myself through the customs when there should be a price on my head, a dutiable metal.

A man passed outside, slowly, testing the wheels; the iron rang out, once, twice, thrice. Base. Metal. Counterfeit. The last passengers hurried into the Pullman. But still the train waited.

At last they started, jerked to a standstill.

"You have to strike back at the cause," said Goodyear, his voice suddenly loud in the carriage.

"What is the cause?"

"Yes, precisely, what?" he lowered his voice. "Ourselves, probably, as much as anything. It's no good meeting evil with evil."

The engine restarted, drowning the true adulterate words, stopped again with a violent, convulsive hissing. Billows of smoke rushed up past the window. Workmen were drilling. Drilling for gas; the terrible hydrocarbons drifting from crevices, expanding, possessing mankind. He peered out through the steaming glass. Poison, he thought. Chaos, change, all was changing: the passengers were changing: a sea change.

Goodyear lay back in his seat. He could feel the change within him, somehow his thoughts were becoming longer: an insidious metallurgy was in practice within him as his ores, his alloys, were isolated. The titanic thunder of the night-shift hammered on his nerves, lacerating them as though it would draw out from him the fine wire of his consciousness.

He knew that he had been altered by the true pattern, the archtype of the events, on the surface so trivial, of the journey. And he sensed that the other passengers, visible for the time being only as that deadly headline *Germany Under Arms,* had also been affected, were even at a crucial point in their lives, turning towards another chaos, a new complexity of melancholy opposites.

Sitting there, for a moment he *was* Firmin, the Firmin who had returned from the war, wounded, to discover only that he had to become somebody else. It was almost as if Goodyear had told the truth to him. And, looking at Firmin, he knew him too to be changed.

Perhaps now, as before, Firmin would have to take a different, unforeseen action.

And an expression of doubt, an hour ago only a shadow on both their faces in an idle conversation, had become part of their features, as years added to them.

Suddenly, cautiously, but with an accelerating motion, the train pulled off once more, slackened for a moment, skidded, and the wheels finding their rhythm, was finally away.

Red and green lights flicked past as the train gathered speed, metal acres stretched and contracted, dilated, narrowed. Folkestone 3 West.

. . . Metal, true metal, counterfeit, said the train. Changkat, Jelapang, liar and cheat. Manganese, chromium, old counterfeit. Goodyear rubbed a patch of steam from the window, peered into the dark. The train rattled over points. Not enough money, not enough money, not enough money for war. Folkestone 4 Circuit. Circuit Fund. Collection. Silver and copper, silver and gold. Suddenly there was his bare-legged boy again, running, running more furiously, more frenziedly, than ever, red and green lights falling on him, silver and copper lights, running through the metal fields with metal furrows spangled with coins of fire. Run-on-little-ghost-of-the-youth-of-the-next-war-there're-still-ox-eye-daisies-to-pick, said the train, going through a tunnel. Goodyear was weary and closed his eyes. He woke with a start. The passengers sat reading quietly or smoking. A girl was knitting in a corner. Down corridors men swayed, tottering like the blind, hands stretched out to wood or glass, men feeling their way through the world, walking in their sleep, somnambulists . . .

His eyes returned to the window. A man digging, sharply illumined by a shower of sparks like red blossoms, slowly raised his spade. Davies' words recurred to him: 'The man who digs his grave, the girl who knits her shroud.' It's never too late, never too late. To start again. You bore in the earth. Silver and copper. Silver and gold. Man makes his cross. With crucible steel. Base metal; counterfeit; manganese; chromium; makes his iron cross; with crucible steel.

The train took a hill. The boy fell in the fire. The knitting needles flashed like bayonets. Steel wool. The red lights flashed. Green lights. Knit. Socks! Knit. Shroud! Knit. Stab! Iron, steel, said the train. Iron, steel. Steel iron. Iron, tin, iron, tin. Steel and iron steel and iron steel and iron steel and iron *steeeeeeeeeel!* . . .

Now they were going at a tremendous pace, but Goodyear and Firmin were fast asleep under the lamp as the express screamed on like a shell, through a metal world.

China

China's like a muddle to me, it's just like a dream, mostly a queer dream. For though I've been there it takes on a quality sometimes that my imagination bestowed on it before I went. But even if I lived there it would still seem to me to be unreal; for the most part I don't think of it and when I do it makes me laugh.

I live down at the docks now in Hoboken, New Jersey, and now and again I wander down there to see a ship that's crossed the Western Ocean. That doesn't make me homesick or stir up in me the old love of the sea or of memories I've got of China. Nor does it make me unhappy when I think I've been there and really have so few memories after all.

I don't believe in China.

You can say I'm like that man you may have read about who spent his life as a sailor on some vessel plying from Liverpool to Lisbon and on retiring was only able to say of Lisbon: The trams go faster there than in Liverpool.

Like Bill Adams I came fresh to sea life from an English public school where I had worn a tophat and carried a silver-topped cane, but there the resemblance ceases. I was a fireman.

There was a terrible war on in China at this time and in this I did not believe either. Just across the river from where we were moored, China thundered her guns Doom! doom! doom! but the whole thing crashed over our heads without touching us. Not that I would have believed in it any more had we been blown all to hell: we do not associate such dooms with ourselves. But it was as if you were dreaming, as I often have, that you are standing unscathed beneath the tumult of an immense waterfall, Niagara for instance.

We were moored nose on to the English battle-cruiser, *H.M.S. Proteus*. Astern lay a high, brightly-painted Ningpo junk. Apart from this, there was little in our surroundings, before the stevedores

49

arrived, to suggest that we were not at home: even the war, palpable as it seemed to be through the river fog eclipsing the opposite bank, did not dissipate this illusion: much might have happened for good or evil in our absence from England. And this perhaps brings me to my only real point. We are always 'here.' You've never felt this? Well, with me this was very cogent. In an English paper I could read about the famous city near at hand, divided against herself, tortured not only by the possibility of invasion but with threats of its own ochlocracy, but when the chief engineer forbade us to cross the river to it, I turned over and went to sleep. I didn't believe I was there at all. And when it was proposed by the chief steward that a cricket match take place between the *Arcturion,* which was the name of our ship, and the *H.M.S. Proteus* I was certain I was not. I had seen this coming, however.

They started it in the Indian Ocean.

I was coming off watch at eight bells and when I got to the galley I knew they were starting it.

The seamen were standing round outside their forecastle winding up strands of heaving line. They were like old maids, holding each other's knitting, I thought. Then I saw that they were making cricket balls. The *Arcturion* carried a spare propellor which was shackled to the break of the poop and the captain was chalking on this. A wicket!

While I was having my chow I knew they were starting it and when I finally came out, they had begun. From the broomlocker to the spare propellor along the seaman's side of the welldock was about the length of a cricket pitch and at the far end Hersey was bowling. He took a long run right down the companion ladder and then bowled. At the wicket chalked on the spare propellor trembled Lofty. He milled about in the air with a bat the carpenter had made him. The ball was returned to Hersey. Fieldmen stood round on the hatches, on the steampiping, among the washing. Now Hersey was bowling again. Lofty had missed. Hersey had the ball once more. One or two were still winding heaving-lines.

When the seamen saw me they started to mince for my benefit. Oh, I say, pass the bally ball,— And so on.

I made up my mind I hated these men and then I wished I could crush them: they would never be anything but underdogs. Unctiousness and servility flowed in their very veins and even now it seems necessary to me to say these things with mere malice. Imitating a workingman's accent, they were even more unpleasant than my own class.

Old bourgeois maidservants with mob cap and broom, that's what English steamboat sailors are.

A few blackened firemen stood around, watching and grinning like niggers. They wouldn't join in. They had solidarity, they had one enemy, the chief steward. The sailors and the others were petty Judases who had to keep in with both sides. They let each other down and they would steal the milk out of your tea. But the firemen were solid. We were prime. And we stood together against the chief steward because of the food.

They had begun by jeering at me: Where is Heton, Hoxford or Cambridge? But in the end they took the attitude, Eton, Oxford, Cambridge and the fireman's forecastle. At any rate he didn't become a seaman and that's something. That was their attitude.

I was a coal passer and worked on the 12 to 4 or duke's watch, and after a while they accepted me silently as one of them. I worked hard and didn't growl. I respected them but to them that was neither here nor there. But now standing together looking at the sailors with contempt, they gave me a sidelong glance as if suspicious that I had gone over to the enemy.

Then the chief steward came out of the galley smoking a cigar, paused imperiously at the top of the companion ladder and descended slowly, puffing.

—Hello boys, give me a knock.

And Lofty handed over the bat to the chief.

Soon he was slogging the balls all over the place; he hit two into the Indian Ocean and it was very clear he fancied himself. Oh it was very clear he thought he had some class.

—Silly sailors, said the firemen in a long drawl.

That night as I was pacing up and down the poop in carpet slippers smoking, the chief steward came up to me.

—Tell me, he began. Surely you play cricket. Now I'm not *just* a chief steward you might say. I've got education. But let me see, you're not *the*—

Suddenly I felt I had to tell him that I was. I told him how I fared in the Eton and Harrow match, how I'd played against the Australians, there was nothing I didn't know about cricket. I also told him to hold his tongue, but I ought to have known better than to trust a sailor.

It was only after he'd gone that I thought of all the things I ought to have said to him.

He kept his promise as long as it suited him, only as long as it suited him. Meantime we were getting nearer and nearer to China.

And the nearer we got the less I believed in it.

What I want to convey to you is that to me it was not China at all but right here, on this wharf. But that's not quite what I wanted to say. What I mean is what it was not was China: somewhere far away. What it was was here, something solid, tactile, impenetrable. But perhaps neither one thing nor the other.

You see, I had worn myself out behind a barrier of sea life, behind a barrier of time, so that when I did get ashore, I only knew it was *here*. Even if I perked up after a few drinks, I always forgot I was in China. I was 'here'. Do you see that?

The first thing I knew when I got there was the extent of this mistake. I don't mean I was disillusioned, I want to make that clear. I didn't feel with Conrad 'that what expected had already gone, had passed unseen in a sigh, in a flash together with the youth, with the strength, with the romance of illusions.' That sigh, that flash, never happened. There was no moment that crystallized the East for me. This moment did not occur. What happened was different. I had been looking forward to something anxiously and I called this China, yet when I reached China I was still looking forward to it from exactly the same position. Perhaps China wasn't there, didn't exist for me just as I could not exist for China.

And I even began to believe my work was unreal, although there was always one voice that said: you get hold of a firebar and you'll soon enough know how real it is.

Then we were alongside and not long after the captain called for me.

—We've arranged a cricket match with the *H.M.S. Proteus* and we want to show them, he said.

—Sure, said the chief steward. We've arranged a cricket match and we'll show them foxy swaddies what we think of them.

—And you're going to play, said the captain.

—Sure, said the chief. And now you've got to titivate yourself up a bit, make yourself look a bit smart you know. You can't play with an old towel round your neck. What would they think of us?

—That's right, said the captain. The last time you went ashore with a towel round your neck, you were a proper disgrace to the ship.

—You were the only man who went ashore without a tie, said the chief.

—I went to have a swim, I began. But what was the use of talking to these old washerwomen anyway? And I was highly amused to be looking right down once more into the corrupt heart of the life I'd left behind; I thought it extremely funny that my existence had not changed at all and that wherever I was I would be evaluated, smelt out, by my own kind.

A little later the chief steward came down to the forecastle with all sorts of fancy white ducks he'd rooted out and pretty soon I found one hanging on the curtain rail of my bunk. As I changed the firemen grinned.

—Now you'll feel at home, Jimmy.

No other fireman had been selected to play and inwardly I raged.

Outside the chief was saying: —We'll show these swaddles we can make a proper respectable turnout.

Then we strolled along the wharf towards the cricket field which was situated between a slagheap and a coaldump. A river mist was rolling thickly over towards the city, but the atmosphere was clear where we were going save for a thin rain of coal which drizzled in our faces from the tips, speckling our white trousers with dust. Now you could make a fine character study out of this. There was old Lofty and Hersey and Sparks and Tubby and the three mates and the doctor and you could make a fine description out of each one. But unfortunately I can't discriminate, maybe it's my loss, but they all looked the same to me, those sailors: they were all sons of bitches and now after so long I can only see them at all through the kind of mist there was then. So I won't bother you with that. They just looked damned funny as they straggled down the wharf. And I must have looked the funniest of all straggling along with them, all of us in the fancy white ducks the steward had given us. Some trousers far too short and some far too long, which made us look more like a bunch of Chinese coolies than a proper respectable turnout.

Then the swaddies came out of the *H.M.S. Proteus* and they hadn't bothered about any whites. Some wore khaki shorts, some dungarees, others singlets and khaki trousers. And now after so long I only see them through a kind of mist. I can't even say, Well, there was one fellow like this. Hell, they were just swaddies, misled, exploited, simple, handsome and ugly like the rest of us.

Their captain and the chief steward spun a coin. The chief steward won.

The captain of the *Arcturion,* who was not playing but who was reported to be 'keen' on cricket, stood behind a godown and watched the proceedings with a heavily critical air.

—It was my call, I laughed. You should have run.

—I thought you said you could play cricket, the chief grumbled.

—I called. It was up to you to run, I laughed.

—Don't laugh, said the chief.

But I went right on laughing. Then the captain appeared and it seemed that he was damned angry too.

—What are you laughing at? I thought you said you could play cricket, he said. And you've run our best man out and been bowled yourself. Why, I thought you said—

—Firemen don't play cricket, I said shortly and walked away from the wharf.

Once I looked back. Lofty was playing hard with a cross bat, defending the honour of the welldock. Then rain sluiced down and stopped play. It was the monsoon season.

I ran for the *Arcturion* and changed quickly.

At the entrance I watched the others shuffling back mournfully into the seaman's forecastle, their white trousers clinging to them like wet rags. Doom! Doom! Doom!

Other firemen joined me at the entrance and we watched the stevedores unloading our cargo, of scouting planes, a bomber, a fighting plane, machine guns, anti-aircraft guns, 25 pound bombs, ammunition. I did not believe in all this. I was not there.

And here's what I want to ask you again. Haven't you felt this too, that you know yourself so well that the ground you tread on is your ground: it is never China or Siberia or England or anywhere else . . . It is always you. It is always the earth of you, the wood, the iron of you, the asphalt you step on is the asphalt of you whether it's on Broadway or the Chien Mon.

And you carry your horizon in your pocket wherever you are.

PART TWO

Malcolm Lowry Remembered

Malcolm Lowry: A Note

by Conrad Aiken

My opinion of Malcolm Lowry as a writer is of course already on record, in the "blurb" which I was asked to write for *Under the Volcano* when it first appeared. More extensively, it can be found in the portrait of Lowry—on the whole, pretty accurate—in *Ushant,* my autobiography, where he appears as Hambo. In the last section of this is a fragment of imaginary dialogue between us which was actually written at Cuernavaca in 1937, when I was staying with him, and which, allowing for the necessary "heightening," is very close to the mark. It will suggest, I think, something of the remarkable spiritual and aesthetic and psychological symbiosis that grew up between us immediately after our first meeting in 1929. He had read my novel *Blue Voyage,* and wrote me about it to Rye, Sussex, where he assumed I was still living; and he asked me to lunch with him, either in London or Cambridge, where he was to matriculate in September. On finding that I was in the other Cambridge—on the Charles River—he at once inquired whether I would consider taking him on as a pupil, the terms to be arranged. The terms were arranged, he set sail on a freighter from Liverpool to Bermuda, on another from Bermuda to Boston, and arrived one day in July on my doorstep in Plympton Street, Cambridge, next door to the Grolier Bookshop, with a taropatch in one hand and a small battered suitcase in the other.

The suitcase contained an exercise book (and not much else) in which was as much as he had then written of his first novel, *Ultramarine*; and it was on this, as I have described at length in *Ushant,* that we were to work all that wonderful summer. *Blue Voyage* he knew better than I did—he knew it by heart. Its influence on him was profound and permanent, and was evident even in that first title—he was delighted with my suggestion that he might well have taken the next step and called the book *Purple Passage.*

But though the influence was to continue even into the later work, a matter that was frequently and amusedly discussed between us, and was also to comprise a great deal that was said by me in conversation, it was much more complicated than that. The fact is that we were uncannily alike in almost everything, found instantly that we spoke the same language, were astonishingly *en rapport*; and it was therefore the most natural thing in the world that a year later, when difficulties arose between him and his father, I was able to act as mediator (I had by then returned to Rye), and, as a result of this, for the next three years, *in loco parentis*. I became his father.

Time and space were to interrupt this quite marvelous relationship, but never to change it. *Tout passe, l'amitie reste.* His first letter to me had begun: "I have lived only nineteen years, most of them badly." Would he have thought that he lived the rest of his short life badly? No, I don't think so. The work speaks for him, and he knew that it was superb.

Call It Misadventure

by Clarissa Lorenz

The current revival of interest in Malcolm Lowry's works takes me back to the thirties, when the late British writer lived with us during my marriage to his mentor, Conrad Aiken, poet and novelist. He was an enigma to me, this mystic and demonologist, this alcoholic who loved life and destroyed himself like Dylan Thomas, with whom he had much in common. A great autobiographical writer grossly neglected, he saw only two of his works published, *Ultramarine,* a novel about his seafaring year, and *Under the Volcano,* a masterpiece documenting the horrors of alcoholism.

We first met Malcolm in 1929. Nothing in his cherubic countenance suggested the crucified genius. A snapshot I took of him in Cambridge, Massachusetts, shows a handsome, rugged youth of twenty with wavy brown hair, a radiant smile, and the intense blue eyes of a visionary. He had crossed the Atlantic impelled to meet the author of *Blue Voyage,* having assumed that my husband's novel had been dedicated to him. (We had the same initials, C.M.L., but he didn't use his first name, Clarence.) Presumptuous, wasn't it, and yet he felt something mystic about the coincidence, destiny pointing to Aiken. Under Conrad's supervision, he tinkered with *Ultramarine* for the next four years. An excerpt, "Seductio ad Absurdum," appeared in O'Brien's *The Best British Short Stories of 1931,* and caused the volume to be banned from British public libraries.

In the early thirties we went to live in Rye, Sussex, where we had Jeake's House, a seventeenth-century edifice named after a family of astrologers and necromancers. This haunt intrigued Malcolm, and it became his second home. As a Cambridge University student, he spent all his vacations with us. His father, a Liverpool cotton broker, staunch Wesleyan, and fox-hunting Conservative, had engaged my husband as tutor and therapist to grapple with his son, a dipsomaniac. I kept my fingers crossed. One genius in the house was enough. For all my maternal feelings toward Malcolm, ten years my junior, I associated him with catastrophe. On his own admission, just to meet him was a disaster. Conrad for a long time suffered fracture headaches—souvenirs of a bibulous wrestling match with his protégé over the lid of the WC tank.

They were both night owls, spending convivial hours at Ping-Pong and literary powwows. Their "pub crawls" stirred gossip in Rye and upset my domestic timetable. I would sit by the front window, chafing, while the dinner dried up in the oven. One foggy night a couple of muddied, blood-streaked apparitions staggered in, looking sheepish. They had fallen into the river—fortunately at low tide. "How much longer will Conrad put up with this madman?" My diary gave him short shrift. "Not to be housebroken . . . Definitely no mixer . . . A caged lion . . ."

Malcolm tried hard not to be a nuisance. A creature of extremes, he either starved himself or gorged—on everything but fish (choking on the bones happened to be one of his many phobias). I kept fearing he would absentmindedly set fire to his mattress or break a leg falling downstairs. He moved like a somnabulist, his blue blazer spotted and rumpled, a necktie holding up his trousers. Keeping him laundered and presentable called for finesse. His socks created minor crises. One day he decided to bury a pair of argyles. "About time, too," Conrad grunted. "But don't go near the gasometer or there might be another Neuenkirchen disaster!" Malcolm's deep belly laugh resounded through the house.

He was given to prescient statements and long, brooding silences, and was never so isolated seemingly as when part of a group. Social occasions paralyzed him. Playing bridge or parlor games like mock murder trials, he would sit in a trance, lost in his private world of daemons and demons. "Wake up, Malc," I would say, snapping my fingers, a liberty that now makes me squirm. I was the one who needed waking up. I missed a golden opportunity to share in a picaresque experience. Cold comfort, the fact that failure to recognize and foster genius early enough is universal! I am the poorer for neglecting the outpourings of a brilliant mind and a unique imagination.

Our demure young housemaid adored him. "He's a real gentleman." Jenny sensed his sweetness, humility, and loneliness. He had endured four years of near-blindness as a boy, forbidden to read, write, or play games because of a chronic ulcerated cornea in both eyes. The youngest of four sons, he called himself the runt of the family, although he won the schoolboy golf championship of England while attending The Leys in Cambridge (where "Mr. Chips" was a master). He was a fine swimmer, a great hiker, and he even broke a record for lifting barbells.

With women he was shy and taciturn. On one of his solitary tramps along Romney Marsh skirting the Channel, he mailed me an apology in rhyme, for what offense I don't recall. The note vanished, doubtless into Jenny's apron pocket. She saved most of his discarded scribblings. However disorganized he may have been in other respects, Malcolm was a disciplined writer, productive for long, sober periods, endlessly revising and turning out draft after draft —totally committed to art. "Do you know which stars are which," he wrote a young friend shortly before he died, "and what bird is flying over your head and what flower blossoming? If you don't, the anguish of not knowing is a very valid field for the artist. Moreover when you learn something it's a good thing to repossess the position of your original ignorance."

His love and knowledge of nature ran deep. I really came to know him through his protagonist in *Ultramarine*—Dana Hilliot, a coal trimmer on a tramp steamer shunned as a toff and razzed as a slovenly drunk. ("Lord God, look down on your unworthy and unwashed servant, Hilliot, the Liverpool-Norwegian, whose knees knock together at thunder, whose filthy hands tremble always in impotent prayer . . . as he stands alone, naked, weaponless, deliver him from his bondage and bring him out of the darkness and the grief and the pain into sunlight.")

An Ishmael longing for Janet, his girl in Liverpool, he progresses from self-pity to compassion. In one of his fantasies he predicted his own death. ("When the door of Dana Hilliot, old-age pensioner, was forced, the police found him dying on the mattress in an emaciated and verminous condition. Death from exhaustion and self-neglect . . .") *Ultramarine* was to spearhead a series of self-portraits entitled "The Voyage That Never Ends." Malcolm was an ardent disciple of Aiken's credo that extension of consciousness warranted the ultimate sacrifice.

In the course of working out his oedipal problems by proxy, he wanted to use Conrad's dream, recounted in *Great Circle,* of eating the father's skeleton. That, he was told, would be carrying things too far. The Aiken touches deleted, *Ultramarine* went off to Chatto & Windus, only to be stolen from the publisher's car, where he left his briefcase momentarily. While the firm advertised in vain for the manuscript, friends of Malcolm's salvaged fragments of the only other copy, and he supplied the missing pages. Jonathan Cape (who had turned down *Great Circle*) accepted *Ultramarine* with a £40 advance.

In April, 1933, Malcolm accompanied us to Spain for a much-needed holiday. A university graduate of twenty-four, with a third-class Tripos in English, he looked neater but much heavier, a beer drinker and "perpetual source of anxiety to a bewildered father," as he confessed. Lowry Senior still trusted Conrad to wean his prodigal son from the bottle, an onerous job for any father surrogate.

We reached Gibraltar in a stuporous state, feverish and muscle-sore from our second typhoid shots. The noise, tropical heat, and violent atmosphere amounted to hallucinations. Radios blared, barrel organs ground out rhumbas, hawkers screeched their wares, beggars clawed us, a female brass band blasted away from a balcony, a voluptuous danseuse clicked castanets at some Russian sailors, and British troops marched down Main Street disrupting a funeral procession. "A mad jumble of the living and dead!" Malcolm remarked as he grinned, his eyes blue as the Mediterranean.

On the ferry to Algeciras he pointed out several feluccas gliding through the Strait, their swallow-shaped lateen sails unchanged for centuries. He took all the vexations and discomforts of travel in stride and ignored gibes about his girth and the ten-gallon sombrero he had bought. "Just as well he doesn't understand Spanish," said Conrad. In Ronda, after Malcolm and Conrad had ordered a triple brandy at one bar, *aguardiente* drinkers stared at them awestruck. The Civil Guard kept us awake with their nocturnal whistles signaling the all's-well.

Conrad dozed fitfully in the train to Granada (a seven-hour endurance test). Malcolm had carried off his hotel key for the second time. He read *Ulysses,* perspiring in his short sleeves. Whenever the locomotive labored uphill at a snail's pace, he leaned out the window and gesticulated at the engineer to hurry up. The closer we came to the Sierra Nevadas, the farther away they seemed, elusive as paradise, their snowy peaks lost in the clouds. Beyond this apparent mirage was the Alhambra, our destination. A request for two rooms had brought a garbled wire from the Carmona pension: "Reserving bath rooms." Conrad said wryly, "They must have known you were coming." Malcolm chuckled. I hoped his sense of humor would survive Ed Burra's darts and barbs. The young sur-realist painter, who would be joining us later, spared no one in his caricatures.

We were parched by the long, hot journey, and longed for a cold beer. The Carmonas' son-in-law, Tende, a scrawny, lynx-eyed youth, met us at the station and invited himself along with us to the Holly-wood Café, where a Negro jazz band performed. "Traveling a thou-sand miles for this?" Malcolm said plaintively. A paunchy Spaniard at the next table hooted, "What a fat belly!" Conrad's retort "Look at your own" jolted him. Tende sniggered and kept goggling at Mal-colm's drinking capacity. I foresaw trouble.

The Villa Carmona had a romantic appeal—a white stucco, near the Moorish palaces, surrounded by flowering bushes and fruit trees, a well and a fountain in the sun-dappled courtyard. We felt we were in good hands after seeing such names in the guest book as Manuel De Falla, Herbert Read, Katherine Lee Bates, and John Singer Sargent. The household consisted of the recently widowed senora; her unmarried sister, Carmen; a son, a daughter (Tende's wife), and their infant, Nina; Luisa the Singing Maid and a mad, mad cook.

Weather permitting, we ate in the patio, pomegranate petals fall-ing into our omelet, soup, or *olla podrida*. The food was delicious, but the odor of olive oil and saffron hung in the air, blending with that of musk and urine. Cats, dogs, chickens, goats, and donkeys swarmed the neighborhood. We heard of stray cats being shot at night for fodder. An emaciated tabby begged for tidbits at every meal but was never fed, even after she had kittens in the cellar. "Probably belongs to the Republic," Malcolm concluded.

While the Carmonas were puzzled by Malcolm, they doted on Conrad, who lent prestige to the establishment. A schoolmarm from Ohio, thrilled to meet him, said that her pupils loved his poetry. "They memorize the most difficult lines of your *Preludes*." When-ever fellow guests buttonholed my husband, Malcolm would slip away, feeling superfluous. But Luisa lost her heart to him. Like my Jenny, the Singing Maid dawdled over her chores in his room, pour-ing out her love in *cante hondo*. "When she brought in the baby one morning, I couldn't decide whether it was just a friendly gesture or deliberate invitation. So I cooed, not knowing any nursery rhymes in whatever language."

His laughter was easily touched off—by my gaffe in a stationery store when I asked for an embrace instead of paper clips, by a Texas rancher who wanted written copies of all of Conrad's

Preludes, or by a sign at the cinema, "Children who are not at the breast must pay for their seats." He relished jokes at his own expense, as when that patient drone, Carmen, asked whether the grubby blue socks she found in the *baño* were his. Conrad, translating, said crisply, "I suggest they are yours, and that they walked into the bathroom looking for soap and water."

Malcolm had a keen eye for symbols. He was fascinated by my account of an ironmonger in Granada wrapping up some nails in a rotogravure page depicting the Crucifixion. One moonlit night while admiring Granada from the embankment, Conrad tossed English pennies over the parapet. They hit the monastery roof 300 feet below with a faint ping. When Malcolm imitated him, his coins dropped soundlessly into a void. "No echoes, no answers—the story of my life," he said with detachment, as we strolled into a wineshop nearby, a rendezvous for artists. There Conrad made a discovery. Among the paintings that patrons had left in lieu of cash were two self-portraits by Sargent and a watercolor of his niece, the Cynthia of *Blue Voyage.* "By Jove, this is uncanny!" Malcolm blinked with amazement. "Coming across your heroine in the Alhambra!"

The Moorish palaces left him underwhelmed—slavish replicas of thirteenth-century grandeur too perfectly restored to convey a sense of antiquity. He ducked our excursions to the gypsy caves in the Albaicin or to charming hamlets like La Zubia. Conventional tourism was anathema to him. He preferred his own inner landscape and orbit, sampling the cantinas. Sober or not, he observed life with an artist's eye, selecting meaningful material, whereas I snapped pictures indiscriminately and filled my diary with a hodgepodge of impressions.

The pension saw less and less of him as the days flew by. Tende would lurk in the background at mealtimes, pointing him out to newcomers with a sly, "Psst, *el borracho!*" A barfly? That nice, quiet young man? The ladies looked at him askance, and he pretended to be oblivious of them. Ed Burra's arrival complicated life still more. The frail, pixilated artist appeared in a dusty green suit and dragging his luggage, which included a laundry bag.

"I took the wrong train from Barcelona and got lost," he said in his languid, epicene voice, "but then wound up in Almeria, a spot so beautiful I wouldn't have missed it for the world!" He was a novelty to the Carmonas, amusing them with music-hall ditties rendered in a falsetto, and cartoons of fellow guests.

Before long my fears were justified. One day at lunch Ed did a caricature of Malcolm as a blimp in a sombrero. Tende pounced on it with glee, passing it around the patio and drawing giggles and guffaws. "That punk," I sputtered, aching to wring his puny neck. Malcolm got to his feet, snatched the sketch, added a pipe to the mouth, tore it up and flung the pieces in Tende's face, then berated the artist. "That was an unkind thing to do," he said with characteristic restraint. "The trouble with you is that people are too good to you." Ed shrugged and twinkled, "Oh, you don't know half the things they say about me!"

Ed could kill his detractors with a pencil. Malcolm had no such outlet. He had been initiated into sadism at a tender age, he told me, in a rare burst of confidence. "My nanny used to whip me daily with brambles until I bled. I thought it was the customary thing so I never complained. My parents gave her the sack only after the family gardener told them he saw her hold me upside down over my bath." Sadism he felt throughout Spain—a terrified urchin held by the heels over a precipice, a donkey hobbling on fettered forelegs, a little girl blithely twisting a dragonfly on a spike.

Ed's mischief had emboldened Tende into stepping up his baiting. He told Conrad that Malcolm was known all over Granada as *el borracho* and the Civil Guard were watching him. "Once I see him in the Hollywood Café, he asked for *aguardiente* and two women." The day I caught sight of him he was lurching through the streets jeered and laughed at, children and adults turning around to poke fun at him. Scattering them would only have doubled his humiliation. He stopped at a music shop, listening to a flamenco record, a fixed smile on his face, then continued on his zigzag course. (". . . man no longer belongs to or understands the world he has created. Man had become a raven staring at a ruined heronry. Well, let him deduce his own ravenhood from it.")

He and Conrad had been talking of little else but the first bullfight of the season. They saw nothing cruel in the *corrida*. It was a battle between evenly matched contestants, a catharsis purging spectators of aggression, an initiation into manhood at worst, blunting the sensibilities and brutalizing men for war. My husband treasured a snapshot of a beaming, mustachioed aficionado crouching beside a live bull, the autograph reading, "Don Ernesto Hemingvia, toreando a un cabestro castrado en Pamplona."

On Easter Sunday we drove to the *corrida* with the English literary critic Professor I. A. Richards and his German-born wife. They had come to the Carmona after learning of Conrad's presence—a meeting long desired. When I told them that Malcolm was with us, they exchanged glances. He sat beside me in the car, morose and glowering, feeling *de trop* and disliked by his former examiner (and hero) at St. Catharine's College. At times like this he took on the menacing majesty of a bull, shoulders hunched, head lowered, ready to lunge. *El toro* was Tende's new name for him.

The *barrera* was packed. Seats in the *sol* cost less than those in the *sombre,* and so we sat in the sun's glare, the Richardses like myself fortified by smelling salts and dark glasses. Behind us tipsy peasants swayed and swore over their goatskin flasks. Throughout the gory spectacle Conrad blazed with excitement. I kept seeing Malcolm in the arena, taunted and goaded by *picadores,* bewildered and maddened by *banderilleros*. When the bull was given the *coup de grâce,* he crumpled in a genuflecting posture before the matador, his death agonies hailed with savage roars of *Ole, Ole!*

One slaughter was enough for the Richardses, and only pride, or cowardice, stopped me from leaving with them. My head was splitting. I kept whiffing spirits of ammonia, as the aesthetics of the "beautiful cape-and-sword dance" continued to elude me.

On the Richardses' last evening at the pension, Malcolm was at his worst, on the defensive and boastful, something alien to his nature. We sat around the table in the patio with our drinks, tobacco smoke spiraling up to a star-studded sky, nightingales competing with owls, Ed looking like a gargoyle in the flickering candlelight, the professor reminiscing about Harvard, where he was currently teaching semantics, Malcolm interrupting him with his drunken maunderings, Conrad increasingly austere.

I could imagine the tongue-lashing Malcolm got next morning on his long walk with Conrad. "Your irresponsible behavior reflects anything but credit on me—a scandal at the pension and *persona non grata* with the police. I'm fed up making excuses and apologizing for your besotted states and disgusting hangovers. Hell's bells, when will you come to your senses? Your father keeps asking me what the score is . . ." Malcolm came back utterly crushed. He wasn't allowed to live in London or go to sea again, and he dreaded being cut off from the parental purse. Conrad began to talk of releasing him, much though we needed those monthly 20-guinea checks. The whole dilemma cast a pall on us.

In the next several weeks his drinking tapered off and he bore

Tende's torments like a Spartan. But even an English gentleman has his breaking point. One afternoon in May, during a period of regression, he started climbing Alhambra Hill when he heard the derisive "*El toro, el toro,*" Tende with some friends cavorting behind and aping his wobbly gait. Malcolm seized his *bête noire* by the scruff of the neck, rammed him uphill a hundred yards or so, flung him down, picked him up again for a repeat performance, then left him in the dust. "Where did you deposit him—at the Puerta da la Justicia?" Conrad inquired sardonically, as his protégé related the triumph with pardonable pride. "Three cheers," I rejoiced. "That's my boy!"

From then on he had no more trouble with Tende. But fate had other entanglements in store for him—an exotic American girl who came to the pension with her French escort. Malcolm, instantly smitten, stole her away, and for the rest of her brief stay they were inseparable, doing the town and roaming the foothills, falling into a brook one morning, he looking like a mesmerized owl, to quote Conrad. I was glad to see him relate to another human being besides his mentor, but I had misgivings about this glamour girl in the large picture hat who found him fascinating and so handsome.

Their romance touched off arguments about virginity and Spanish morality, causing a flutter. The ladies mellowed toward our paying guest, waxing lyrical over his transformation. He had come out of his shell, reborn, shedding radiance in all directions, loving everybody, kissing little Nina, and cuddling the ugly kitten. Now he bathed daily, shined his shoes, borrowed my nail file, and absentmindedly wore his shirts wrong side out. Conrad's violent reaction mystified me. "All this primping and preening is positively revolting!" There were acrimonious exchanges after Jan left with her Frenchman.

Late one night they staged a terrific row in the patio. I returned from a stroll to hear Malcolm bellowing, "And what about incestuous Susie?" a reference to *Great Circle.* In an alcoholic stupor he then threatened to kill Conrad, not for the first time either. Ed turned a ghastly green. I asked, "What's all the rumpus about?" An ominous silence broken only by the whoo-i of owls, Conrad mute as a graven image.

Twenty years later he supplied the answer in his autobiography, *Ushant,* Hambo speaking. ("Well, it was . . . understood between us . . . You had eaten your father's skeleton—why then shouldn't I eat yours? Not symbolically only, either, my dear old fellow . . .

You as much as admitted that now it was my turn—my turn to kill you. First by taking Nita. Yes. For of course we both knew that both of us were powerfully drawn to that open wound . . . Not so? Yes—in the shadow of the Hundred Fountains, at the Alhambra, you proposed to share her, as foul a sort of voyeur's incest as any second-rate god could imagine. . . .")

The rift shortened our holiday by a week, Conrad now determined to drop his protégé. Adios, adios—Spanish farewells are like Beethoven finales. The Carmonas loaded us with lunch baskets, wine, and two enormous bouquets. A melancholy quartet entrained for Algeciras. Malcolm was in a blue funk and suffering from an intestinal bug. Having forgotten to take his two volumes of *Ulysses,* he had nothing to read for ten hours. The flowers wilting in my lap represented my hopes of Spain's producing a miracle.

From Algeciras we dragged Ed along to Morocco on a whirlwind tour of Ceuta and Tetuán. He sulked and we sweltered, Malcolm remaining in Gibraltar to search for solace and adventure. He must have found these, for the Civil Guard were downright nasty when we returned, until Conrad assured them that our *amigo* would be sailing with us.

Next morning we boarded the *Straithaird,* encumbered with baskets, shawls, donkey trappings, Spanish posters, and Egyptian runners. Frayed nerves and edgy tempers prevailed. Conrad, almost knocked down by playful moppets, was tempted to pitch the noisy brats overboard. Malcolm shared a cabin on that hectic voyage with "three Somerset Maugham Colonels who were dying of the hiccups." His evil genie pursued him. A disenchanting letter from Jan in Lisbon kept him fastened to the desk, penning an interminable ship's log, when he wasn't in the bar. What Conrad called the first fine careless rupture marked the beginning of an ill-starred marriage.

("Hilliot leaned on the rail and looked out to sea. Suddenly he put his hands over his head to shut out the frantic din of the winches. He felt as if he were lost in a dark tunnel, and all at once he saw light at the end of it; and the light was sunshine in a quiet garden, with windblown roses and peonies and Janet was there and stroked his forehead with her cool hands, while they listened to the singing of a tap; and the flower bed was all runnelled with water. Oh Jesus! he was on a ship, he was just a dirty sailor looking out to sea, nothing more . . .")

England's green, restful landscape was a reprieve, although homecomings are usually a letdown. Important mail had been lost, the house looked a mess, our Jenny had taken another job, and dental troubles compounded Malcolm's misery. The Spanish bacillus still caused ructions. So did his drinking. The thorny issue was again thrashed out, he begging for Conrad's respect and permission to come again, for he loved Jeake's House. "Please tell the pater that I'm solving my problem," he implored, after one week's abstinence. The morning he left for London he couldn't find his ticket. I offered to hunt for it. "Don't bother," he said with a feeble smile. "I think perhaps I chewed it up." I found it near the rubbish can later that day.

A suicidal letter came within a fortnight. He was being taken to a nursing home for dysentery complicated by alcoholism, thence to the "pump room" to be dried out. *Ultramarine* had spawned a few piddling reviews. "If the art of writing is imitation, the author has mastered it," said the London *Times*. He couldn't bear to look at his brainchild. His family, meanwhile, prayed for him and urged him to try advertising copy.

Still *in loco parentis,* Conrad was in the States the fall of 1933 when Malcolm brought Jan down to Rye. Friends who put them up told me he intended to marry her without his father's knowledge or consent. "He hopes that we'll stake him to a honeymoon in Paris, where she wants to live. But we can't and won't lend him any more cash. They're both drinking up his allotments and she tampers with his writings. Needless to say, he's not doing any serious work. In fact, he's nothing but denatured alcohol, and getting barmier by the hour. His eccentricities have reached a point where we'll simply have to kick him out. Of course he's got to clean up his own messes, but we feel that Conrad should know about his predicament." Physicians who subsequently treated Malcolm for a chronic glandular infection marveled that he was still alive. The toxic effects might conceivably have accounted for his irrationalities for twelve years.

I last saw Malcolm in the summer of 1936. That winter he and Jan went to Mexico. The marriage cracked up a year later. He began writing *Under the Volcano,* a ten-year stint interrupted by the DT's, imprisonment as a Communist spy (so he wrote Conrad), attempts to castrate him ("unsuccessfully, I regret to report"), deportation, mental collapse and incarceration, rejection slips, penury, self-exile to British Columbia, and a holocaust.

His marriage to Margerie Bonner, a mystery-story writer, was the only happiness he ever knew, "the only thing holding me to life and sanity." She shared conditions "which made Gorky's *Lower Depths* look like a drawingroom comedy." For fourteen years they lived in a squatter's shack near Vancouver, with no wall insulation or heating stove. When fire destroyed their home in 1944, they rebuilt it themselves. Malcolm was badly burned rescuing some of his manuscripts. A novel, "Ballad of the White Sea," went up in flames, but he saved all of his masterpiece, and on Christmas Eve finished a fourth revision in a Lake Ontario pub.

". . . only a person whose whole existence is his work, who had dominated and disciplined the volcano within him, at what a cost of suffering even I do not wholly understand, could have written such a book." So Mrs. Lowry wrote their literary agent. Both London and New York houses accepted *Under the Volcano* the same day. It came out in 1947 (fourteen years after *Ultramarine*), three years after another alcoholic's saga, *The Lost Weekend*—the law of series at work, Malcolm observed wryly.

A season of fame, then relative oblivion. He couldn't duplicate or surpass his magnum opus. (For lack of a new radio battery, the Lowrys missed a broadcast eulogizing "Canada's greatest, most successful writer.") The rest of his works appeared posthumously—two volumes of short stories, *Dark as the Grave Wherein My Friend Is Laid,* and *Hear Us O Lord from Heaven Thy Dwelling Place.* "Lunar Caustic," a novella describing his experiences in a psychiatric ward, underwent changes for twenty years. *October Ferry to Gabriola,* another novel, will be published this year.[1]

As for his *Selected Letters,* they reflect man's inhumanity to a man of tremendous integrity, charity, and good humor. Cheerfulness was indeed "always breaking out." Once, recovering from surgery, he explained his presence in the maternity wing, to an alarmed expectant father, as one of those new, larger atomic babies just recently on the market.

His friendship with Conrad Aiken continued to the end. Paying tribute to his mentor in Wake, he recalled the time he lived in a squalid basement flat in Manhattan and his landlady announced a visitor, a "Mr. the Kraken." That tickled Malcolm. "Mr. Kraken. Well, well, sometimes when feeling gloomy, I find I only have to think of this incident to start chuckling: finally the chuckle becomes a roar of laughter, and melancholy is banished. And then again I think of myself: who the hell am I? What an incredible privilege!

[1] A hardcover edition was published by World Publishing Company, 1970, and a paperback edition by New American Library (Plume), 1971.

Did I really know Conrad Aiken? And did he once actually come to see me? Or did I make that up?"

His odyssey ended in 1957 at age forty-eight, when, in a drunken state, he took an overdose of sleeping tablets. The coroner's verdict was misadventure.

Malcolm Lowry: A First Impression

by James Stern

The first time I set eyes on him was one wintry night in Paris, in 1933.

But before speaking of that night, I should say that a few weeks previously I had read by chance a book, just published, called *Ultramarine*. It was one of those thinly disguised autobiographical first novels. The author's name meant nothing to me, but the book did. It was about an Englishman, an educated young man, who had signed on to a ship in Liverpool as a deckhand, or trimmer. Indeed the writer had evidently, as the romantic phrase goes, "run away to sea." I thought that was wonderful. Here was someone, probably of my own age, who had done what I had always wanted to do. In fact, I had wanted so much to "go to sea" that I had been willing, at the age of twelve, to face the years at an English naval college; until one day someone had warned the Irish-born Protestant boy that in order to pass into such a college he would have to stand before a group of medical men—naked! No. That, for this twelve-year old, was too much: if not actually hitting, it was surely snooping, below the belt.

So what, finally, did I do? I did "run away." Not, however, to sea, but to a somewhat remote region of Africa. And from that experience, some time later, I had written a number of thinly disguised autobiographical stories. Eventually, a year or so before that night in Paris, these grim tales had been published in book form under the highly unsalable title: *The Heartless Land*.

It was pelting with rain that night in Paris. I was on my way to a party in the studio of a friend, another impecunious writer, who lived in the Rue Daguerre. By the time I had turned the corner of what was then the Avenue d'Orleans, water was trickling down my neck, my feet were squelching in my shoes. Only in Africa, however, had I been obliged to relieve thirst with rain. I was also empty-handed. In the company I kept in those days a man who turned up at a party without at least one bottle of wine got what most of us considered he deserved: a dirty look, and sometimes the door as well. So I ducked into a bistro.

To me one of the many glories of Paris is that its inhabitants are practically immune to human eccentricity. Neither to the patron behind the bar, nor to the customer sitting alone at one of four small tables, did it seem in the least surprising that between them on the sawdust-covered floor there lay stretched, flat on his back, evidently asleep, a robust-looking fellow with a week of stiff red stubble on his face, and across his stomach a guitar. Round his neck the recumbent figure wore a scarlet bandanna, over his Herculean chest a jacket of royal blue tweed, and on his legs a pair of dirty gray flannel trousers. What I also could not help noticing was that, although the rain had been coming down in torrents all afternoon and evening, the sturdy brown shoes on his remarkably small feet appeared to be dry. . . .

Standing at the bar, I asked the patron for a *coup de rouge* and two bottles of white wine: *ordinaire—pour emporter*. As the glass of red wine was being placed upon the bar, I heard behind me what sounded like a stifled yawn or groan. And turning my head, I saw that the figure on the floor had risen to his feet. He was considerably shorter than I had expected. Guitar gripped in his left hand, he approached the bar in slow, very deliberate steps, until his right elbow was within a few inches of my left. Alert, we squinted at each other out of the corners of our eyes.

"Excuse me, sir," he suddenly said, in a very English English, "but could you possibly be—er—British?"

To my surprise and embarrassment, I heard myself reply: "Oh, is my French as bad as all that?"

"Oh, not at all. On the contrary. It's just those flannel—those bags!"

He let out a chuckle. He smiled. His teeth were white, and even. Instantly his whole scrubby face lit up, expressing an indefinable charm.

"We at least have them in common," he said. "Let us try not to lose them." And he put out his hand—a surprisingly small hand, I noticed later, with short stubby fingers. But I winced in their vise.

Then it happened.

"The name's Lowry," he said, "Malcolm."

I stared. And told him mine.

To my amazement, he stared, his hairy mouth agape.

It was I who managed to find words first. "Liverpool?" I uttered. "Ultra-Liverpool?"

"Liverpool. Yes," he flashed. "Painted white across my stern!"

I had not time to laugh, for up went his arms, guitar and all, and I found myself enveloped in a rib-crushing hug—and a cloud of absinth. "Bound," came his hoarse voice in my ear, "bound for the Cape, lud! All aboard for the heartless land!"

Then, falling apart, we looked each other over, like two dogs whose tails did not wag, but were held high: the prospects for the immediate future seemed boundless. At last, as a substitute for all the things that clamored to—and would, we knew, in time—be said, we shattered the silence of the bistro with brust after burst of laughter.

"*Patron!*" boomed Malcolm Lowry in his very English French. "*Un pernod fils, s'il vous plait. Et pour mon ami . . .*"

"*Un rouge,*" I added. "*Un ballon.*"

The grimace of the future author of *Under the Volcano* was not lost on me. By midnight, however, each of us had convinced the other that he was a budding genius. Of himself I believe Malcolm laughingly boasted that he would soon be "out-Mobying Melville."

Now one might have thought that to any young person such an encounter would have been a memorable occasion, an incident sufficiently surprising to be recorded or resurrected in conversation over the years by one as well as the other of the participants. Yet in retrospect it seems quite in keeping with Lowry's enigmatic character that from that night in Paris until his death in Sussex in 1957 not once, in our correspondence or in my presence, do I remember his referring to this first meeting. And although I grew to realize that of facts Malcolm, like many other writers of fiction, was no passionate lover, whenever I heard someone ask rhetorically: "But can you really believe what Lowry says?" I would be reminded of what I can only presume was his inability or refusal to recognize the coincidental aspects of our first encounter. Personally, I have always been inclined to think that Lowry looked upon coincidences as unphenomenal phenomena; that he took them for granted as the permanent and necessary clothing for his own particular psyche. Nor do I feel it a contradiction to say that I believe he loved coincidences enough to miss them when they failed to recur, whereupon I can imagine him, in secret and with a grin of infinite cunning, setting about to create one—more unlikely than those that hitherto had caused his friends to shake their heads in disbelief! Here I am hazarding a guess, of course, but how else can one account for his erratic, restless, self-obsessed life having been so packed with eerie happenings, with inexplicable signs and portents, with stolen manuscripts, with sudden mysterious conflagrations in which houses, including his own, would be burned to the ground, his books and chunks of huge unfinished novels lost? From such natural or man-made catastrophes and accidents on land Lowry himself would escape intact by what invariably seemed a miracle, and he would manage to survive at sea (though this was largely thanks to his prowess in the water) when other men would surely have drowned.

Did Lowry himself offer any explanation for such a peculiar concurrence of events? To this question he might insist that all his life he had felt haunted by coincidences, or he might add to the aura of largely self-created mystery by an involved dissertation on the mystical dogmas of voodoo and cabalism. When confronted, he would not deny that he possessed magic powers. "Ah!" he would breathe, his whole face alight with pleasure. Then I used to think I had never seen a smile so infectious, a pair of eyes so sly. Yes indeed, Malcolm was quick to create his own legend.

A major factor in the Lowry legend was the man's physical strength. Something of this power I was soon to learn from personal experience, for that night in Paris did not end in the bistro in the Rue Daguerre. In fact, like other nights I was to spend with Lowry, this first one had, in the conventional bedtime sense, no end. . . .

Whether my newly found friend had been invited to the party up the street, whether I suggested he should come along, or whether he himself had tacitly decided to accompany me, I no longer remember. I am certain, however, that we arrived at the studio together. I am also sure that by midnight "full swing" would be too mild a term to describe the state the party had reached. The studio, ill-lit and under a haze of tobacco smoke, was jammed with young people, many of whom I knew and most of whom were dancing with the abandon appropriate to the latest jazz from Louis Armstrong, to their ages, and the hour.

No sooner had I stepped across the threshold than I did a most unfortunate thing. What I had meant to do, at sight of so many familiar faces, was clap my hands above my head. What I had not taken into account was that each hand held a full bottle of wine.

The immediate result of my absent-mindedness can probably be imagined. Following the splintering crack there fell on my head and down my neck a cascade of glass and wine. A roar of laughter went up, and in my effort to cross the room I found myself severely buffeted by whirling couples. Suddenly I tripped over someone's feet; lost my balance; was about to fall. To check the fall my hands shot out to the first object that caught my eye. This object was a stove . . . one of those black, innocent-looking Victorian stoves from the top of which rises what the French call a *tuyau*, or pipe. It was at this *tuyau* that my fingers tried to grab. And succeeded. The yell of agony that I uttered must, I feel sure, have silenced, if only for an instant, even that crowded room. The next thing I knew I was being hoisted like a sack of potatoes upon someone's shoulders. I was riding, head down, up a ladder. Then I felt myself being deposited slowly, with infinite care, upon a bed.

"I could have told you!" came the hoarse, indignant voice close to my ear. "That beastly wine! Red wine, too! The ruin of many a good man! . . ."

To identify himself there was no need for my good Samaritan to have spoken, such was the overpowering stench of pernod.

An hour or two later, after my friend had bathed my hands in balm—butter, olive oil, or maybe raw meat, until at least the pain had receded—I told him, sitting on the terrace of the Café Dome, that since a certain night on the Mediterranean, in a sailor's tavern named the Zanzibar ("Zanzibar," Malcolm repeated in a whisper, and I can see him storing away the syllables in his fabulous memory), I told him that since that night I had never again been able to face anything that even reminded me of anise. "The very sight of it!" I said, as I watched him raise the muddy-yellow liquid to his lips.

"But, my dear chap!" he exclaimed in genuine surprise. "Surely you were taught always to return to the saddle immediately after a fall?"

"Well," I faltered, "there are falls and falls. . . ."

"Ah, yes. Those from that old mare name Grace! Don't I know! Don't I know!" He paused, then added with funeral solemnity: "To avoid the fall, one should always take great care to lie prone. Preferably on God's earth. Or the floor."

He sighed, raised his glass, then embarked upon a story about a bordello he claimed to have known in the port of Zanzibar. By the time the story ended the waiters of the Dome had started piling the chairs on to the terrace tables, the great shutters came rolling down, and over the city the night sky began slowly giving way to a steel-gray dawn. It was then, without plan or prearrangement, that we set out upon the first of what Malcolm called "little walks." As may be imagined, nothing connected with Lowry, save perhaps his feet and hands, could be considered "little." Of this first walk certain vivid memories stand out. I know where we walked to, and, more surprising perhaps, the hour at which we finally landed up in my flat in a house in what was then the Rue René Pauline. Briefly, we walked from the Dome to the Place Pigalle, and back to Montparnasse by way of Les Halles. Not far as the crow flies. But we were not crows. Moreover, when we stopped for what Malcolm called a "breather," it was not on a branch. This, the first, but not the longest of our "little walks," lasted twenty-eight hours. . . .

As walking companions Malcolm and I were not well matched. Unlike me, he was short in the leg. His gait, incidentally, was something special. No one who saw it could disbelieve that he had been a seaman. One landlubber we knew used to claim that he had only to catch sight of Lowry approaching to feel his stomach begin to heave and his hand go out to the rail. Unlike me Malcolm was, need I say, a talker, or rather a monologist. Unlike mine, his bump of locality on land was erratic. In cities, I don't think he ever knew where he was. Yet should I hesitate too long at a street corner, he would complain that I had "becalmed the ship," that "one should never set sail without a compass," or that "your canvas, mate, is not fully spread." Again, unlike me, Malcolm was not a visual person, or rather our eyes absorbed different aspects of the visible world. At night when I would be observing the faces of other pedestrians, searching for the name of an alley, looking at buildings, Malcolm's interest would be limited to bars and stars. He would be constantly gazing skyward, attempting to give me lessons in astronomy, a favorite subject, my ignorance of which genuinely grieved him. He also held grievances against astronomers. "See," he would proclaim, standing stockstill and raising his face in the midst of traffic, "see that luminous band, those countless gems? Know what they call 'em? The Milky Way! Milk-my-eye!" he would growl. "Pah!"

Well, Malcolm certainly could not complain that there was anything milky about our "way" across Paris. On this "little walk" we started off, I remember, on the first lap of what I still call "La

Route des Grands Hommes"—that is, a somewhat circuitous course, roughly by way of St. Germain-des-Pres, "just to fire a salvo," as Malcolm put it, as Pascal and other *grands garçons* who served the "intellectual world" at the Cafés Flore and Magots (both closed, of course, at five a.m.); a brief halt before the Hotel d'Alsace to pay our respects to the author of "The Ballad of Reading Gaol"; back down the cavernous, shopless, cat-and-history-infested Rue Visconti, to bow to Balzac; then along the Quai de Voltaire, over the river, round the Place de la Concorde, to the Rue d'Amsterdam, to hail Heinrich Heine.

To those acquainted with the city of Paris these proper names may convey some sense of direction; what I cannot hope to express in a few pages is the passage of time, the hours it took us to cover the distance, not—as my sea-hating, horse-loving family would have said—from "point-to-point," but "as hounds ran." Somewhere along the line this fox took, in any case, after many a "breather" and an occasional "sonvich" in bistros catering to the very late and the early, we reached a restaurant in the *huitième arrondissement*, a region through which in days and nights to come I used to attempt to increase the speed of Malcolm's crawl. The restaurant I remember as being elegant even from the outside, and the hour must have been approaching noon, for I could see from the streets that the stools at the bar were being swiftly occupied by members of the international *louche* and *beau monde*, who kept passing under our jaundiced eyes through the polished swing doors. Aware of the appearance of both the place and the people, I hesitated to enter: I had an unhealthy suspicion that such seats as might be free at the bar would, once the management caught sight of us, promptly become *"réservés, Messieurs, je regrette."* But Malcolm, I realized, was determined. "Ah," he breathed, "I smell something good." So in we marched.

As I had also anticipated, no sooner had we circumnavigated the doors than every man and woman at the bar stopped eating— to stare. However, once seated on a couple of stools two enormous menus fell miraculously in front of us. "We're over Becher's!" I muttered. "Aintree to starboard!" echoed my friend, "full steam ahead!" And he ordered an aquavit—*"un double!"* As it turned out, our unorthodox attire in the plush setting, not to mention what must have radiated from our skins, enabled us both swiftly to acquire at the crowded bar a comfortably wide berth.

"Now then, old chum," said Malcolm, spreading his arms and

studying *la carte* with unusual care, "let us relax. It isn't every day that deckhands travel first-class to Oslo!"

It was then that I began to learn more about Lowry's life. It soon transpired that what had attracted him to this three-star restaurant had been its name, La Scandinavie, which he kept repeating to himself in a nostalgic whisper as he threw back his head and demanded more of *"la même chose.* Best appetizer in the world, my dear fellow! Unlike pernod, guaranteed not to make you into a humpty-dumpty again!" (Here I should add that hours ago, in deference to my companion, I had switched from red to white wine.) From a few words I heard him exchange with the barman, I then discovered Lowry's talent for learning languages. Like his master, James Joyce, Malcolm had taught himself Norwegian in order to read the works of Ibsen in the original. This led him to tell the story about how he had once jumped ship in the port of Oslo with the express purpose of meeting the Norwegian poet Nordahl Grieg, whose novel *The Ship Sails On* had sent Lowry "rushing up to the poop" in excitement.

Once launched upon a story Malcolm was liable, as in his longer fiction, to digress, to associate so freely that one would find oneself carried away on currents that turned out to be but tributaries of his subject's main stream. His monologues had the quality of dreams, and to reconstruct such talk uttered and heard as a rule "under the influence" and at night—nights in themselves like dreams—is impossible. Before embarking on his voyage to Norway in search of the novelist, Lowry, I believe, had not been in correspondence with Grieg, nor had he made inquiries at the consulate in London or elsewhere.[1] He thus arrived in Oslo not only alone but without a clue as to the whereabouts of the man he intended to visit. Only after hours of wandering about the city did he discover that Grieg lived not in Oslo at all, but Heaven knows how many scores of miles away in the north of the country. Never one for shortcuts, for modern means of transport (even in later life and married, he would travel only by freighter, the smaller, the slower, the better), Lowry acquired a map and there and then, armed presumably with a compass, set out into the foreign land on foot through the snow. That he eventually succeeded in finding Nordahl Grieg I know, but how long the journey took him, how far he walked, how he was

[1] Since this memoir was written I have learned that Lowry wrote several long letters to Grieg, but failed to post them. —J.S.

greeted on arrival, I cannot remember. There remains in my mind after thirty-four years only a vague memory of Malcolm, footsore and hungry, knocking diffidently on the door of a remote mountain cabin in the middle of the night. . . .

The area between La Scandinavie and the Rue d'Amsterdam was, I think, the largest we managed to cover that day without "heaving-to" en route for a "breather." Having recited in doleful unison:

> *Ich weiss nicht, was soll es bedeuten,*
> *Das ich so traurig bin . . .*

outside the house where *"der grosser Heinrich"* and his fat Mathilde had lived a hundred years before, we crossed the street into the Gare St. Lazare—ostensibly, as I remember Malcolm saying on future occasions, "to cock a metaphorical finger at my countrymen, as they emerge from the Heart of Darkness into the City of Light." In reality, we "put in" at the Gare for the simple reason that we happened to share a romantic passion for railway stations. The restaurant at the St. Lazare, moreover, has a convenient "deck" on which one can "sit out" on earthbound wicker chairs while traveling vicariously the Seven Seas—seas which my twenty-four-year-old companion had already sailed.

In his life, in most of his work, in conversation, Lowry invariably returned to the sea. Sitting in the Paris station, swopping stories of our early wanderings, he began telling me how he had set out on his first long voyage from home (to China via the West Indies), while still in his teens.

"So did I."

"Ah, thought so. Shake, chum!"

Although his earliest love, I think, had been for the works of Conrad, it was under the impact of the first plays of the living dramatist O'Neill that Lowry had written *Ultramarine,* for whose central character he chose the name of Eugene Dana Hilliot. Malcolm then told me the story of his first literary pilgrimage, in 1929, from England to Cambridge, Massachusetts, to meet the American poet, Conrad Aiken, an occasion that marked the beginning of a lifelong friendship. This story struck me as so similar to that of his voyage to Norway that I felt inclined to take them both with more than a grain of salt. Years later, however, I learned that the two tales were perfectly true. In 1929, at the time Lowry was homeward bound from his visit to America, I happened to have set out from England to the United States in the hope of eventually making my way round the world—a piece of information that caused my companion to clap his hands and burst into doggerel: "I knew our paths had crossed before! But 'twas night, chum, the seas were high. So was the bosun. So was I. . . ."

So far as I knew, he could have been "high" ever since! In Paris, at our age, in those early days of our not so easily won freedom, such consciences as we had about indolence and our chosen profession were soon drowned by words and what we consumed. As for Time, it neither dragged nor flew: it had no meaning. Of the fact that night had fallen when Malcolm muttered in the station that we might "weigh anchor," that as we mounted the steep incline towards the Place Pigalle the clocks of Montmartre were probably striking ten or eleven, or indeed that a night and a day had passed since we met, neither of us was aware.

Here, in Utrillo-land, having long since forsaken "La Route des Grands Hommes," I have a vague recollection of my friend suddenly halting on the *trottoir* to deliver to passersby a speech on the glories of French civilization. These impromptu remarks he attempted to utter, unfortunately, in French, so that very soon a considerable crowd gathered, to cheer or jeer, as a result of which we were asked, most politely by a local gendarme, to move on. Which we did. But at a pace which by now had dropped almost imperceptibly from a crawl to a bedroom-slipper shuffle. The night sky had lost its fascination; the past, even the sea, had for once been exhausted as subjects for another monologue. Now ladies of all ages, but not of the oldest profession, found themselves confronted at close quarters by bloodshot eyes in a hairy face in which a mouth would open to growl:

> *"Ah, mademoiselle,*
> *Comme vous êtes belle . . . !"*

Followed by a glance of panic and the sound of fast-retreating heels.

By the time we reached Les Halles the carts and the *camions,* carrying in from the country every conceivable raw material that man can consume, were clattering over the Pont Neuf into the great market. In a tiny tavern frequently by fishmongers Malcolm had an altercation with the *patronne*—a woman with the neck and biceps of an all-in wrestler—over the glass in which she had served him his calvados. "A mere thimble!" he spluttered, fitting the empty glass

on to a finger and holding up his hand. *"Voilà,* Madame, *un—
un* thimble!" And turning to me: "I say, old fellow, what the hell's
the French for thimble?" Just as I was expecting a shout of *"sale
étranger"* from our rear, I heard my friend settling the dispute by
demanding a whole bottle of calvados—which he proceeded to ram
into his coat pocket. Then, with the courtesy of a *grand seigneur,*
he offered his hand to the giantess, leaned forward over the bar, put
his lips to her awe-inspiring forearm, bowed to the French fishmongers and, blowing out his cheeks, shuffled from the tavern in
my wake.

After dawn in the Luxembourg, that dreamworld of all France's
public gardens, we both broke into what would be blasphemy to
call song. What we hummed, crooned, and howled, Heaven knows.
The combination of our unmusical roars must have been appalling.
We were still blissfully yelling when, rounding that lovely tree-
covered corner opposite the Place Edmond Rostand, Malcolm
caught sight of the figure of George Sand reclining on the grass.
I can see him still, in his jacket of royal-blue tweed, the bottle
protruding from his pocket, lumbering off the gravel path onto the
forbidden lawn. Reaching the silent novelist in stone, he gazed
affectionately down at her, settled himself on one elbow beside her,
laid an arm round her neck, and then, as though suddenly remembering his manners, reached for the bottle and solemnly offered
it to the lifeless lips of the woman who had loved one of my
friend's favorite composers. At last, with a disappointed wag of his
head, he raised the bottle high and turned it upon his own insatiable
throat.

How, from where, did I witness this scene? From a wooden bench
not twenty feet away, where I sat huddled in such convulsions of
laughter that finally Malcolm felt sufficiently concerned to take leave
of the lady and thump me on the back, to raise me up for the last
lap of our walk through the sunlit morning.

"Oh, I'm tired," I moaned, "I want to go to bed, I had a little
drink about an hour ago . . ."

Instead of finishing off the ditty, Malcom raised one arm and
pointing northwest, recited in resonant if somewhat slurred tones:

> "Must we to bed indeed? Well then,
> Let us arise and go like men,
> And face with an undaunted tread
> The long black passage up to bed. . . ."

Little does he know . . . I thought, as we rose and together tot-
tered away under the trees.

My flat in the Rue René Pauline was on the sixth and top floor.
Long accustomed to the steep ascent, I knew how to take it, slowly,
in my own particular stride. But I could see, leaning over the
banisters at every other *étage*, that my friend, on conquering one
flight and before embarking upon the next, was feeling the need
for "stoking up the boiler." By the time he had reached my door
he was panting for breath and his eyes seemed to have receded into
his head. He stood in the narrow hall, leaning his weight on one
hand flat against the wall, the other on his hip. "I say, old fellow,"
he gasped. "You must be parched. Here, have—have a drink!" And
pulling the almost empty bottle from his pocket, he thrust it out at
arm's length.

"No thanks, old chap," I managed to say, "I've just had one."
But I took the bottle from him.

An instant later I almost gave it him back—for suddenly his head
drooped, one leg buckled, and like a bull at the end of battle, he
began to crumble. Down the wall he slowly slithered. Flat, prone
he lay, his head in the crook of one arm, face to the floor. I bent
over, laid my hand on his head. "Where's my guitar?" he gargled.
And began to snore.

This, on almost any other morning of the year, would have put
an end to my first impression of the man whose acquaintance
I had made in a bistro thirty-four hours before. Alas, this was no
ordinary morning. . . .

I had thrown a blanket over the recumbent figure, taken off my
clothes, and was about to fall into bed when I caught sight on the
mantelpiece of a sheet of paper on which I read, scrawled in my
own hand: Rose in Paris, breakfast here Tuesday.

My eyes fled to the clock, to the calendar on the wall—and,
clutching my aching head, I stifled a scream.

Rose was my "little sister," most innocent and tender-hearted of
girls, barely out of her teens. Rose was a girl who until now had
never ventured "abroad." Rose was a girl on a visit to an aunt who
lived in Paris. Rose was a girl whose Big Brother also lived, for
some unaccountable reason, "out there." Rose was a girl who had
never had a drink. Rose was a girl who was coming to breakfast

. . . any minute. My head began to reel. Oh Rose was a girl was a girl was a girl. . . .

At last I grew calm. I even grew resolute. I marched toward my snoring friend. I bent down, put my arms round his waist. Between him and the bathroom lay eight feet of floor: those feet might as well have been miles. I marched into the bathroom, put my head under the cold tap. Without looking in the mirror I began to shave. . . .

Oh, him? He's a friend. . . . He isn't feeling very well. . . . I should leave him. . . . No, he doesn't like to be touched. . . . Oh, he's really very nice but—to tell you the truth—he bites!

No, that wouldn't do, muttered the shaven face with the aching eyes, when—the doorbell rang, the heart gave a bound, and trembling hands grabbed a pair of trousers and a coat.

"Ah, there you are!"

"I say, you do live high up! Mummy sends her love—Oh!—Oh, look! What's happened? The poor man! Is he hurt?"

"Not a bit of it, Rose. Come on in—or rather, if you wait one second I'll come out with you. Malcolm won't want to be disturbed—"

"Oh, but the poor man! Why is he on the floor? I'm sure he ought to be in bed?"

"Not a bit of it, he loves floors—"

"But he can't be all right. . . ."

"Perfectly all right. Now I'm ready—"

"But couldn't we lift him? Together? Why does he snore so loud? I'm sure he's ill—"

"Not a bit of it, Rose."

I was dressed, ready, my hand was on the doorknob. "Look here, I'll tell you," I said in exasperation. "He has been out celebrating. Yesterday was his—his birthday—and he's just sleeping it off. He'll be—"

"You mean," asked my little sister as I guided her over the threshold, "you mean he's—drunk?"

"That's it," I gasped. "Drunk. But not disorderly."

"Oh dear, how awful!" she groaned, following me down the stairs.

That should indeed be the end of my first impression of Malcolm Lowry. Yet I feel it would be incomplete, that it would be doing an injustice to him, to his enigmatic character, above all to his memory, if I were to omit a brief epilogue. I have said that Lowry never mentioned our first meeting. This is not strictly true. He did refer to it once, in February of the year 1947—fourteen years after the event.

The occasion was the beginning of a momentous month in Lowry's life: the month that saw the publication in New York of his novel *Under the Volcano*—a book grossly underrated in the author's native land. Malcolm had been working on the novel for some ten years; he had rewritten it three times, and I forget how many times it had been rejected. I had read the final version in proof in New York and sent him a lengthy cable of congratulations to Haiti, where he and his wife were spending a week or two en route to America from their home in Vancouver.

In pencil on a picture postcard, Lowry had replied to that cable as follows:

Dear old Jimmy,

You rendered me speechless, and I still am, having been laid up in hospital here with a cough and Lady Hamilton on the wall by George Romney. There was a mocking bird too, and a bird that piped, and a man next door that mooed with pain. I am ok now. We leave to-morrow for Miami, thence proceed by bus to New York— reaching there mid-February sometime. Can you find us some hole to crawl into—a previous hole fell through. Thank you a million.

Malcolm.

I cannot remember whether I succeeded in finding the Lowry's a "hole" in New York, but I do know that on the afternoon of his arrival I arranged to meet Malcolm in the large mid-Victorian bar of the now defunct Murray Hill Hotel. When I entered he was already there, the only customer in the huge room, standing in his most characteristic posture, his hands flat on the bar, his right foot on the brass rail, eyes raised as though gazing out to sea. I had not seen him for more than thirteen years. His face had a weather-beaten look, his forehead was furrowed; otherwise Time had changed him astonishingly little. We greeted each other Spanish-fashion and I called him Consul. Then my eye fell on the glass that stood before him on the bar. It was a wine glass and in it I saw wine and the color of the wine was red. . . . I glanced from the glass to him and back. Would that bell ring in Lowry's fabulous memory? Evidently not, for he began telling me about Haiti, about voodoo rites as practiced on that island, until suddenly he stopped and in the silence bestowed on me a look that struck me as almost aggressive.

"By the way, old boy," he said at last, choosing the words with care and speaking with slow deliberation, "I have a little bone to pick with you. By now there isn't much flesh on it. It remains, nevertheless, a bone. You probably won't remember. But I do. Would you mind telling me why you told the girl who came to visit you that day in Paris—I have a hunch she was your sister—would you mind telling me why you informed her I was drunk?"

My Friend Malcolm

by Clarisse Francillon

In 1948, the people living in the back streets off the Place Saint-Germain-des-Pres could see a strange figure passing: it was Lowry walking day after day with the same slow, regular stride; he was going as in dream, seeming to look at nothing, nobody. His somewhat threadbare raglan overcoat, the colour of moss on a stone wall, opened on a tweed jacket and baggy trousers. The pupils of his eyes, the deep blue of underwater caves, his short arms almost like a child's, his chubby hands, we only noticed these later.

Paris did not interest him. Never during his stay here have I seen him look up to the top of a column, or wonder at an archivolt or at the grooves on a stone. One evening, as we were walking together down the rue de Babylone, he stopped for a long while to gaze up at clouds madly racing among the winter stars. That was all. Once or perhaps twice, he felt like going to the movies; we saw *Monsieur Verdoux* and also, I am afraid, *Le Diable Boiteux*, a very poor production. The poster of *The Grapes of Wrath*, whose opening scenes he had once admired, drew his attention. But we never got to the movie-house where they were showing this film by John Ford: in a town, there are uncountable stages on the road to drink.

Sun and trees, these he no longer knew how to appreciate. At the home of the English lady with whom the Lowrys were staying, he always disdained the garden with its closely cropped lawns and the delphinium beds in full bloom; he never looked out the window. Whether it was in this house or in mine, the ritual never changed. On emerging from an opaque sleep that lasted well on into the morning, he would, in a frenzy of impatience, slip on his grey woollen turtleneck sweater, thinking only of reaching the kitchen as soon as possible. The nervous trembling which shook his limbs only stopped once he had drunk the first glasses of red wine and water.

87

This beverage was prepared for him in a small decanter, the stopper of which coming in contact with the neck punctuated the greater part of the day. In our worried minds, this clinking took on huge proportions, swelling to the clanging of an alarm-bell on a ship adrift in the mists. This lasted till Lowry would vanish eventually and, do or say what we would, escape from us.

He showed a marked preference for those dim taverns off the beaten track, little frequented unless by a handful of workmen in dungarees with a bag slung over their shoulder—rue Jacob, rue Gozlin, rue des Ciseaux, rue de l'Amiral-Mouchez . . . As often as not, he stood at the bar for hours on end, ordering glasses of rum, fine beer, or else of heavy red wine, which, however, he thoroughly detested. He drank without haste, as if in a dream, treating to a glass the clients who happened to be standing next to him, some immediately recognized member of what he called the Great Brotherhood of Drunkards. In halting French, he would sometimes join in a ragged conversation; or he would snatch up a joke or a scrap of a story that interested him. To the proprietress of the *Perroquet,* whose sign was hanging near the Parc Montsouris, a lady he thought particularly open to pity, he expounded one evening the difficulties of translating into French the preposition "under". Should it be "sous", "au-dessous", or "en dessous"? The patronne gave her sober advice.

With hands which were beginning to suffer from the shakes again, how did he manage to get a few crumpled notes out of his pockets and lay them on the bar? And then, he would come quietly, letting himself be led away by one of us, unless the proprietors had to throw him out of the door, for it was often closing time when the floor had to be swept and the chairs piled up on to the table. Once in the street, he sometimes declared of a sudden: "Just wait for me, I'll be back in a few minutes." He never used to come back— we could search for him; we'd catch sight of him through the steamed-up windows of a neighbouring bar, his face flushed with a kind of glee at his release.

Only rarely did he give direct proof of his tremendous store of knowledge or his stupendous learning. No more than of his generosity, of that sympathy with his fellow-men, together with a quivering, agonizing compassion. These could only be guessed at in flashes. But there was his book that bore witness to them abundantly. At the most, he would now and then explain a point of etymology or a cabalistic symbol. I can also remember how, one evening, at dinner—he ate little as drink took away his appetite— and though he had more than crossed the frontiers into drunkenness, he was still able within two or three minutes to find a passage in the complete works of Shakespeare, and read to us some of Timon of Athens magnificent curses:

> " . . . Thou . . . whose self-same mettle,
> Whereof thy proud child, arrogant man, is puff'd,
> Engenders the black toad and adder blue,
> The gilded newt and eyeless venom'd worm,
> With all the abhorred births below crisp heaven
> Whereon Hyperion's quickening fire doth shine. . . ."

In most people, this type of memory, which I like to call culture, stands in contrast to that which I call the memory of things lived, and they go in inverse proportions. Just try an experiment: the more able a person is to quote, for example, such or such an aphorism by Nietzsche giving, if possible, an accurate reference of chapter or page, the less he will remember the shimmering of a slice of lemon floating in the glass over which you have one evening confessed to him your reasons for murdering the rich old lady next door. The same is also true the other way round. By what miracle did both types coexist equally in Lowry? The first memory vivifying the second, one supporting the other, made for an extraordinary verbal inspiration, not unlike that of Rabelais.

Who was the "I," how to find this "I," where had it got to? the Consul asks, and similarly we can imagine Malcolm, always more or less drunk, yet still coherent, a little mad but never altogether out of control, never having quite lost grip on himself, with the thought that the drunker a gentleman became, the more sober he should appear. To put it in Jacques Laruelle's somewhat moralizing words: an honest man in spite of all, and brave; who might have shown great capacity for good, an *hombre noble:* such was the Consul . . .

To drink or not to drink, that *was* the question. On the one hand you had the most vigorous, lucid, sanest man that ever walked on earth, of exceptional strength, an outstanding capacity for work going as far as asceticism; on the other, the maniac, the madman, a victim pursued by demons, the plaything of evil forces, who lets himself be driven out of the gardens of this world, to totter at the brink of the abyss outside. All his life, he had been that pendulum unceasingly and relentlessly impelled from one extreme to the other. Only Death put an end to this swinging back and forth.

He died in England, where he had been born on July 28th, 1909, at Birkenhead, Cheshire. During World War I, his eldest brother had been conscripted. From the Lowrys' garden could be seen a weathercock on a steeple. "If I come back home all right, I shall climb up there and fetch that cock down," declared the soldier, who did eventually come back all right. Their father asked him, pulling his leg, "Well son, what about trat cock?" Everybody laughed except Malcolm, the youngest, who remained silent and upset. He adored his brother, whose return he had been expecting every hour of every day, and could not understand the joke: he thought their father was really going to compel the young man to climb up that building and bring down the bird.

In his early youth, Lowry had made up his mind to become a writer. He never changed his plans. This did not prevent him from practising sports, especially golf, with enthusiasm. Golf plays a great part in his work; it reminds him of holes and thus of chasms and the abyss,—the abyss which each of us carries in himself or, in a non-figurative sense, the barranca which meanders through the town of Quauhnahuac and symbolizes cleavage and separation. Yvonne has left the Consul. She can try to come back and to take him away, to beg him to follow her far away towards the North, to start a new life: it is all a waste of time. But if Yvonne was unfaithful to the Consul, it is because he had (so to say) driven her towards his half-brother and then to his friend: he had subrogated his powers to them, there is no doubt of that. For he is more or less one with this half-brother who represents that younger, more chivalrous and freer part of himself; he is also one with his friend, the French film director Laruelle. "From chapter 2 on, if you read properly [he once wrote to me], the whole book can be considered as a film made by Jacques Laruelle, which is a way for me of honouring the French Cinema. For this film is certainly not American . . ."

About his grandfather on his mother's side, who was a Norwegian captain on the windjammer *The Scottish Isles*, extraordinary tales were told in the family. The contrast between his exploits and the dull money-making business of Malcolm's father, a cotton-broker by trade, roused the imagination of the boy, who moreover was a great reader of Conrad. Fearing the spell of a protected milieu, he ran off to sea.

His father stopped him on his way. A violent quarrel ensued, with reproaches and threats. The whole affair ended up with a compromise in pure English style: if he was allowed to go to sea for a year, then Malcolm promised to become a student at Cambridge. He was seventeen years old.

The ship on which he enlisted as a sailor was bound for the Far East, tramping along the Siberian coast, round China where a civil war was raging and where, while the ship had put in, he managed to get himself shot in the knee. On the way back, the ship carried a load of wild animals among which a she-elephant whom he met again years later in a Roman zoo, as he tells in one of his as yet unpublished tales: "Elephant and Colosseum".

As it was not yet time to go up to university, he went on another voyage to the West Indies. He stayed at the governor's house, did some business on his father's behalf and undertook to climb a mountain whose top had never yet been reached. He took the altitude and, all his money spent, ended up playing the ukelele in a brothel. Having enlisted on another cargo boat, he went on to Boston, where he wished to meet Conrad Aiken, who was to have a considerable influence on his writing.

As good as his word, he went up to Cambridge, where he was rather proud to live in Marlow's rooms at Saint Catharine's college. He got an honours degree, then an M.A. Cantab. On his first summer holiday, he took to the sea again, bound for Arkhangelsk. In Norway, he met Nordhal Grieg, the second writer who influenced his life as a writer. He then wrote "In Ballast to the White Sea," his first novel, the manuscript of which (together with the notes taken during the voyage) would be lost later in a fire that destroyed their log cabin in Canada. The following summer he spent in Spain with Conrad Aiken; there he met the girl who was to become his first wife.

At nineteen, he writes another novel: *Ultramarine*, in which we find sketched out some of the themes which were to reappear in *Volcano*: the sea, of course, and his search for purity, and the double, triple or quadruple gins swallowed down at an hour when the portside lights are not to be clearly distinguished from the peppermint-liqueurs taken in wharfside cafés. A feeling for dialogue is already present, incomparably. And a sense of humour; not slashing irony, but that sudden reversal of things that turns objects upside down revealing their absurd and sudden poetry.

Ultramarine was published in London by Jonathan Cape in about 1932. A few fragments translated by André Gide appeared in France in a magazine whose name Lowry was never able to tell me. A first trip to the continent had made him love Chartres and the surrounding countryside. In Paris, he got married, met Cocteau, who invited him to a performance or two of *La Machine Infernale*. Lowry was enthusiastic. Later his copy of the play was to be stolen from him in Mexico City in a pulcheria by a bearded Indian brandishing two pistols, who galloped away carrying off on top of it all Lowry's sun glasses.

America attracted Lowry. The homeland of Jazz and Melville. He spent some time in New York, where he earned his living on various jobs and wrote "Lunar Caustic," a novella, which has remained unpublished in English. *Esprit* published a translation of it in the spring of 1956 under the title of *Le Caustique Lunaire*. A drunkard roams for a whole day around a hospital, where he finally gets himself admitted for disintoxication. On his release, the janitor gives him back the bottle of whisky which he had left at the lodge on entering. The patient cured would not need it any longer, would he? He would only have to throw it away. He does throw it away into the first garbage can and then, on second thoughts, he fishes it out again. He starts drinking again, at first timidly, then triumphantly. And in a church at that.

In Hollywood, glad to be working for the Cinema which had been always a passion with him, he wrote a few film-scripts, but very soon was disgusted by the poor quality of writing which was expected of him. Separated from his first wife, he went to Mexico, where he stayed for about two years. During a second stay in Hollywood, he met his second wife, Margerie Bonner, whom he married at Vancouver in December 1940. When war was declared, he tried to volunteer but the army turned him down because of his old wound in the knee.

He had already at hand a first draft of *Under the Volcano*. He started rewriting it, without however laying aside "In Ballast to the White Sea." He and his wife had settled in British Columbia in the English speaking section of Canada. Dollarton is a small community of fishermen and boat-builders.

Standing on an inlet of the Pacific, the cabin with its back to the forest, and which appears so often in the *Volcano* in the conditional mood, really existed. The homemade curtains, the stove which burnt driftwood picked up on the beach, the tiny jetty from which one could dive into the sea and on which would sit hooded mergansers, and other big sea-birds, Malcolm knew all these things. "It is indeed the most beautiful country in the world," he used to say to me. They had a kerosene lamp and drew water from a well adorned with a ship's figurehead which they had picked up on the beach and which served as guardian angel. "We were still on earth," he wrote in "The Forest Path to the Spring," another unpublished story, "but if someone had charged us with the notion that we had gone to heaven and that this was the after life we would not have said him nay for long. Moreover if we had been charged with formerly having been in hell for a while we could probably have had to say yes too, though adding that on the whole we liked that fine, as long as we were together, and were sometimes even homesick for it, though this life had many advantages over the other . . ."

And Lowry went on writing, sawing up logs, facing the difficulties of life, the rough Canadian climate. At this point, their shack and all that was inside it were destroyed by fire. Ineradicably, fire was to be inscribed along the whole course of their existence. The manuscript of "In Ballast" was irretrievably lost, that of the *Volcano* rescued. (The last version, lost in a Mexican bar, found again thanks to a football champion, was finished at Xmas 1944 in a pub, on the shores of Lake Ontario.)

The novel was accepted both by English and American publishers. The letters from London and New York announcing the news reached the author on the very same day in Mexico. Then, he went back to Canada with his wife. They both spent the summer over the galley proofs. As we can imagine, Malcolm corrected them again and again and infinite number of times, in fact practically re-writing the book, coming near to driving Margerie and his publishers to distraction. In the end she told me, "I got hold of the whole bunch and sent it off. Malcolm affirmed that he could not let them publish it before having worked again on it, but since he had rewritten the whole book at least twenty times and destroyed thousands of pages, I thought it was high time to put a stop to it." *Under the Volcano* was published in 1947 by Raynal and Hitchcock. Once the proofs had been sent in, the Lowrys went to Haiti. Sick with desperation and anguish, Malcolm thought he was courting disaster.

It was just the reverse that happened. The book met with considerable success. For a few months even, it was a best seller. Encyclopedia Britannica hailed it in these terms: "No more valuable voice has made itself heard this year. *Under the Volcano* opens a new prospect in the line of young novel-writing."

It was then in 1948 that Lowry made his second visit to France, this time to help with a translation of his book. Helping meant for him to sit down now and then at a table all the time he was there, to extract a bit of pencil from his pocket, jot down a fragment of the preface or the forewords he had planned, which he had solemnly promised and which he judged to be indispensable. The Greek e's, the d's like flying buttresses, the t's like solitary crosses by the road-side . . . That is how he himself characterized his hand writing. Then suddenly he would drop it all: his brain did not work as he wished, not did his hand; he felt it impossible to go on. After he had left for America, we were compelled somehow or other to finish the preface of the *Volcano*, filling up the gaps, blending into a whole by drawing inspiration from recalled conversations or memories the various paragraphs—if we could call them paragraphs. As to the preface of "Lunar Caustic," he never got further than the ten first lines.

Either he would take up a copy of the *Volcano* to point to an allusion to the Kabala, or look for a passage which might be a stumbling block to us. Or he explained a pun, or a joke; the bar-room floor was meant as a pun on ballroom floor, a phrase derived from an American popular song, which a little further on became the bathroom floor; the beginning of Chapter 11 contains an accurate quotation from a poem, deliberately misquoted at the end of Chapter 2; throughout the book, one may find without the usual quotation marks sentences by Marcus Aurelius, Keats, Shelley, a Hindoo text and innumerable allusions to history, legend and folklore . . . We leave it to some future writers of glosses and notes to unravel them in their critical editions.

From much thumbing, the pages of our working copy became limp, yellow, and sticky: it was indeed a pithy book. The thought that it was going to come out in French pleased Lowry very much. He feared only one thing: that the work would not go fast enough, that he would die before its completion. This thought was enough to make the perspiration pour down his ruddy face, under the hair as bushy as the short reddish moustache. *Au-dessous du Volcan* came off press in January 1950, only a year after the Lowrys had gone back to their little dream cottage, rebuilt by Malcolm with the help of his friends the villagers.

Where had he found the strength to overcome the obsession with fire, the terror of some new disaster or that of insanity? Roofless, having lost all that they had owned, Margerie and Malcolm went to watch the sunrise in the ruins of their house, which still smelt of fire, several weeks after the catastrophe. Not only had they resolved to rebuild the walls which were dear to them, but they perceived in the whole matter something reassuring or even comical. They wolfed down their sandwiches amidst the charred beams, thus driving away the ghost of what Malcolm would have wagered to be the devil in person, "that sworn enemy of all humour in misfortune as well as of all human happiness, and who desires nothing so much as that man should believe in the hostility of the forces that surround him."

"And the spring? Here it was. It still ran," he wrote in "The Forest Path to the Spring." ". . . with a faint tang of mushrooms, earth, dead leaves, pine-needles, mud and snow, on its way down to the inlet and out to the Pacific. In the deeper reaches of the forest, in the sombre damp caves, where the dead branches hang bowed down with moss . . . it was haggard and chill and tragic, unsure measurer of its path. Feeling its way underground, it must have had its dark moments. But here in springtime, on its last leap to the sea, it was as at its source a happy joyous little stream . . . Laughing we stooped down to the stream and drank."

This Paradise: what force could have driven him out of it? Three or four years later, we find the Lowrys in Sicily at Taormina, then in England. They settled at Ripe, a tiny village in Sussex. Good and hard times followed each other, whatever we might mean by good or hard. Finally, in the summer of 1957, I received the following letters from Margerie. "I have some very bad news. Malcolm is dead and was buried here in the churchyard a month ago. I should have let you know long since but the shock was terrible. He died in his sleep and I found him in the morning dead . . ." (dated July 25th, 1957). "It was a terrible shock and you can imagine that it very nearly killed me. I still cannot believe it. He was working the day before and late that night. So he went to the extra bedroom so as not to disturb me, there I found him in the morning. Clarisse, you cannot imagine how well and happy he had been this last year, never like it before and I was so happy . . . Malcolm died on the night of the 27th to 28th June. We had rented a beautiful little cottage built in 1730 with a charming walled garden, and there we have lived very quietly, Malcolm working hard and me helping him and gardening. On May 27th this year . . . he took me for a beautiful holiday in the Lake District. We stayed at Grassmere where Wordsworth lived and took long walks over the mountains every day, carrying the volume of Wordsworth's poems and our lunch. He was quite thin, and very tanned and looked really beautiful . . ." (dated August 9th, 1957).

Malcolm Lowry left a volume of short stories, two of which have been published in *Lettres Nouvelles*: "The Bravest Boat" and "Strange Comfort." [1] In this volume we publish two others, that is to say the longest: *Through the Panama,* which seemed to us the most important. In it, Lowry speaks of the technical problems he had to solve, of his tentative efforts in the search for a new hero (and indeed after the Consul, this was not an easy task). The story also contains what I might call one of the keys to the *Volcano*: "Everything written about drink is incidentally absurd. Have to do it all over again, what about conflict, appalling sadness that can lead equally to participation in the tragic human condition, self-knowledge, discipline. Conflict is all-important. Gin and orange juice best cure for alcoholism real cause of which is ugliness and complete baffling sterility of existence as sold to you. Otherwise it would be greed . . ."

In addition, Margerie has in her possession the manuscript of a more or less finished novel entitled *October Ferry to Gabriola* and which forms one of the wings of that triptych of which the *Volcano* and the volume of short stories were intended to be the other two. In it, some of the characters whom we know already follow the course of their destinies. No doubt it will be published some day.

—Translated from Clarisse Francillon:
"Malcolm, mon ami" in *Lettres Nouvelles*,
5 July-August 1960,
by Suzanne Kim, Paris, June 1972.

[1] "The Bravest Boat," November, 1953; "Strange Comfort," September, 1955.

Second Encounter

by Norman Matson

I saw him first at a distance. He always had a quality of standing alone, of seeming to be far away, not because he himself felt aloof but because he *was* solitary, and was horrified by the world. When I came into the recently converted speakeasy he was at my right, and though we had not before seen each other he at once raised a hand and smiled. Lowry was born (the bookflap tells me) in 1909, so then around 1934 he was rather young, much younger than I, but he did not seem of any particular age. We had a mutual friend who had arranged this encounter without himself taking part. Now, having met, we moved to the bar and were served whiskey by a fat, unamiable crook, a veteran of the illegal days.

Both of us, Lowry and I, had been to sea for long voyages. Not much before this he had been in the Orient, and he was then involved in a novel whose name and subject escapes me. He was different from anyone I had ever met. He was a stranger, from Canada.

He said with a friendly, self-commenting smile, "You know I'm a Norwegian, too."

But he was only half, unlike me. He said after a third drink that I should try to remember his other half was Irish.

In his pictures he is a handsome man. What I remember from this first meeting was a muscular, medium-sized (my size) man, gray as of face and hair, though his hair couldn't have been. We talked about something or other but not politics or "ideologies" —he didn't give a damn. He was a writer with a capital W, unpublished, but confident and wholly—a writer. I might have asked him why he was, being that kind of metaphysical bore—why was it important to be a writer? I didn't, but I think that then, at least, the question would have made no sense to him, as one may ask a psychologist (for instance), "What is a psyche?" There isn't any

answer because if there is, oh, even if it is merely considered, all
the words are emptied of importance and with them their speaker.
What was important to Lowry then, that moment, was the drink
he was drinking and the dark little joint we were sharing, as drink
is important only to writers and maybe painters who are so to speak
pulling themselves up by their own bootstraps, who are each day
making their world and turning the red blood their mothers poured
into their veins into ink so that it may be used for words, a fantastic
ambition and drive when harnessed to some un-God, some Nowhere.

He didn't have a job, and unlike an American made no apology
for that. He had regular money from somewhere, enough for living
and enough for liquor. At the rate he consumed it, even then, that
was expensive, not as expensive as, say, heroin, but expensive and
as insistent. The cost he never questioned, nor added up: literary
drunks don't, not at least those I have known. I liked him but he
was more literary than I. There was a slight shadow of Oxford
between us. I don't think he mentioned Oxford. But I was earning
money at writing, which he wasn't, and of course I didn't mention
that either. I don't know what I mean when I say that I felt he was
Norwegian—but I felt that we were alike in something. We were
friends at once.

After this encounter things happened to him, but I have forgotten
what. He was published in highbrow magazines that I could not
afford to write for and probably couldn't have "made," either.
Twenty years later I was back in Paris pursuing what Allan Ross
Macdougal told me were ghosts (he was right) and one afternoon
sitting on the terrace of Lipps, an artistic pansy, trailed by a
furtive French punk, who had learned from tourists that he didn't
have to run errands or lay bricks or whatever for a living, told me
that a friend of mine named Lowry ("says he is a writer") lived
in a small hotel back of the Deux Magots. I went to the dark, lower-
class *zinc* of this hotel and there was my friend Malcolm Lowry.
He waved at me. He always drank standing up and sweated as if
he were swallowing some metallic poison that was even more alien
to the human bloodstream than alcohol. He fought his liquor, as
they say, but managed from time to time to smile about it.

We met as if there had been no years between, and he seemed
no older. He named the exact place and date of our last meeting.
He explained the Deux Magots no longer wanted him around and
so he had retreated to this cave. He smiled and a clear, visible
stream of sweat poured off his face. He raised his hands and said

that this was where he spent his days. Not with friends but alone. I can't say that I understood Lowry. Who "understands" an artist? He wasn't crazy, far from it, nor sick. When he went on the wagon, which he did occasionally, his natural muscular strength returned in a day or two as if he hadn't been abusing it, and he was again an athlete, although not a happy one. He poisoned himself on purpose. As he did so to stand alongside of him took more endurance than I had.

The part of this second encounter I think about when I read the beautiful and somehow faulty pages he left behind after finally doing himself in for good, and which are now being published, has its location on the rue de Cels up beyond the rue de Lambre where we had a tiny house and where my wife and Margerie (Mrs. Lowry), who were friends by now, arranged a later afternoon tea or cocktail gathering in the second-floor "living room" (a measured ten feet by ten feet), but when she, Margerie, arrived it was to say that Malcolm had come only as far as our front doorstep and there decided that he could not just then meet strange people. He was not drunker than usual, but his need for solitude was uncontradictable, like some law of nature. Margerie, a little breathless and white with anxiety because she had left him alone, came up to our spiral dollhouse stairway. In the hallway she whispered to my wife, Anna, that they had found a bistro in our block and that was where he was. Maybe I would join him? He is lonely, she said.

It was the kind of bistro that is scattered through France, a neighborhood *zinc*. I had often passed it without seeing it. Malcolm had not only found it but recognized it. There was a tense, a dramatic situation in there as I entered. Madame, a thin and alas an ugly woman, dressed in old black, was controlling her hostility and her contempt with difficulty. Only she and Malcolm were there. She hated my friend for a number of reasons, because he was an "American," because he drank rum as if it were water, mostly because he thought her bistro was funny. He certainly had not said he did but he had said when she had asked him why he was inspecting her café with such close interest that he found it "uniquely interesting." When the rum bottle was finished he asked for more and she brought a different brand, a terrible drink made in some cellar perhaps. He suggested nevertheless that he buy the whole bottle at once. She wouldn't have it. He showed her his money. She said No —it was her last bottle, she had other clients. He asked me to note the iron chairs, on the wall last year's calendar and a gilt-framed photograph of a group of 1914 conscripts, sad with youth and distance. He tiptoed to the back of the place where an arch was curtained across with folds of dark dusty cloth.

Madame, her bony face a white flame of hatred, stood behind her *zinc* wishing, I think, she could call the gendarmes to throw us out. Malcolm raised dust touching the curtains, making an opening, and dared me to look into the alcove behind, which was saved from utter dark by a small window, a bit of gray and dusty light in the back wall. In a corner, his relaxed feet two or three feet above the floor, a man, his black tongue showing, hung by his neck. I believed in it for a moment, while Malcolm watched my face, and then I saw it was an effigy, life-sized, fully dressed, some dismal fellow-Christian's idea of a joke. We went back to Madame for another of the dark harsh drink, the flavored mixture she was selling us as rum.

Malcolm said, "This place is like no other. It is complete. They even have an aquarium. Have you looked at it?" There was a square glass tank of water sentineled by bottles of cheap apéritifs with strange unconvincing names. "There is a fish in it." There was, too, a creature too big for the tank. "Tell me," he whispered, "is it or is it not a herring?" I said I thought it was a herring. "But not a pickled one?"

"No," I said, "it is alive. It swims back and forth." All he wanted was this corroboration.

"I find places like this," he told me, "dark small places with their own meaning, everywhere. I'm prone to them. Sometimes I think I first imagine them, see them in a nightmare and then find them actual and existent in the world. But the herring was special, wasn't it?"

We had at last left Madame and were standing outside her dingy doorway. As soon as we had closed the door behind us the lights had gone off, a sudden comment, like "Good riddance."

I don't know how much "rum" or whatever other alcohol Malcolm had downed that day, a long day now drawing to a close, but he showed no signs of it except only the sweat of agony that dripped off his cheeks. I looked along the rue de Cols, treeless, gray, with sharp geometrical shadows on its housefronts: all its detail bulged out at me. The man and woman who passed, she shoving a kind of cart with handles to it, stared at us, and they were real and separate as ships far out at sea, real as ghosts, and fated, doomed, precisely like the rest of us, beginning with Malcolm

Lowry and myself. The sky above Paris was alight with the last of the sun, the first of the night's electricity, and there was one long pink cloud. For a moment it seemed to me (but how would I know?) that I saw the world with Lowry's eyes, and I thought as I have thought this last week reading the static, staring clarity of his "Hear Us O Lord from Heaven Thy Dwelling Place," in which he startles you with beauty, that if his world had been mine I, also, would have devised ways to avoid it for long whiles, if I could, but at the same time held desperately onto life.

Malcolm Lowry Visits the Doctor

by C. G. McNeill

My acquaintance with Malcolm Lowry goes back to his days at Dollarton when he was writing *Under the Volcano*. I had just started in private practice and had opened up a branch office in Deep Cove, where there had previously been no physician.

He came to the office one morning accompanied as always by his wife Margerie. He was a short, sturdy, pink-faced man with an absent manner. His speech was clipped and slurred. There were frequent pauses as he stopped for the right word. During the course of the interview I asked him what he did.

"I am a writer," he said. I wondered at the time if he wrote radio commercials, advertising copy, or did more serious writing but did not develop the point.

His complaint was that his legs hurt. When I was at medical school we were taught to say, "Of what do you complain?" Most of us stop asking this question soon after graduation because the answer so frequently comes back:

"Oh, I'm not complaining. I have this pain in my stomach (chest, back, etc.) but I'm not really complaining."

Later I used to ask them simply: "What's your trouble?" or "What's troubling you?" I stopped this after a while because so many times the answer would annoyingly come back: "That's what I came to you to find out."

I forget now what approach I used to elicit Malcolm Lowry's complaint, but at any rate he was literate enough to tell me that it was the ache in his legs and that it was interfering with his work.

"I'm a writer," he said, "but I have to dictate. My wife takes down what I say." Later I was to find that he had a mental block against holding a pen or pencil.

"Most embarrassing. Sometimes I have been in places where I was supposed to sign my name and when I pick up a pen my mind goes completely blank. My wife Margerie does all the business. This has even happened to me in the bank."

"A saving block," I interposed, "if you were about to sign a check."

"Malcolm dictates standing up," said his wife. "He leans with the back of his hands on the top of the desk. Sometimes he will stand that way for what seems an hour thinking for the proper word. At the end of the day his legs are all swollen and aching. Show him your hands, Malcolm."

He held out his hands. They were short, stubby, muscular. On the backs of the knuckles and first joints of the fingers there were calluses.

"But these are anthropoid pads," I exclaimed. "The apes have these from leaning and dragging the backs of their hands on the ground. I have never seen calluses in this area before." Nor was I ever to see them again.

Malcolm smiled. "We have been trying to simplify our lives by living in this remote place away from everybody. Actually we are squatters in a house on the beach. But I did not know I had regressed as far back as the apes." One could see that my comment had pleased him, and I believe that with the term "anthropoid pads" I had established a rapport that was to bring him back to me in the succeeding years. His wife also I was to look after, more particularly in the difficult period after his death when she was arranging his works for posthumous publication.

And I remember Malcolm and his numerous violences, his intense concentration and yet neglect of his own body's physiology. How one part of him could be in the room talking to you and yet the sensation was that part of him was outside looking in, watching critically, evaluating; words streaming forth but not emerging above his subconscious; his numerous "hang-ups" and phobias; his fear of syphilis, rashes and body distortion; his ruthlessness in condemning his own work when it did not come up to standards he himself had set.

I then asked him to strip for the physical examination. He was, as I have said, short and sturdy. He had a good-sized chest and I commented on his tan. His wife told me that he went swimming every day and was able to dive off their porch when the tide was right. Their house was built on piles partly over the water, and from it he could leap or dive directly into the sea.

"Malcolm swims like a fish," his wife told me, "but I have to keep an eye on him because he likes to float on his back and think. Sometimes he goes to sleep like this. Once on the Riviera he went to sleep under a blazing sun and slept for several hours, still floating. He had the most frightful burn on his face and chest. His eyelids were puffed closed, his lips all raw, and he was ill for days after."

I finished my examination of his chest and abdomen. He seemed fit and I directed my attention to his legs. It was immediately apparent what his trouble was. Although still a young man, he had developed varicose veins from long periods of standing. Both legs were involved to above the knees. I explained to him that if he were to take the weight off his feet and dictate lying or sitting with his feet up his legs would stop aching—even walking around was preferable—or he could bandage his legs or wear an elastic-style stocking. None of these suggestions was an acceptable solution.

"It is not possible for me to dictate while walking about, or lying or sitting. The words will not come unless I am standing in just this position and leaning with the back of my hands on the desk."

Surgery was then suggested, that of ligation and stripping to remove the varicose veins from the groin to the ankle. When he found that only a few days were required in hospital and that he would be able to resume his dictation in three to four weeks, both he and his wife thought this the only solution and asked me to arrange it.

While we had been talking Malcolm had dressed himself. All except his shoes and socks. These he now proceeded to put on. Sitting on the low stool that I had used in examining his legs, he reached out for his shoe and started to slip it over his toes.

"No, dear," said his wife, "put your sock on first." He dropped his gaze momentarily, grunted and put on his right sock. Then the shoe. Then he reached out to the left side, groping, still talking to me. I was watching him fascinatedly and by golly he did it. He picked up the other shoe and started to put it on his bare left foot.

"No, dear," said Margerie, "you must put on the sock first." Malcolm looked down, grunted, and did as he was told. Margerie and I looked at one another and both of us shook our heads. This was a man who needed a lot of looking after.

In due course of time a hospital bed became available. Malcolm went in and had his veins stripped. There were no complications and he was able to resume dictation. The book was finished and published. It was a sensation. Malcolm brought me a copy. He was very grateful.

"I should like to have autographed this for you, but unfortunately I have this mental block and am unable to sign my name. But look, give me a bit of paper and when the block passes I will write on it and you can paste it in the book."

I tore off a blank from my prescription pad and he put it in his pocket. Two months later it came back to me in an envelope addressed by his wife. On my prescription blank was written in ink,

with affection
Malcolm Lowry.

Malcolm Lowry: 1930

by Gerald Noxon

It was in the fall of 1929 that I first met Malcolm Lowry. I was then an undergraduate at Trinity College, Cambridge, in my second year at the University, while Malcolm, although a year older than I, had just come up. His arrival had in fact been delayed for some two years which he had spent working his way around the world as a merchant seaman. He had come up to St. Catharine's College, which was not one with a contemporary literary reputation.

Our meeting, since we were in different years and at different colleges, would have been most unlikely had it not been for the fact that I was the publisher of a small undergraduate literary magazine called *Experiment*.

Malcolm was at that time, and continued to be, for the most part, a very shy fellow whose acquaintance at Cambridge was composed not primarily of his fellow undergraduates, but of a wide variety of persons, both of "town" and "gown," ranging from bookmakers (turf) to bookmakers (literary). However, shy though he was of most of the academic fraternity, Malcolm was above all a writer, and he knew it. This fact soon became known to the editorial board of *Experiment,* which consisted basically of J. Bronowski, Hugh Sykes-Davies, and William Empson.

A story entitled "Port Swettenham," submitted to the magazine by Malcolm, was promptly accepted and printed in the February, 1930, issue of *Experiment*. It was, although very rough and uncertain in many ways, quite obviously a work of genuine literary merit and one of original talent. This was the first publication of work by Malcolm Lowry. He was at the time already well on the way with a novel entitled *Ultramarine,* which was eventually to be published by Jonathan Cape several years later.

By the time his story had been published in our magazine, I had of course had reason to meet the author. It was not easy to know

106

what sort of person he was. I knew nothing whatsoever about his background except that he had been to sea and he appeared to be, through what I later learned to be an extreme shyness, a rather surly, uncooperative, and not very communicative individual. Drink in sufficient quantity would for a time tend to loosen his tongue, but that did not always mean that he was any the more able to communicate his thoughts and feelings to others.

It was quite obvious to me, however, that Malcolm was having a difficult time at Cambridge, not so much on account of Cambridge itself, but on account of what seemed to be the serious problems which occupied his mind and dominated his spirit.

At first, after the publication of his story, I met Malcolm only accidentally, in the street, in pubs, or sometimes at parties. Then, on his own account, towards the spring of 1930 he began to come to visit me in my rooms in Trinity. He was passionately fond of jazz and fascinated by the cinema. I had a phonograph, a small but respectable collection of jazz records—old Deccas and Parlophones, as I recall—mostly blues, for which Malcolm and I shared a particular fondness. I also had a long shelf of film books, which were not very common around Cambridge at that time.

During these visits, which always occurred at night, Malcolm usually stayed only a comparatively short time. If he found someone else with me when he arrived he would usually either refuse to come in at all, or sit silently for a few moments and then, mumbling some sort of an excuse, take his leave.

Our conversations, apart from the subjects of jazz and movies, were nearly always concerned with the technical problems of the writer. Malcolm was at that time trying very hard to discover a way in which to write the kind of book he wanted to write, a mode of writing which would not only fulfill his own purposes but would at the same time conform to a certain extent to established literary values which he acknowledged and respected. He was deeply concerned with questions of "metier" as well as the problems of self-expression. Two writers seemed to have an overwhelming importance for him at the time. They were Herman Melville and Conrad Aiken. Later I learnt that a third writer, a Norwegian by the name of Nordhal Grieg, was also very important to Malcolm, but he never mentioned Grieg to me during the Cambridge days as far as I can remember. We did, however, discuss at some length a novel which Malcolm had already started writing, entitled "In Ballast to the White Sea," and it was in connection with this project in particular that Nordhal Grieg had influenced Malcolm, as I later learnt. The manuscript of this novel was destroyed, according to Malcolm, in a fire at Dollarton in British Columbia in 1944.

In *Ultramarine,* too, the novel which Malcolm was trying to complete while he was at Cambridge, there was certainly some debt to Grieg, but on the whole *Ultramarine* was predominantly influenced by the works of Conrad Aiken in general and by the novels *Blue Voyage* and *Great Circle* in particular.

With me Malcolm chose to discuss principally problems of style and language, not content. He seemed to know what he wanted to say, which was most unusual in so young a writer, but he was terribly concerned with how he should say it. The question always was, how should a serious novelist write in that year 1930? Naturally we discussed the kind of solutions put forward by such writers as Joyce, Faulkner, and Hemingway as well as those put forward in the works of Aiken, Melville, Bunyan, and a host of others.

Basically Malcolm was unwilling to repudiate the legacy which he had found awaiting him in the works of nineteenth-century novelists. While discarding the aridity of a purely realistic style, he was unwilling to adopt the kind of personal stenography which made the works of writers like Joyce and Faulkner superficially difficult for the reader. Nor was Malcolm to be reduced by the apparent simplicity of Hemingway, whose writing he found much too flat for his own purposes. For Malcolm it was necessary that his writing should have a perfectly wrought surface meaning, in the sense of the term established by Flaubert. A competent and thoroughly understandable narrative technique, however complex it might be in form, was a necessity, as was a sound dramaturgy of classical origin. And above all Malcolm knew that he had to use the full range of the English language as it had been given to him to know it and use it. And even in 1930 his command of the English language was amazingly authoritative.

But while fulfilling all the conditions mentioned above, Malcolm insisted that his writing must be capable of carrying meaning at many different depths, on the many different levels of intellectual and emotional communication which he discerned so clearly in Melville, for instance.

Truly, Malcolm Lowry had set himself a problem to which there could be no single, simple answer. He had already committed himself to a struggle which he himself realized could never have a definite outcome. There was no help for it. He could not borrow nor adopt a style. He had to create one of his own to fulfill his own needs, and it had to be forged out of the extraordinary complex alloys which were constantly being produced in what must be called the furnace of his mind. For, internally, Malcolm was a man on fire. His external appearance in 1930 did not give much evidence of his internal condition.

He was a short, compact man, very broad in the shoulders and exceptionally strong. His arms were rather long for his height and when standing he let them hang down at his sides in a curiously fixed curvature. I remember thinking that Malcolm was not bow-legged but bow-armed. His eyes, of an extreme blue, were the most striking feature of his face. I learnt that you could always tell more about Malcolm's state of mind by the look in his eyes than by anything he might say, or fail to say.

In spite of our fairly frequent visits together, with the jazz and the movie books and the discussions of literary style and methods, I did not feel that I knew Malcolm very well, nor could I form any exact notion of the personal problems from which he was obviously suffering but to which he did not refer. All I knew was that I liked him and I knew instinctively that he was a friend.

Much later in 1930 when the summer vacation was drawing to a close—it must have been in September—I found myself in the town of Rye in Sussex. I do not now remember exactly how I came to be there, but I was alone and I was planning to stay the night. I was strolling idly down the main street of the town enjoying the sunshine when I ran into Malcolm. I mean, I literally ran into him. I was not looking where I was going and he was busy staring into the window of a hardware store. As we stepped back to examine one another I thought how extraordinarily well he looked. He greeted me with a truly jolly air, showing a kind of exuberant delight in our encounter which I had never seen him display at Cambridge. It turned out that he had arrived just that day in Rye in the company of Conrad Aiken and his wife, Clarissa, who were moving back into Conrad Aiken's old house in Mermaid Street. Although I knew much of Aiken's work, I had never met him. I did so that evening, introduced by Malcolm, and there began a friendship which has lasted more than thirty years.

And in front of the hardware store in Rye there began, too, a new and much more intimate phase in my relations with Malcolm Lowry. For two or three days of magically fine, warm weather, the kind of thing that England produces once in a decade or two just to prove you wrong, Malcolm and I roamed the town of Rye together, wandering from pub to pub—unbelievable how many there were in such a small place, but Malcolm knew them all—putting down vast quantities of Sussex Ale and taking the little narrow-gauge railway out past the golf course to Camber Sands to swim in the Channel waters, for once almost reasonably warm as the tide came in over the sun-warmed flats. In those few days I discovered a new Malcolm, a man full of laughter and joy, conscious, though never confident, of his talent and ability. For the first time he talked to me about his childhood, of his father, his mother and his brothers, of Liverpool and Merseyside, of his illness about the age of ten which had so seriously affected his eyesight that he had gone almost blind, of his longing to go to sea, of his going to sea.

I began to understand something of the personal problems which obsessed him and which were the source of much of his sometimes very odd behavior.

We talked a great deal and we smoked a great deal—it was a time of pipes for both of us and I had just discovered what was to me a new tobacco—Balkan Sobranie No. 10, it was, a mixture with a bit of cigar leaf added. Malcolm found this extraordinarily good. To smoke it was, he said, exactly like eating, only much superior to that overrated exercise. And it was a fact that we seemed to be eating only sausage rolls, miniature pork pies, and scraps of fish and chips wrapped in pieces of newspaper—the fish was elegantly described as rock salmon, but we both knew that it was dogfish or catfish, and that was all right too.

During those few days Malcolm proved himself a fascinating companion. The brilliance of his mind, his extraordinary memory, the amazing range of depth of his knowledge, his fund of really funny stories in which the jokes were most often at his own expense, all astonished and captivated me as did the warmth and friendliness of his nature, which was revealed to me in its true condition for the first time.

My time ran out and I had to return to London. Malcolm came to see me off at the little station in Rye where the local toy train stood waiting to trundle off to catch the express at Ashford junction. I can still see him, flapping his arms at his sides in a farewell gesture, like a kind of fledgling. The weather had stayed fine. I left Malcolm, as I had found him, in sunshine.

As soon as I got back to town I went to a tobacconist's in Piccadilly and had them send a tin of Balkan Sobranie No. 10 to Malcolm Lowry, Care of Conrad Aiken, Jeake's House, Mermaid Street, Rye, Sussex. Almost at once I had a note from Malcolm written in his almost indecipherable hand, tiny and crawling up the paper.

"Thank you for the tobacco," he wrote, "It is the first time anyone ever gave me anything like that."

It was not until many years later that I discovered that what he wrote may well have been true. Certainly the small gesture meant much to him at the time.

Malcolm's second year at Cambridge was, I think, a pretty hectic one. I saw very little of him. It was my last year at Trinity and almost immediately afterwards I went to live in Italy. In his final year Malcolm, with his amazing tenacity in recuperation, pulled himself together and emerged from the academic wringer with a first class honors degree in English, which, of course, he thoroughly deserved but which few of us believed he would get.

More Than Music:
Glimpses of Malcolm Lowry

by Downie Kirk

> Sir, more than kisses, letters mingle
> souls;
> For, thus friends absent speak.
>
> —JOHN DONNE

It would take a symposium of the friends with whom Malcolm Lowry corresponded to describe him adequately from his letters. Yet, one correspondent, basing his impressions upon letters which were written during the decade that was the most productive period of his literary career, can still give a significant view of the man and the artist. One naturally wonders, of course, what right one really has to quote from the private letters of an author; one is sharply reminded of Heine's remark: "To publish even one line of an author which he himself has not intended for the public at large—especially letters which are addressed to private persons—is to commit a despicable act of felony."

But in the case of Malcolm Lowry one may perhaps be pardoned, for obviously some of the care that made him revise almost every paragraph he wrote went into the composition of his letters, although it is doubtful that he wrote them with a view to publication. In fact, it is their very naturalness that makes them valuable. He obviously wrote many of them under pressure, at a time when he was absorbed in the composition of his novels and his poetry; for he makes frequent references to the long stretches of strain caused by his creative work, in the midst of which he would write a letter in reply to an invitation to spend an evening of complete relaxation from his creative endeavours.

> When I'm working at very high intensity [he says on one occasion] the writing of even the smallest note often takes an incredibly

long time—an occupational psychological aberration of some sort doubtless due to the fact that the narcissistic care which one sometimes expends on prose makes a fellow forget a letter should be spontaneous and to hell with the semicolons, since your friend doesn't want to look at them anyway but is simply interested in hearing from you.

Joseph Conrad once said that he could compare the strain of writing *Nostromo* only to the everlasting somber stress of the westward winter passage around Cape Horn. So it must have been with Malcolm Lowry; for he drove himself mercilessly to produce his works: with him there was a passionate necessity to reflect and to distill in its purest form something within him that would not give him peace. And many of the letters—"the only true heart-talkers," as someone has said—are as revelatory of Lowry as his autobiographical fiction. The expression of his thought is neither cryptic nor obscure. His commentary on life and literature is all the more precious because it is good vivid talk by the Lowry whom not many could listen to with complete comprehension for any length of time because of the abstruseness of his references and the broad leaps in his thoughts. He was, of course, shy, and although he was dying to communicate, he often remained silent; when he did open his mouth, it was to release a flood of words that dazzled you with its brilliance but frequently left you bewildered about its meaning.

We are now aware of Malcolm Lowry as an outstanding novelist, as a distinguished short-story writer and as a considerable poet, but his power as a critic is practically unknown. His book reviews and literary criticisms, although not numerous, are penetrating. His letters, moreover, reveal him as a sensitive critic of literature, politics, music, art and philosophy; in them he discusses with acute perception and in clear style a wide range of unusual subjects.

In one letter he tells about reading José Ortega y Gasset—especially his wonderful lecture on Goethe, and his *Towards a Philosophy of History*. In the latter work the Spanish philosopher suggests that human life in its most human dimension is like a work of fiction, that man is a sort of novelist of himself, who conceives the fanciful figure of a personage with its unreal occupations and then, for the sake of converting it into reality, does all the things he does. Lowry says this idea recommends itself to him because he feels that man is a kind of novelist of himself. He thinks, too, that there is something valuable from a philosophic point of view in trying to put down what actually takes place in a novelist's mind when he conceives what he conceives to be the fanciful figure of a personage.

> The part that never gets written, with which is included the true impulses that made him a novelist or dramatist in the first place, and the modifications of life around him through his own eyes as those impulses were realized, would be the true drama, and I hope to finish something of this sort one day.

At this point he inserts a long parenthesis in minute handwriting in the margin of his typed letter, which I quote in full, because its remarks on Pirandello exhibit the honesty, fairness and insight of his literary criticism:

> This would be not unlike Pirandello who—I quote from an article in The Partisan Review—"inverts the convention of modern realism, instead of pretending that the stage is not a stage at all, but the familiar parlor, he pretends that the familiar parlor is not real as a photograph but a stage containing many realities." This is Shakespeare's speech come true. My feeling is that Pirandello may not have wholly appreciated how close to truth his view of human life might be, as a consequence of which the realities of "Six Characters in Search of an Author," say, do not measure up to the profundity of the view, though I have not studied him sufficiently, and the accepted critical opinion upon Pirandello is apparently faulty.

Lowry continues his analysis of Ortega's *Towards A Philosophy of History* by stating that although Ortega is not concerned in this work, at any rate, with fiction, it is the thesis upon which he bases his view of history—namely, that man is what has happened to him. This thought interests Lowry because it is a philosophy that begins with one's existence, links up with Heidegger and Kierkegaard, and hence with Existentialism. Writing in June, 1950, he notes that Existentialism has already become a music-hall joke in France and that it contains an element of despair that is absent in Ortega. Sartre's Existentialism, as far as he can understand it, strikes him as "a sort of reach-me-down or second-hand philosophy," changed dramatically to fit the anguish of the French in their struggle against the German occupation. In conclusion, however, he says:

> Even so, it's refreshing to read a philosophy that gives value to the drama of life itself, of the dramatic value of your own life at the very moment you are reading.

Commenting on Ortega's thought that the snob is hostile to liberalism, with the hostility of a deaf man for words, that liberty has always been understood in Europe as the freedom to be one's real self and that it is not surprising that a man who knows that he has no mission to fulfil should want to be rid of it, Lowry says that this idea at first sight appeared to him, among other things, one of the most convincing arguments against communism that he had ever read in such a short space, but that on second thought he realized it was only a statement in defense of the old school of liberalism, and he states that such a school could not exist without the possibility of free discussion of revolutionary tenets, including even those contained in communism for that matter, or without the right to practical absorption of revolutionary tenets where desirable.

The political situation in the world looked grim to Lowry in 1950, although it did not seem to him half so hopeless as it had in 1939 or even in 1938. In one letter, for instance, he writes: "Sometimes I get the impression that not even the people who are actually in the process of making history know in the least what is really going on. Or if they do, it seems appalling that they should be in the position that they are." As for the eventual outcome of the present human predicament, he felt that mankind, striving toward a rebirth, would probably achieve a better world in the not-too-distant future. He was familiar, of course, with the pessimistic picture drawn by Orwell in his *1984,* as he often talked about the novel; but he was more hopeful than Orwell, and although he was painfully aware that man, if he did not take care, might destroy himself—as we might infer from *Under the Volcano*—he felt that the revolutionary forces of our time would change for the better the present shocking situation in world politics. He says, optimistically, that "anything that is a revolution must keep moving or it doesn't revolute: by its nature it contains within it the seeds of its own destruction; so by 1989, say, everything ought to be hunky-dory, all of which certainly doesn't make it any easier to live in 1950."

Elsewhere Lowry discusses at length religion, witchcraft and Voodooism—subjects in which he took an intense interest. Referring to *Mythologie Vodou,* a book on witchcraft, by his Haitian friend Milo Marcelin, he takes exception to a review of it in *Time* magazine; he explains that it is a book not about Voodoo chiefly but about witchcraft, and that there is a difference, although it is not perhaps apparent to the layman.

Lowry points out that Voodoo is essentially a religion to be regarded with reverence, since it is without question a matter-

transcending religion based upon the actual existence of the supernatural—a fact that is fundamental to man himself, compared with
which most other religions are simply techniques to hide that fact
or at least to keep the supernatural at relatively safe distances. He
feels that only the Negroes are powerful enough or holy enough to
be able to handle it, and that even they of course abuse it. He
thinks, furthermore, that the white man should regard with awe
the great dignity and discipline that is behind Voodooism at its
highest, its conception of God and the meaning it gives to life—
and this he says is the religion of a race that we so often glibly think
of as inferior, or comprising medicine men, or the powers of darkness, etc. He appeals for greater understanding of the colored people
with words that are as timely today as when he wrote them ten
years ago:

> Heart of Darkness indeed! Joseph Conrad should have been to
> Haiti. What he failed to understand was that the savages of the
> Congo had, to some extent, subdued the dark forces that are in
> nature by creating their religion in the first place in order to subdue
> them, that that, in its way, was a civilizing almost a pragmatic
> process . . . It is clear that Comrade Joseph did not allow himself
> to be corrupted by any savages though; he stayed in Polish aloofness
> on board in company with some a priori ideas.

Lowry himself felt that in his rich and varied life there had been
many communications between his mind and others by means outside the channels of sense, and he was so convinced of the existence
of thought transference that he could not dismiss it as mere coincidence. The subject of telepathy occurs often in his letters. Once
a "mysterious" crossing of our letters (this resulted in much confusion and the resort to telegrams) caused him to write:

> I am being so supermeticulous about what is more or less spon-
> taneous because I perceive, having been reading Bergson, that the
> difficulties on one plane of communication and the too great facili-
> ties on another (if telepathic ones can be called such) might have
> led you into some inconvenience, than which little is worse on
> Saturday afternoon . . .

Malcolm Lowry was blessed with a keen sense of humour,
though critics seem to have overlooked this priceless quality in his
writings. He once said that he intended to write a book dealing with
the peculiar punishment that is meted out to people who lack the
sense of humour to write books like *Under the Volcano*. He was, in

fact, a very witty person, and his wit could not help overflowing into his letters. It usually appears in a tone of good-natured banter. Commenting on the reception *Under the Volcano* received in France, he writes facetiously:

> Finally, I thought that you would be tickled to know, The Volcano has made a hit in France, where it is coming out three times in the next month: first in a classic series, then Correa, and it is also being serialized in the Paris daily newspaper, Combat. They have decided that it is the writing on the wall, that your amigo is everything from the Four Quartets (which he has never read) to Joyce (whom he dislikes)—finally relate him to the Jewish prophetic Zohar (of which he knows nothing)—they have some other comments, too, about Macbeth, but that is nothing to what someone is just going to say in Victoria, over the C.B.C., where they have decided that the Consul is really Moby Dick, masquerading as the unconscious aspect of the Cadborosaurus in the Book of Jonah, or words to that effect.

A knowledgeable devotee of the cinematographic art, Lowry once said that if *Under the Volcano* were filmed in his lifetime, he would insist on helping to direct it, and in his letters he makes many interesting references to films. He tells, for instance, of going to see the film *The Hairy Ape,* which he had heard was good; he considered it *djevelsk* (Scandinavian for devilish) in the worst sense, although the suspense was subtly increased by the accident of the lights failing for an hour right in the middle of the showing. He recalls that people looked very sinister and strange standing about in the foyer, and he made a note that he ought to use this in a book; then he remembered that he had done so in *Under the Volcano.* In another letter he says that he went to see the old silent film *Intolerance,* played straight through without any music at all, which he considered a great mistake as Griffith wrote his own score. "Very few silent films," he remarks, "will stand being played like that, without music, which I think is interesting. *The Passion of Joan of Arc* is an exception."

With regard to C. F. Ramuz's novel *When the Mountain Fell,* Lowry makes some enlightening remarks on the author's style, in which he detects the influence of the movies. From his reading of Clifton Fadiman's remarks printed on the cover of *When the Mountain Fell,* he had gained the impression that Ramuz's style was being approached in an odd way, that it was supposed to be natural— that is, artless, unsophisticated, stark, stern, unintellectual, above all uninfluenced. He says he cannot see how a style, no matter how arrived at—often he imagines largely by cutting—can hope fundamentally to be much more than simply appropriate, in the fullest sense, to what the author is writing about. He says also that he did not find Ramuz's style particularly simple and that he can detect many sophisticated influences including avant-garde cinema. But as far as he is concerned the story is none the worse for that. His concluding remarks on style are illuminating:

> Just the same one is all in favour of a clear, pure, concrete style, and one with the utmost of simplicity, etc. But if one has arrived at that position, it is unlikely that the style has been uninfluenced. Doubtless one has to pass through a maximum of influences before achieving a style at all. It is difficult to see how a style like Ramuz', even if it achieves great clarity, can be called unsophisticated. Anyhow his simplicity, such as it is, strikes me as having cost a great intellectual effort.

Lowry's lifelong interest in style, as well as his deep love of language and his ready championship of the outcast, mark him as a kindred spirit of the great Austrian critic and poet Karl Kraus, who, like Lowry, concerned himself throughout his life with literary style and poetics, carried on an unending campaign against inaccurate and slovenly use of language, and fought against injustice, corruption and hypocrisy wherever he found them. Lowry doubtless knew the work of Kraus, because he was steeped in the writings of the authors of Central Europe. He often spoke in admiration of Kraus's compatriot and contemporary Hermann Broch. But he talked most about the German-Jewish novelist Franz Kafka, who like himself was definitely influenced by the cabala and the works of Soren Kierkegaard. There is much of Kafka's philosophical and religious symbolism—as well as traces of his compact, intense and closely reasoned style—in *Under the Volcano*. In his conversations Lowry made frequent references to *The Trial* and *The Castle,* and in one letter he writes that he appreciates a Kafka-like scrupulousness on my part, but hastens to remind me that "Kafka believed that while the demand on the part of the divine powers for absolute righteousness even in the smallest matters was unconditional, human effort, even at its highest, was always in the wrong."

Lowry had great sympathy for the younger authors who were struggling for recognition and was most generous in assisting them. When he reviewed their work, he made his criticism in the spirit of kindness, but he could be caustic, as when he reviewed Thomas Merton's *The Seven Storey Mountain*. He considered it a very questionable book—a paradox, in fact; for Merton had gone into a Trappist monastery pretending to give up everything and yet went on writing books. But even in Merton's book Lowry recognized a kind of sincerity or dedication and felt that the book was important enough at this point in history to be considered on another plane altogether. He ends his entertaining review with a timely, striking thought: "That a Monastery might, in essence, be the capital of the world at this juncture is a possibility which not even Nietzsche were he alive would care to question—or would he?"

No account of Malcolm Lowry's life and work at Dollarton could be complete without mention of his love of British Columbia and especially the country closely surrounding his shack on Burrard Inlet. His descriptions of it permeate his fiction and the abundance of feeling he had for the place overflows into his letters. The fear that he might be evicted from his beloved house on the beach caused him much anxiety, which he expresses in his letters. Nor did these feelings end on his departing to Europe in 1954. From Ripe, near Lewes, in Sussex, he wrote in April, 1956: "Though we like this place quite a bit, please don't think we have abandoned Dollarton; we have not and think of it constantly." And finally, about seven months before his untimely death, he wrote these nostalgic words: "I am writing like mad on October Ferry to Gabriola. . . . It is better than the Volcano, a veritable symphony of longing for the beach. We hope to return D.V., meantime think of you often and are often homesick."

Reading Lowry's letters again was a great pleasure to me. The immense vitality, the exuberant humour, the depth of thought and the broad humanity expressed on almost every page, often in the richest of poetic imagery, gave me moments of sheer delight. As a tribute to Malcolm Lowry—the man and the artist—I should like to quote, in closing, from a poem his friend, Conrad Aiken, for whom he had the greatest admiration and who in turn cherished him as if he were his own son:

> Music I heard with you was more than music,
> And bread I broke with you was more than bread.

Malcolm Lowry: A Reminiscence

by David Markson

For seven or eight days, in the summer of 1952, I visited with Malcolm Lowry in the squatter's shack on the beach beyond Vancouver where he had written most of *Under the Volcano*. In September, 1954, while they were awaiting the departure of a freighter to Italy, he and his wife Margerie lived for two weeks in my New York apartment. The duration of both visits seems greater in retrospect, since time spent with Lowry was somehow concentrated, or distilled.

Speaking of Dylan Thomas, Lowry told me once: "You know, I never saw him when he wasn't drunk." I have to begin with the same qualification about Lowry. The man could not shave himself. In lieu of a belt, he knotted a rope or a discarded necktie around his waist. Mornings, he needed two or three ounces of gin in his orange juice if he was to steady his hand to eat the breakfast that would very likely prove his only meal of the day. Thereafter a diminishing yellow tint in the glass might belie for a time the fact that now he was drinking the gin neat, which he did for as many hours as it took him to collapse—sometimes sensible enough of his condition to lurch toward a bed, though more often he would crash down into a chair, and once it was across my phonograph. Then he would hack and sputter through the night like some great defective machine breaking apart.

Yet what one remembers is less the excess than Lowry's own attitude toward it, an incredible impression he conveyed that he could never take any of it quite seriously. He had an acute sense of his own dissolution, eternally chagrined at being a nuisance, apologizing hourly for small disasters, but what he sensed equally was the underlying absurdity in it all: the very idea, a grown man and that is the third burning cigarette I have misplaced tonight.

One afternoon in New York we had to leave him alone for a time, though safely within the apartment. Because a party was being given

120

for him that evening, Margerie had done her best to establish what Lowry termed her "tyranny of five o'clock"—no hard liquor before then. What gin we possessed was hidden, and we left him with six or eight cans of beer. I returned first, about three hours later. Within moments, Lowry had commenced to giggle. Sheepish, but no less transparently gleeful, he glanced about furtively before he confessed: "I have a funny story to tell you, about something that happened when you were out." Something had happened, as opposed to being done. A day or two before, I had bought fresh shaving lotion. I did not ask what it had used to dilute itself.

One jokes because Lowry joked: this was mischief only. Though the mischief was somehow cosmic too, as if ordained. In his autobiographical narrative, *Ushant,* Conrad Aiken remembers a younger Lowry as "visibly and happily alight with genius," and the phrase means exactly what it says. Lowry looked like a genius; there was a gleam not within but behind the eyes that seemed to transcend any ordinary alertness or mirth. The notion will be more provocative if one recalls the Consul's "demons" in *Under the Volcano*—another surely autobiographical work—and how often those demons are "in possession." He had Scandinavian eyes, with a certain whiteness in the pigmentation of the lids which complemented that demonic glitter. But his upper teeth protruded slightly, suggesting a grin whether one was intended or not, making of him a roguishly improbable Faustus at best.

And he was really too "bookish" for the role, even if there was a distinct manner in which he cared far less about the written word than about the personality of the man who had put it down. A book became a kind of introduction, for Lowry, to the author personally. Voicing some insight or other, he might preface it thus: "As old Melville would say . . ." What followed would be a notion that Melville (or whoever) had never anywhere expressed, but that only he among authors might have.

He chose his men, however: "You cannot trust the ones who are too careful. As writers or drinkers. Old Goethe cannot have been so good a man as Keats or Chatterton. Or Rimbaud. The ones that burn."

He delighted in repeating an anecdote about having known "a poet" of seventeen or so, in London—"a wild boy who insisted he was already dying, smashing glasses after each drink, that sort of thing." Some years later, he had begun to admire the work of "one"

Dylan Thomas, whom Margerie then met during a visit to England on her own. "And how is ruddy old Malc?" Dylan asked. Margerie was certain that Lowry did not know the man. Nor could Lowry himself make the connection until a new Thomas collection appeared with an Augustus John portrait as a frontispiece.

Then again his "familiars" were not necessarily always his peers. During one New York conversation, and after a lengthy pause on Lowry's part, the talk had been taken up again for some moments before he announced: "Incidentally, there was an owl perched outside there just now. You saw it, of course?"

An owl. On West 113th Street. Well, it was not impossible—though with Lowry there was also the question of what sort of owl. One morning when he was alone at the Dollarton shack, for example, a bird several times plummeted from a tree to crash against a window. The question to be asked at Margerie's return, for one with Lowry's occult orientation, was self-evident: "Is there mail? Someone is trying to get in touch with me." As Lowry related the incident, it was almost redundant that Margerie carried a letter from a total stranger, the last line of which read: "You have got to write to me." There would be a merriment in the telling, perhaps even a hint of self-mockery. Doubtless it sounds stagy; in reality, it was unsettling.

In any case such dimensions were more than appropriate to Lowry's talk, which, again like the Consul's, was wholly remarkable, wholly implausible, if not to say so full of involution and subordinate phrases that even simple declarations were rarely completed: every owl reminded Lowry of twelve other owls. One afternoon, out with friends, he began an anecdote about a French hospital where, apparently, several kindly but ill-advised nuns had supplied him with liter after liter of red wine. The story was started at least eight times. But after digressions about everything from Manx fishing customs to the reading habits of James Joyce, it spiraled finally into absolute incoherence:

"Malc, will you for heaven's sake tell us what you are talking about?"

"Well, it's difficult. But you have to listen. It's . . . contrapuntal!"

The tale of the nuns was told, insofar as it was, in an exclusive East Side hotel, under circumstances themselves characteristic. Lowry was to meet his agent there at about noon. After various confusions he arrived at approximately four, wearing baggy denim trousers, a boyish sports shirt without a necktie, and a zippered denim jacket. In fact, he was in the process of being turned away, until another member of our party was recognized by the doorman —though Viscount Peter Churchill's status at the hotel has presumably been in question since.

A point should be made that such situations did not occur because of the drink alone, though they had nothing to do with anything like Bohemian protest either; rather, there was a kind of naïveté in the man, and a considerable innocence. He had lived in isolation for so long, in Cuernavaca and in British Columbia, that he simply did not think about such things as neckties. In the Dollarton woods, where the Lowrys had neither electricity nor plumbing, an "appointment" meant a casual invitation to look in at the shanty of some fellow squatter 100 yards down a stony beach.

As it happens, Lowry and I did take a more "formal" excursion up there one day, or what began as such. The Dollarton house was situated on one of the deep-water Pacific inlets east of Vancouver Island. Somewhere to the south, though "just around the bend," was a town called Port Moody that Lowry decided we might inspect. In bathing trunks, carrying our clothes, we set out via dinghy: "Around the Horn to Valparaiso!"

The latter was more like it. After an hour investigating flora and fauna along the wooded shoreline, we were next evidently in the great strait itself, banging about amid currents, inspecting the looming, rusted underbellies of freighters at anchor a mile or so from any docks, absurd though maybe intrepid too in our tiny craft. Four hours had elapsed before we made fast—to discover that we might venture no farther than to the first dockside tavern. Somehow, en route, Lowry had lost his pants over the side.

Undaunted, we had the required drinks. Yet even well into dark Lowry was reluctant to depart, though now what held him was a special flavor of the tavern itself—of the sea at its door and of men who followed the sea. More often than literature, or Mexico, the sea colored Lowry's talk, recollections of his one boyhood voyage as a coal trimmer, of other passages thereafter, and for all his removal from it now it lured him still. This stocky, clumsy, shy little man just turned 43, without a cent in his pockets, for that matter without pockets, appearing on the threshold and grinning ingenuously, yet timidly too, which was characteristic of him among strangers . . . and yet within a moment being grinned at in turn, his obvious joy infectious and winning. Men lifted their glasses, they called hello. "The very sight of that old bastard makes me happy

for five days. No bloody fooling." Long after recording it Lowry
remained too pleased to admit he had overheard it being said about
himself.

But at last, departure. Once Port Moody was behind us and the
random lamps of the freighters at mooring had faded to port the
darkness was absolute. "Now listen, Malc, do you recognize this
inlet?" "Oh, it's near, it's near." He, himself, all but invisible in
the stern, sprawling, dragging one arm or the other in our wake.
"There are whales here now and then, have I told you?" Then,
from somewhere in the mountains, the eerie "Zinnnnnng!
Zinnnnnng!" of a sawmill running through the night. "Ha! There is
old Kafka, leading his orchestra. He must have been a splendid
fellow, Kafka. I prayed to him once, and he answered my prayer."
It is well past midnight when we locate the solitary dim gleam in
the distance. Still, we may be rowing an additional half-mile out
of the way. But no, it is the shack: Margerie has left a kerosene
lamp in the window. "Oh, I knew you chaps would have some adventure or other." To which, Odysseus: "I say, you do have the
decency to offer us a drink?"

Up there in the wilderness, Lowry swam for half an hour or more
each morning, whatever the weather. It may have saved him—
certainly it postponed the inevitable. He was all chest, though in
that athlete's way of going to fat where chest and stomach become
one, and he had short arms that often seemed to flop about ineptly,
like the appendages of some beached sea thing.

Yet he had been handsome and, as the photos show, with his
beard the face expressed a kind of gravity and wisdom in the last
days. But at this time he was weathered and turning fleshy. In-
terestingly, the older Errol Flynn, cast as the boozy Mike in *The
Sun Also Rises*, took on a look very like Lowry's.

I have said there was something naive or ingenuous about him.
On another level it was simply honesty; one was convinced he had
never in his life been motivated by pettiness. But he was also able
to talk about love, in an essentially masculine, platonic sense,
without inviting accusations of mawkishness, or worse. A case in
point involves Conrad Aiken, who had filled an *in loco parentis*
role for him in his youth, and whom he had not seen for nineteen
years before the New York visit.

Aiken was on Cape Cod when the Lowrys arrived, and Margerie
sent a telegram. After two decades, and though he was 65 then

himself, Aiken still knew his man. It was the poet who made the trip.

Unfortunately, his arrival coincided with the aforementioned party. For some years Aiken has maintained a walk-up in the East 30s, and we went there first. Lowry was still in fair shape outwardly, the after-shave "bracer" to the contrary. (He had this faculty: musing, perplexed by unmentioned private visions, he could be teetering at the edge of the abyss and for a time not seem drunk at all, merely abstracted. Eventually, of course, he would come back to reality like a bridge collapsing.) At Aiken's, the fare is martinis. Lowry had been elated for days over the prospect of seeing the man again, but here too he was initially shy, and there were false starts. In rough form at the moment was a novel, *October Ferry to Gabriola*, the most nearly finished of the several to be left at his death. For some minutes Lowry endeavored to summarize a nonexistent plot, after which: "Well, nothing happens. Nothing should, in a novel." Whereupon Aiken, whose *Blue Voyage* Lowry readily acknowledged as the critical influence on his own concept of fictional subjectivity: "No. No incidents."

Lowry also talked a good deal about his condition, laying it in part to his pain at having to leave Dollarton, where the squatters faced eviction. "I have to slide through this time of crisis on my unconscious," he repeated more than once. During the conversation he was beset by the shakes, and discussed this also. (Shortly after his arrival in New York, having to sign a paper before a notary, he was unable to write his name. Three martinis effected a remedy, though he spilled the first and the second had to be held for him.)

Margerie had gotten him into a tie and jacket for the evening, and I had shaved him, so at the party itself his appearance again may have been briefly deceptive. Present were his friends James Agee and James Stern, his editors Frank Taylor and Albert Erskine, and two or three wives. The night was exceptionally hot; Agee, apparently already ill himself, stood through most of it in a pool of sweat that had literally dripped from his chin to the floor. Almost at once, Lowry drifted into a kind of rapt silence, likewise sweating profusely, gazing at nothing; perhaps an hour passed in which he spoke to no one at all, nor did he move from his chair. Then, suddenly, cupping his hands to his mouth, he began to make sounds that can only be called "beeps"—though one who knew could infer jazz, and more specifically tunes associated with Bix Beiderbecke: "Singin' the Blues"; "I'm Comin', Virginia"; "In a Mist." For thirty minutes at least, even more absolutely lost to the rest of us now, the man rendered the Dixieland he had loved as a youth. ("I learned to write listening to Beiderbecke," he had remarked in Dollarton. He owned an ancient, hand-cranked phonograph, and a collection of scarred recordings to which he could listen for hours. "Oh, what pure art!" he might cry, or, "Ah, the discipline!" Amid the New York baggage was a ukulele, but with strings missing.)

The private recital ceased only when Aiken announced his departure: "Good night, disgrace." Then, however, Lowry insisted upon seeing him home—this with no idea where Aiken was headed and, chances were, with no money in his possession either, since Margerie normally handled all cash. In the street, in jest but in sadness, Aiken had to wrestle him off as a taxi drew up. Breaking Lowry's hold, the older man tumbled to the floor as the vehicle took him away.

Those next moments, gazing into the empty street where only now a small rain, like a mist, had begun to fall, Lowry could not have appeared more sober. "He is an old man," he said, "and now I will never see him again." He was right, if for a wrong reason; and for a time he wept.

By morning, the twinkle had returned. Aiken had spoken of a nine-o'clock train, and Lowry did not begin to function until well past that hour, but he insisted upon seeing the poet off. "After all, he is my father, and I haven't seen him in fifty-eight years. How can you keep me from him?" And again: "Of course, I would have gone to Massachusetts myself if I had to, even on all fours." In the end he settled for a telegram: "Was on deck 7 a.m. to see you off Wednesday but was offset by hurricane am going to encounter Monday afternoon off Cape Hatteras . . ." (There was, in fact, a hurricane along the coast that week, called "Edna," which Lowry talked about incessantly and which he insisted he had "invoked.")

At the same time he was able to regret what he determined had been "rudeness" at the party, apologizing too for the mounting havoc in my own apartment—glasses broken, books and bottles and half-smoked cigarettes scattered everywhere, if not to mention the sheaf of manuscript poems reposing for days now beneath the kitchen sink—or the blood that had mysteriously appeared on his blanket.

Similarly, whenever we were out together, always the generous impulse: "Here, here, let me pay." Then the hand at the pocket, the sigh of frustration. "Well, later, Margerie has money." Neither would he forget, ultimately demanding that she contribute $10 or $20—"my share, at least"—on an accounting that had come to infinitely less.

They were to sail, via an Italian line, from Brooklyn—on a ship he gleefully proclaimed was certain to carry high explosives.

En route to the docks, he was much taken by the Brooklyn Bridge, and he was "almost tempted" to revise a judgment on Hart Crane (he felt the bridge a static symbol). Loyally, he remembered to remind me that I must read both Stern and Agee, as well as Aiken's *Great Circle*—"Though I did not write that. The one I wrote in another life was *Blue Voyage*." And throughout the drive he repeated a line, in a spurious Mississippi accent, that he attributed to Faulkner: "Ah can stand anything. Ain't nothing wrong with me that a good bour-bon won't cure."

In fact he stood the first few hours well. At breakfast the shakes had been extreme, but he had acknowledged without argument that a shave was necessary. The sailing was to be seven or eight hours delayed, however, by which time he was semi-conscious in his bunk.

"I must see the skipper. If he is not a company man, this will be a happy ship." Meanwhile he impressed upon Margerie the urgency of tipping the steward at once. "Italian ships have holds full of Chianti."

Then, final words which will perhaps be allowed in a reminiscence of this sort: "I'm a pretty bad man, but you should really come to Sicily with us. We love you, you know, but not so that you have to shove a cork up your arse, old man."

Three years and intermittent letters later, the cablegram: Malcolm Suddenly Dead—Margerie.

And *vale*, since he eludes one's poor words anyway. One was convinced that the demons were real. But what one remembers, in the end, is the innocence withal, the mirth, the sheer abundance.

Recollections of Malcolm Lowry

by William McConnell

On May 14th, 1927, Malcolm Lowry was seventeen years old. On that day the Liverpool Correspondent for the London *Evening News* interviewed him just before he sailed on the cargo steamer *Pyrrhus* as a deckhand at 50/- per month. He told the Correspondent: "No sick-cushion youth for me. I want to see the world and rub shoulders with its oddities, and get some experience of life before I go back to Cambridge University." The Correspondent interviewed his rich cotton-broker father and his mother, too, but only her comments are on record: "He is bent on a literary career, and his short-story writing is all to him," said Mrs. Lowry, when the ship had left.

On his return from Port Said, Shanghai and Yokohama Lowry was again interviewed, this time by *The Daily Mail*. With characteristic candor he announced he didn't intend to go to sea again, since a fourteen-hour day chipping paint, scrubbing decks and polishing brass was not to his liking. He said he intended to go on to university, compose foxtrots and write fiction.

One of his intentions was realized, as we know, for Malcolm Lowry wrote, among many other works, one of the great novels of the twentieth century, *Under the Volcano*. Despite the early experience of his four-month voyage as deckhand, he returned to sea, traveling to every ocean, beachcombed in the South Seas, settled for troubled spates in Mexico, Haiti, Germany, until he finally found, again close to the sea, a waterfront shack at Dollarton, ten miles from Vancouver, where he could write and live in his own peculiar, uneasy peace.

It was during this last period of his life that I met Malcolm and his wife, Margerie (who published many fictional works under her maiden name, Margerie Bonner). It was at a cocktail party at the Caulfield home of Alan Crawley. A. J. M. Smith and the American poet Theodore Roethke had persuaded Malcolm to attend. He was pathologically shy and any group of more than four usually caused perspiration to drip from his face, but on this occasion there was no shyness. It was a gathering of writers, of like beings, of natural and mutual acceptance. He hated literary people; to the same degree he accepted and loved those he felt were dedicated to literature. Quite often this blind acceptance caused him self-hurt and disappointment, but more often it created deep friendship.

Physically, Lowry was a powerful man: short, broad-shouldered, with a tremendous chest. His gait was rolling, whether as accommodation to his bulk or the result of years at sea, or simply the acquisition of an imagined habit, I don't know. He was fair-headed, with muscular arms and small feet. Most impressive of all were his intense blue eyes, which looked into and through your own, which gazed into the distance, which altered in hue as his mood varied.

Most of his life from the time he left university until he discovered Dollarton was spent in physical activity in odd corners of the globe, but, like the scattered notes which he wrote on bus transfers, cigarette papers or any other chance piece of paper, all of his life was lived for metamorphosis into short story, poem or novel. He could discard nothing and, consequently, writing to him was not the usual casting for idea, figure of speech, or character portrayal, but rather a painful, tortuous process of selection and arrangement.

He had that rare (and rather frightening) gift of near total recall. I saw him sometimes after intervals of several months. For the first five minutes he would stare contemplatively across Burrard Inlet at the evening outline of Burnaby Mountain, then reflectively at a gull sweeping low over the water, then finally at me. Out of the air with magic, it seemed to one like myself who had little memory whatever, he would recount word-perfect an argument we had had on our previous meeting. He would review exactly what each of us had said, then quietly announce that he had been (or I had been, it doesn't matter) in error in a particular statement. Accuracy, even on trivial matters, was an obsession.

This accuracy was one of the strengthening qualities of his writing. By exact physical depiction, razor-edged characterization, evocation of mood, he had some alchemy which would make each line true in detail, yet with layers of meaning which could be peeled off by the reader without the onion becoming smaller. In his great novel, *Under the Volcano*, this is revealed in many pages. For example, I recall Malcolm describing to me how, when a young man in Wales, he had come across an amusing insertion in a Visitors' Book in a hotel. He described it on several occasions, each time not really adding anything, yet casting a different spell over the event on each telling. Consider my delight, then, when I encountered it in another guise on page 181:

> "Climbed the Parson's Nose," one had written, in the visitors' book at the little Welsh rock-climbing hotel, "in twenty minutes. Found the rocks very easy." "Came down the Parson's Nose," some immortal wag had added a day late, "in twenty seconds. Found the rocks very hard." . . . So now, as I approach the second half of my life, unheralded, unsung, and without a guitar, I am going back to sea again: perhaps these days of waiting are more like that droll descent, to be survived in order to repeat the climb. At the top of the Parson's Nose you could walk home to tea over the hills if you wished, just as the actor in the Passion Play can get off his cross and go home to his hotel for a Pilsener.

We walked along the beach one late afternoon—a warm afternoon when the tide was full, the salt-chuck quiet as if it had been fed to satiety and didn't want the never-changing chore of accommodating itself to the tug of the moon. We were having one of those intense and enjoyable silences which can cement each to the other without any mortar of words. We came across the oil-encrusted corpse of a seagull. I knew, of course, how passionately fond of birds Malcolm was (a well-marked pocket-size volume of Peterson's *Field Guide* was usually beside him) and I made some remark about someone's criminality in dumping bunker oil in the harbor. Malcolm nodded, then pointed without a word to the flares of the oil refineries on the other shore, his hand sweeping even further to indicate the smog which sawmills in Vancouver's False Creek were emitting to soot the landscape. Later, when we had doubled back up the hillside and through the evergreen forest, his fingers felt the new sharp green needles which had contributed to the forest loam. A deep observer, he believed nothing was or could be wasted in nature and that death itself was necessary for creation.

Was this knowledge, perhaps, the reason for Lowry's bouts of alcoholism? Unlike most of his friends I never saw him during such times. He did discuss everything but the reason for them with me candidly and simply (there was no false pride, no pantomiming of excuse, but simple direct statement). On several occasions I know his fear of groups triggered him off. Once he arrived at an august tea party staggering and all but speechless, wanting to hammer rag-time on the piano instead of being listened to with respect and awe. There were other occasions when he was alone and his lone-liness simply could not be borne. I suspect that sometimes the creativity which constantly welled up from within himself could not be channeled as he wished it and had to be deadened by some anodyne. He didn't possess the routine and familiar antidotes with which the majority of us are equipped. During these frightening periods his understanding and devoted wife and the few friends, such as Einar and Muriel Neilson of Bowen Island, to whom he turned like a child, carried him through and, more important, beyond, during the even more bitter period of contriteness.

He told me one day that during the long months when he had written *Under the Volcano* he had not taken a drink even of wine, though he had been staying with a friend who had vineyards and made wine while he wrote. I mentioned earlier how every tag end of event was of importance to him, and somehow incorporated into his writing. This was true even of his attempts at forgetfulness, his wild occasional descents to escape the unbidden imagery he could not momentarily harness. He describes just such a period experienced by the Consul:

> . . . Why then should he be sitting in the bathroom? Was he asleep? dead? passed out? Was he in the bathroom now or half an hour ago? Was it night? Where were the others? But now he heard some of the others' voices on the porch. Some of the others? It was just Hugh and Yvonne, of course, for the doctor had gone. Yet for a moment he could have sworn the house had been full of people; why it was still this morning, or barely afternoon, only 12:15 in fact by his watch. At eleven he'd been talking to Mr. Quincey. "Oh. . . . Oh." The Consul groaned aloud. . . . It came to him he was supposed to be getting ready to go to Tomalin. But how had he managed to persuade anyone he was sober enough to go to Tomalin? And why, anyhow, Tomalin?
>
> A procession of thoughts like little elderly animals filed through the Consul's mind, and in his mind too he was steadily crossing the porch again, as he had done an hour ago, immediately after he'd seen the insect flying away out of the cat's mouth.

Unlike most of us, Malcolm had not lost the wise-eyed innocence of childhood. In fact, many of the incidents of his childhood re-mained in his mind vivid as current events. He told us on several occasions, for example, of a nurse his wealthy family employed when he was very young. She had loved his older brother and to his horror hated him. Once she had wheeled his cart along the cliff-edge, high above the rolling sea. He described with quiet exactitude her features as she leaned over with a blanket to smother him, how he screamed (the exact key), and then the saving running footsteps of his favored older brother which interrupted the scene.

I used to steal glances at my seven-year-old son when Malcolm and Margerie visited the cottage by the lake in which we were then living. His features were as mobile as Malcolm's when Malcolm was talking, as intent, and as unspoiled by conditioned attitudes. Those two instinctively understood what each other was feeling as well as taking in the surface articulation.

Don't let me suggest that Malcolm was somber. He had a huge Rabelaisian sense of humour and, oh rare quality, could laugh with gusto at himself. One afternoon we were visiting Malcolm and Margerie at their shack. It was several months after he had injured his leg badly when he fell from his wharf onto lowtide rocks (pre-occupied with dialogue, so he said, dialogue to finish off a discussion he, Margerie, my wife and myself had had months before). He described the horror of the Catholic hospital where he had been taken (the cowled nuns, for some reason, were the opposite to Sisters of Charity to his pain-wracked mind) and the even greater horror of later visiting his orthopoedic specialist, who sat examining his leg and remarking he might lose it. Malcolm graphically detailed the whole room, his utterances of despair that he might lose the leg, then the aseptic smile of the doctor who casually remarked, as he reached behind and brought out a new nickel shining artificial limb and stroked it, that it was as good as a natural one for the classical case of amputation on another patient he had. Desultory talk followed this devilish recount, then Malcolm, who was always fascinated by the law, asked me whether I had had any interesting law cases recently. I was young in my profession then and, perhaps over-enthusiastically, I described a Motor Manslaughter case I had defended. I described the difficulties. The accused was on the wrong side of a straight road, he had spent the afternoon drinking beer in a pub, and the police had found a half-finished bottle of whiskey in his truck after the accident. In recounting all the evidence against my client, then finally the jury's acquittal verdict, I gleefully remarked, "It was a classical case!" I looked up and there was Malcolm stroking an imaginary artificial steel limb, murmuring "classical case," then he erupted into roars of gargantuan laughter. His interesting thesis of "never trust an expert" probably had some merit.

Malcolm personally knew a number of great writers who admired his work and communicated their admiration to him. I think, from recalling our conversation, one of his special friends was Conrad Aiken. Aiken recognized his genius long before the public success of *Under the Volcano*. While still at Cambridge some of Lowry's short stories were published in America, and in 1932 his first novel, *Ultramarine,* received a rather indifferent public response. It was during this period, as I recall, that Aiken encouraged and stimulated him.

He had known well, while in England, Dylan Thomas. Upon the occasion when Thomas first came to Vancouver for a public poetry reading, Malcolm, the shyest man I have ever known, remarked laconically that Dylan Thomas for all his flamboyant public personality was really a very shy person. After Dylan Thomas' reading a reception was arranged to which the Lowrys and ourselves were invited. Despite Malcolm's dislike of people in groups ("individuals lose their most precious possession—their identity") and his antipathy towards "literary people" ("they don't write, they talk aseptically about it as if there were no bloody birth pangs and the work emerges well-scrubbed") he wanted to meet Dylan. In the many-roomed converted old house where the reception was held both were for a long time in separate rooms, both being lionized and hating it. At length friends managed to bring them together. They warmly clasped hands and Malcolm said simply: "Hullo, Dylan," while Dylan Thomas replied with equal shyness, "Hullo, Malcolm." In retrospect I feel similar inner fires were burning in each because they could not render the whole of their experience into a creative mould.

In Malcolm's relaxed periods he strummed a huge repertoire of songs, chanties and tunes he had composed (including a lively national anthem) on a battered ukulele, and he was never so happy as when he was immersed in this music of his own making, whether bawdy Spanish tunes picked up in some waterfront bistro in North Africa, or plaintive Chinese rise and fall he had heard in Singapore. Hours would pass delightfully, for he took it for granted you shared his happiness.

After the publication of *Under the Volcano* Malcolm and his wife traveled for a year, visiting Haiti, England and the Continent. With his habitual generosity he shared his royalties with the many he encountered who claimed to be able to put words onto paper. When he returned to his beloved shack at Dollarton there were periods of acute financial want, and it was during one of these periods there occurred a minor event which highlighted two of his characteristics—naïveté and the ability to laugh at himself.

About this time one of our popular national magazines printed, as an advertisement for a bank, a single-page short story headed: "We Printed This Because We Like It." At its conclusion there was an invitation to other writers to make submissions.

Many months later Malcolm laughingly told me of his submission. It started off as a well-planned anecdote but somehow it became longer and longer. Feverish weeks were spent as the anecdote dilated and expanded into the eventually completed whole—a piece of work which would have required ten issues of the whole magazine instead of a single page. He had waited patiently for weeks to receive the bank's check before he gradually realized the violent sea-change his creativity had caused. Fortunately, about this time royalties from some of the translated editions of *Under the Volcano* began trickling in.

Many are generous, as he was, with material possessions, but few extend the intellectual generosity he was capable of. It mattered not to Malcolm whether someone was famous or unknown, skilled in the craft of writing or a fumbling tyro. He, who knew how difficult it was to piece together common words so they sang and wreathed in rich meaning, gave consideration, time, advice (but never didactically, always subjectively) and encouragement to all who asked for it. He not only loved language and the individual warp and woof rendered by a writer, but revered it. He, a master, considered himself a tyro and anyone who tackled the same task with love he viewed as a potential genius.

Malcolm's relationship with his wife was far more than the customary one. They were partners in everything they did, sharing the successes or the periods of actual want with equal zest. He was proud of her attractive gaiety and her theatrical (she had been an actress) manner. More important, he was as concerned with her writing as he was with his own—and as proud of it. Margerie's opinion was constantly sought and considered. Equally, her concern and consideration for his welfare, her honest and penetrating appraisals of his work supplied Malcolm with a reserve of strength and stimulation which always carried him through the bleak non-productive periods every writer encounters. Margerie possessed that rare quality—intellectual honesty and forthrightness. They admired and respected as well as loved each other.

I recall Malcolm's delight when I introduced him to T. E. Lawrence's *Seven Pillars of Wisdom*. I was a bit taken aback at his enthusiasm until I realized that Lawrence had a similar quality in his writing (not often encountered), that of concern with metaphysics. "I must write to him," he told me. I reminded him that Lawrence had been dead for decades. Malcolm ignored this, for to him a writer never died. He accepted it on the surface, of course, so improvised long verbal letters instead which enlivened our walks. The symbolism in Lowry's work is not confined to the work itself. It was part of his daily life. His world was peopled with black and white forces. His daily swim (even when light skim ice scummed the surface of the deep North Arm) was not merely a swim but a metaphysical experience. I've mentioned the gas flares at the cracking plant. For hours he would discuss them, not as hot crackling oil flames spurting into the evening's darkness, but as living sentient forces which peopled his world. In the same way the Consul, towards the end of *Under the Volcano*, symbolically invests a calendar.

> He saw again in his mind's eye that extraordinary picture on Laruelle's wall, Los Borrachones, only now it took on a somewhat different aspect. Mightn't it have another meaning, that picture, unintentional as its humour, beyond the symbolically obvious? He saw those people like spirits appearing to grow more free, more separate, their distinctive noble faces more distinctive, more noble the higher they ascended into the light; those florid people resembling huddled fiends, becoming more like each other, more joined together, more as one fiend, the further down they hurled into the darkness.

His last novel (unfortunately the middle section was taken out and never replaced) was typical of this. For several years there had been recurrent rumors that the waterfront shacks, including his own, were to be bulldozed and the occupant squatters forced out of the beach strip. This had a terrible effect upon him. Here, as I said, he had found his uneasy peace. For a month he and Margerie had searched the Gulf Islands and Vancouver Island for an alternate home. The novel was, on the surface, about the search for a home and dispossession, but the recurrent symbolism of many facets raced through it contrapuntally. Just as *Under the Volcano* had been written four times (once completely rewritten in a month when the previous draft had perished in a fire), so did this final and tremendous work undergo many changes and alterations.

One afternoon—early, about 2:30—he started to read the first draft of his last novel to myself, Margerie and my wife. The typescript was interlineated with his spidery written additions and changes. He would finish a page and, without dropping a word, walk into the bedroom to pick up a scrap of waste paper on which was an inserted paragraph. We had brought a bottle of gin. As it was a festive and important occasion he had bought two himself. Margerie, my wife and I had several drinks, but were spellbound after that by his resonant voice and the wonder of his prose. He read on and on, drinking in sips straight gin, without slurring a syllable or slighting a word. Finally, at 2:30 in the morning, he finished the last paragraph, the three bottles empty. My wife and I were terribly exhausted, but elated. When we got up to leave Malcolm was immersed in a paragraph he wanted to rewrite again, but rose to light our way up the trail with warmness and thanks,, as if it had been we who had performed the favor. "God bless you," he would always say, instead of "Goodbye." This is the Malcolm we'll remember, and the one to be seen in his verse and prose.

Last month we drove by on the cliff road overlooking the former Dollarton shacks. Bulldozers were matting the underbrush to make way for a park. The squatters' shacks, Malcolm's included, had long since disappeared. We were sad and spoke retrospectively, then brightened, remembering the seagull dead from oil, the dropped needles which made the forest floor. He surpassed all of these, Malcolm did, for during his lifetime, not after it, he created life from his own.

PART THREE

The Luminous Wheel:
The Evolution of
Malcolm Lowry's Style

Malcolm Lowry: The Writer [1]

by A. C Nyland

A. The Apprentice

From September 1923 to March 1927, Malcolm Lowry was at The Leys. At this time and in this place he made his debut as a writer. His initials, C.M.L. (Clarence Malcolm Lowry), expanded into CAMEL, formed the pen name which identifies his writing. It appears in print with ever-increasing frequency in the school paper, *The Leys Fortnightly*.

His housemaster, W. H. Balgarnie, "Mr. Chips," had helped James Hilton in his ambition to be a writer. No doubt Lowry was also encouraged by this educator, but no specific record of such help or acknowledgment of it can be found among the Lowry papers. All that can be proved is that he wrote poetry, short stories, and sports reports and that these were accepted and published in *The Leys Fortnightly* from 1924, during his second year at the school, until 1927, when he left it. His work received some measure of recognition, since he won the first and second prizes for news reporting in 1924–25, and in the fall of 1925 was elected to the editorial staff.

His early stories foreshadow his later work in several ways, especially in the importance given to autobiographical elements. In a young writer this is hardly surprising. Lowry's experience was limited. His world was bounded as well as expressed by that limited experience. He was wise enough to use what he knew and to use it as well as he was able. His first published story is an example of this. "The Light That Failed Not" tells of a student who was caught reading a story during study, given a detention, and saved by a

[1] This is Chapter II of a doctoral thesis, *The Luminous Wheel: The Evolution of Malcolm Lowry's Style,* written for the University of Ottawa.

power failure which, by plunging the room into darkness, made dismissal necessary. There is nothing very remarkable in this; nothing except CAMEL's choice of a subject that would appeal to his schoolboy readers.

In this early writing certain characteristics which became dominant in his later work make their appearance. Easy familiarity with his subject and friendly informality towards his reader mark the opening sentences of "Travelling Light." It begins,

> For the perpetuation of the human race it is necessary and desirable that people marry. If one is so lucky as to have a brother doing this in the middle of term and to go home oneself for the ceremony, one may heartily endorse that statement without fears of conscience, however infinitesimal.

The protagonist in this story must take part in a full-dress Corps parade as soon as he returns to school. Lowry speaks of this:

> All through my stay at home the black dog of this parade had sat on my back with its two front paws, as it were, down my neck. Just as I might be transporting myself to the heights of bliss, for instance, at the reception, it would bark in a rather sceptical fashion, and whisper into my ears that not only was my uniform uncleaned, but that my cap badge was missing, my puttees still retained the mud of the last field-day but one—and countless other things which would pain you as well as me if you read them.

Years later, in describing the Consul's inability to escape the fate that was closing in upon him, Lowry says that the man felt "as if a black dog had settled on his back, pressing him to his seat." This is just one of the many "dog" images or references that help to build up the symbolic pattern in *Under the Volcano*; they are, obviously, deeply rooted in Lowry's past.

The passage cited above from the early writing also gives a hint of something else he used cleverly in his later work. *Under the Volcano* recounts what seems to be complete understanding between the Consul and Mr. Quincey's cat. "Elephant and Colosseum" has a similar projection of ideas through an animal's response. These links with an animal provided Lowry with a means for intensifying the expression of the protagonist's thoughts. A recurrent idea takes on a new emphasis from this blending of human consciousness with animal awareness.

Another characteristic of his mature work that appears in this early writing is his complete and conscious identification of himself as the writer in the story he is telling. One gets the impression that here it is a schoolboy's way of meeting the possible taunts of his peers. Later it becomes a significant aspect of his way of looking at life. Under any circumstances, an author is always present, consciously or unconsciously, in his work since his ability to show and even to imagine situations, characters, actions and reactions is colored by his own experience. With Lowry, experience was more than this. It was a standard by which he judged his own life and achievement and one against which he measured his characters. His commitment as an author is evident from his voluminous notes, in which everything he has experienced has been recorded. He was always the conscious craftsman desirous of setting down in the best possible way each experience and every facet of each experience that came his way. His use of this criterion for his characters is shown later in the number of his protagonists who are writers, among them Wilderness, Cosnahan, the Consul, Hugh, and Dana Hilliot. Even in his school stories there is a writer, Lucius Bright, the protagonist in "The Repulsive Tragedy of the Incredulous Englishman."

Schoolboy humor is shown in a murder story, "The Blue Bonnet," which begins offhandedly, "Said one of these charming people: 'Yes, it certainly was a very nasty murder now I come to think about it'." The influence of his mathematics courses is evident in the naming of the characters, but a typical touch of humor lends variety and local color; they are called Macexe, Macwye, Macay, and Macbee. The setting is, of course, "the wilds of Scotland." There is a tongue-in-cheek description of the murder. Macwye shot Macexe, "but not before he had turned the handle of his telephone and gasped 'Police!' in a rather futile fashion down the mouthpiece. He died just before the close of the inverted commas."

His ability to describe accurately and arrestingly begins to appear in these early stories. In "A Rainy Night" he gives a picture of a golf links on a wet day when "the flags of the greens, which are full of troubled pools, are so soaked as to have lost most of their flapping power."

The story, however, is not about golf. It is the treatment of a theme that would haunt him all his life, the theme of suffering, and even death, that results from man's inability to communicate except in words which, under some circumstances, he cannot say. One man leaves the train, an unopened package of sandwiches in his bag, and leaves behind the other man to whom he had been casually kind, pitying one whom he thinks is addicted to drink. This man had really been dying of starvation. Melodramatic and jejune this is, no doubt, but starvation, here physcial, later mental and moral, furnishes the theme for much of Lowry's writing, and the inability to communicate is the reason for the mental and moral hunger that becomes at times almost an obsession with him. The schoolboy very strongly foreshadows the man.

This story shows three other traits which became Lowry trademarks. The Swede is the first of a long succession of seamen; he is a ship's fireman. Even before his first voyage Lowry was interested in the sea and the men who sailed in its ships. No doubt some of this interest can be traced to the seafaring grandfather who was part legend, part hero to the boy. Some of it too is the natural interest of an intelligent boy in the life he sees around him. He grew up near of the world's great seaports overlooking an estuary that was always alive with ships.

The second mark is the use of advertisements as links with the background. Sometimes, in the mature work, advertisements serve as anchors by which the character is moored to reality; sometimes they are bridges by which the characters make the transition from thought to thought, or from present time to past time. In this early story such skillful usage does not appear. The advertisements are mentioned as being part of the scene noted by the protagonist from the train: "Everywhere sodden advertisements clung like wet rags." From his consciousness of the need to identify a scene by the use of specific details grew the ability to use what the advertisements were saying as a means of emphasis, or to form a link in the development of complicated thought. This small point of observation developed later into a means by which texture could be obtained.

The third mark of identification with his mature work lies in the thoughts that go through one man's mind as he judges, and misjudges, the other. Drunkenness is supposed to be the malady from which the Swede suffers. The protagonist judges him, kindly, but very definitely on almost nonexistent evidence. His tolerant aloofness is an adumbration of Mr. Quincey's attitude toward the Consul in *Under the Volcano*. Alcoholism, the problem which forms a constantly recurring subject in his later works, appears here for the first time.

Even in this early writing Lowry seeks the significant word, the fresh expression of his idea. In "Satan in a Barrel," which Lowry calls "pirated history" about Jeffreys of the Bloody Assize fame, the warder speaks "in a voice like a cracked phonograph record." Later when the warder replies to one of Jeffreys' speeches Lowry writes, " 'I don't,' phonographed the warder. 'My reasons are as follows.' They followed." Lowry does not give the reasons. He leaves them to the reader's imagination, showing that he knew even then that some things are much more emphatic when left unsaid. The word "phonographed" is a neat reference to his earlier simile. It is perfectly suited to the story, which is a serio-comic treatment of a supposedly authentic historical incident.

In the same story he attempts to describe sound with a visual image; a daring flight into imagery that would challenge him again and again. The Voice of Grace speaks to Jeffreys, trying to bring him to repentance. Lowry describes it: "A kindly voice! it breathed good will! I could almost see it: it looked like violets in a mud-bank." This is not too successful; but the attempt to describe the indescribable has been made.

In his later work Lowry showed great skill in presenting the passage of time. The reader almost hears the minutes tick off while some action, seemingly insignificant, is described. This is, of course, the reason for the use of that action. It is described in detail to arrest the flow of thought and to make the reader conscious of the passing of time and often of the boredom of the protagonist for whom the slight action takes on an undue importance. "The Repulsive Tragedy of the Incredulous Englishman" is noteworthy mainly for the strength and sureness with which this device is used. The protagonist, a writer, bound for Australia, is on board the *S. S. Chian* which "furrowed white on a blue ocean, an easy-going plough of fifteen knots." His wife is ill, so he is left to his own devices. The peace of the sea voyage has become monotonous and he wishes something would happen:

> Couldn't there be an alarm that the boat was going to sink or something? Not sink, really, of course. . . . A good change from writing novels, but he did wish something would happen. He relit his pipe. The match flared up, and, its work done, warped and went out. A black curled useless chip, he threw it over the side, and watched it rebound off the bilge-keel to disappear astern. What a fuss, he thought, for his mind to make about a match! The smoke from his pipe flew towards the stern, and mingled in the black smoke of the funnels. Well—well.

A trivial little description? Perhaps. But how perfectly it shows how trivia assume gigantic proportions in the emptiness of monotony.

In the same story the antagonist, an Armenian hypnotist, criticizes the wordiness of the protagonist, an English writer: "The less adjectives, the more forcible the remark. Avoid always bombast and arrogance." This thought occurs many times in Lowry's revisions of his own work. It even appears, thirty years later, and couched in slightly different terms, in his criticism of the work of others. He does use adjectives, it is true, in much of his writing, but their use is always controlled and when the work reaches its point of highest intensity it is stripped to the essential words, each one of which carries its full load of meaning.

Another pattern of expression that has become characteristic of his mature work is also evident in his school writing; this is the use of a journey. Lowry's characters are always going somewhere— for a walk, a boatride, a canter, or perhaps on a real journey by boat, train, bus, or airplane; they seldom just sit and talk. Movement acts as a release for stream-of-consciousness comment or for interior monologue by which the reader is told all he needs to know. Sometimes the journey is short, an afternoon walk, as in "The Bravest Boat" and "Gin and Goldenrod." In this case the story is threaded on the things described as the protagonists walk along. Sometimes it takes a considerable time to develop, as in "Through the Panama," in which he gradually sorts out the background and fits it in, piece by piece, almost as if he were completing a jigsaw puzzle. Sometimes the story is almost completely unraveled by the protagonist's digressions or distractions on a bus ride, as in *October Ferry to Gabriola*, or during a plane and bus journey as in *Dark as the Grave Wherein My Friend Is Laid*.

Three of the early stories, "Travelling Light," "A Rainy Night," and "The Repulsive Tragedy of the Incredulous Englishman," use this device. It even appears in one of the poems, "The Old Woman Who Buried Cats." By means of this device, Lowry keeps the characters together in a situation in which their minds can wander to fill in the background for the reader. At the same time, it holds them fixed in their relative positions toward one another and enables them to break into each other's thoughts with no manipulating on the part of the author. The characters might be said to form a captive audience for one another, always within reach when the need arises. Lowry used this device with ever-increasing skill until the pattern of movement, the enclosing of a group within some sort of vehicle, became dominant in his writing to such an extent that one feels it is an expression of his life, that is, a long seeking, a long journey toward self mastery and fulfilment.

In addition to the stories discussed above, CAMEL contributed reports on sports. It is reporting with a fresh approach. He states that a drawn game (1-1) was extremely poor and uninteresting, "Poor because the defence would not defend nor the attack attack: uninteresting because of the apparent sulkiness of the whole team." The score had remained unchanged "not because of the brilliant defence of each side but because of their parallel mediocrity." Then his writer's instinct makes him present a human action and he states that the most interesting incident in the whole game occurred when one of the referees brought off a catch from a hard hit "not only with the utmost nonchalance, but with hardly removing one hand from his pocket, and with absolute immobility of expression."

His disgust with poorly played games sometimes brought forth caustic comments. Of one match he says, "the centre half and the backs spent the rest of the game wandering round like mislaid ewes and hitting at this and that." The game raised itself "slightly off its pillow at the beginning of the second half." His originality even leads him to describe a game entirely in terms of a poorly mounted stage play in which the "actors" miss their "cues" or forget their "lines." He claims that the first act is about as "diverting as a musical comedy without any music," the second as amusing "as a farce without a single laugh, without a single epigram." This was played, however, "in a theatre of excellent traditions and many previous successes." Having set the stage, he introduces the principal actors and apportions to them the blame for the "play's" failure. He describes the acting of the other "artists" in the cast, and then concludes, "It was slightly before the final curtain that I crept (complete with hump) towards a door which, had it been there would have been surmounted tactfully with the legend EXIT."

Two final extracts are of interest because they show that this young reporter brought his whole self and his whole experience to his job. Literature as often borrowed ideas and similes from sport; sport has seldom done so from literature. One does not often find sports writing like this: "It seems almost inconceivable that a team which played so well should, five days later, give such a dismal display. Still, Shakespeare had his 'Pericles'; comfort in that."

In the same number, reporting an earlier game, he made two remarks which brought a flood of letters to the editor protesting his method of reporting. CAMEL had written, "Haller, our goalkeeper, who was compelled to fox for the majority of the game, made one save for us, just before half time, with a Pantagruelian kick." This, and his habit of using dots to express the inexpressible, sparked the criticism to which he replied in part:

> There seems to be a yet further objection concerning my reports, on which I have attempted to bestow a little sadly needed originality; you ask "What can I mean by Pantagruelian?" Is it a confession that you yourselves do not know your Rabelais, and perhaps a further confession that you are not old enough to read it: and "fox"—what can I mean by "fox"? A fox, I may state for your benefit, is an animal which, in its spare time, foxes. Hence the verb, to fox.
>
> And dots. I admit (being of a generous mood) on reading through my story, that there were, maybe, just too many of them for some tastes: but this error was partly due to the printers, who are liable to print . . as . . . . But even so they (the dots) remained much less offensive than your letters.

CAMEL makes a few remarks on his critics' error in etiquette in saying that he has "undoubted talent" and promises to make no such mistake about them. He finishes, "Therefore, I say, dots to you, Sirs. And, I may be permitted to add, having a bad cold, that I shall continue to write as I wish, dotwithstanding. This place is reserved for conventional salutations. CAMEL"

One further point remains to be noted regarding Lowry's work as a reporter. Even at this early stage he shows his ability to turn a phrase. A few examples of his precision of expression have been noted above in other connections, for example, the center half and the back described as "mislaid ewes" and the game raising "itself slightly off its pillow." He also has play moving "at a snail's pace" and the ball that "scarfed itself round our circle in a most listless and clinging fashion." For one gifted with such ease of expression, the reporting of a game in which nothing happened must have been a truly stultifying experience.

CAMEL contributed to the *Fortnightly* in another genre. From time to time a poem appears over his signature. Except for the last of these poems, this work does not show the freshness or the originality evident in his prose. One of the earliest, "The Old Woman Who Buried Cats," parodies a well-known nursery rhyme in its opening lines: "There was an old woman who lived in a nice/Little house that was badly infected with mice." The serio-comic note is well sustained throughout and the poem must have amused its schoolboy readers.

The next poem to appear, "The Rain Fell Heavily," is a lugubrious description of a graveyard and the inscription on a headstone. The young poet's use of contrast by the change of stanza form, tempo, and imagery is good, but the lines "The mourners slowly crept away/ And left me to my solitude" hint that the source of inspiration was the Graveyard School of poets, and this was not the company the lad was really seeking. His inspiration lay elsewhere, as his last poem printed in the *Fortnightly* shows.

A year after he left school he made his final contribution to his old school paper. During that year he had made his first voyage and had learned a good deal about life and about himself. He had also learned how to express himself with the simplicity and the strength that indicate the end of his apprenticeship and the beginning of the next stage in his development. That the experience at sea had given him a new dimension is evident in "Number 8 Fireman," in which the man comes up from the stokehole "supping the wind." He pictures Jesus counting all creatures, beginning with the sand on the seashore:

> The gulls that wheel, *Klio,*
> And mew around the funnel;
> The sharks and the dolphins;
> Red sponges, fiddler crabs,
> Snouted squids umbrella-winged
> Squeezing and buzzing,
> Coiling and heaving;
> Stars that are reeling:
> And all of his children
> He counts for his Father.

Then the young poet sweeps to his climax by using a dramatic contrast:

> But I have no father:
> The fire is my mother,
> And roaring she bore me;
> She washed me in coal dust,
> And fed me on cinders;
> She parched me, then maimed me;
> And I am her stoker.

As God cannot count me,
The Board of Trade count me,
Like winches and derricks
Or boilers; like pistons
Revolving and gleaming;
Like brass-silled white cabin-doors
Windily creaking.

Quite obviously no body of criticism of this early work exists. In his second letter to Conrad Aiken, the young writer—now twenty years old and at work on his first novel—indicates that he had received encouragement from those whose opinion he valued, "the only other department that I have had any success in" is in writing seriously and "that success rarely meant acceptance but quite often sincere encouragement from people whose opinion could hardly be taken to be humble." The phrase "that success rarely meant acceptance" is revealing. It indicates that what had appeared in print was but a small portion of what had been written. Whether he realized it or not this was an advantage; he needed the discipline of rejection as much as he needed the encouragement of acceptance.

In her study of his early work, Suzanne Kim describes the schoolboy writer and makes this comment on the point he has reached in his development:

> Le reproche le plus grave à lui adresser consiste dans le manque de diversité à la fois du fond et de la forme. La production de cette période se rattache trop à l'immédiat; même l'argot d'écolier qu'il utilise n'échappe pas à ce reproche. Mais un point reste acquis: c'est tout naturellement qu'il ancre son langage dans la réalité du temps. A présent c'est l'argot des écoles, plus tard il utilisera et reproduira celui des bateaux et des bars. Dès ces premières oeuvres, le processus semble inevitable, congenital pour ainsi dire.[1]

This criticism is made by one who, having knowledge of his later work, looks for traces of that work in the early writing, that is, she approaches the past but illuminates it from the present. Again, to limit his later use of language to that of boats and bars is to limit almost to the point of nullity prose which has infinite variety. But

---

[1] The most serious fault to charge him with is a lack of variety of both matter and manner. The works of this period are excessively bound to the now; even his schoolboy slang deserves this criticism. But one thing is already clear: it is entirely natural for him to anchor his language in the reality of the present. Now it is the argot of school; later he will use and recreate that of ships and bars. From the time of these early works on, the process seems inevitable—one might say inborn.

her point on the style of that early period is well made. He did write from a limited experience and in the speech of the schools for the most part, but the comments from his schoolmates which have been cited show how far he is above the average, or the typical, in this expression.

His work must be allowed to speak for itself. The young writer is clearly striving to express himself, drawing on his experience and on his reading, shaping his material in the furnace of his imagination. But the most important trait of all is the fact that he was not concerned about the judgment of his peers. He wrote what he thought should be expressed. This independence, or fidelity to his vision, stayed with him to find eloquent expression in his defense of his novel *Under the Volcano* when editors requested changes he was not willing to make. He had begun early to establish his own viewpoint and to demand freedom to express it and, when attacked, showed himself well able to defend his position. Having advanced to this point he was ready for further growth. The apprentice has acquired a certain skill in handling his tools, he has some idea of what he wants to do with them. The journeyman must now produce some original work, and this was to be shaped from life as he saw it when he deliberately went out and lived it as a deckhand on a freighter.

B.   The Journeyman

What has been examined thus far of Malcolm Lowry's work shows that, as a schoolboy, he has made contributions to his school paper in poetry, the short story, and sports reporting. His letters to the editor, although cleverly handled, are incidental, arising from a specific need, and, as such, represent but a phase in his prose writing. In poetry he is obviously trying to find his voice and, in the last poem treated, there are indications of a definite advance toward surety of expression. In the short story his work is mannered but there are hints that, given something worth saying, he would find his own way of phrasing it. In the sports writing there is a deliberate attempt to bring freshness to a form that, for most writers in this field, too often degenerates into jargon or into inane comment cloaked in clichés. He realized that these faults marred most sports writing and he consciously tried to avoid them. This section, "The Journeyman," will treat of his development prior to the publication of *Under the Volcano.*

Malcolm left The Leys at the end of the spring term, 1927. Normally he would have gone on to Cambridge; he had been registered at Christ's College for that fall. But he wanted to be a writer and he knew that he could never write aseptically, sealed off from the world around him. He wanted to see life and to gain experience, so, from May to October, he worked as cabin boy and deckhand, and sailed to the storied ports of the Far East. With mind and notebooks crammed with incidents and images he returned to England and began his first novel.

He had already done considerable work on *Ultramarine* before he went, in the summer of 1929, to Cambridge, Mass., to meet Conrad Aiken. Something of Lowry's ability to see double or multiple significance in words is shown in his choice of a title for his work. He had been greatly impressed by Aiken's novel *Blue Voyage* —Aiken claims he knew it by heart. The title *Blue Voyage* expresses much of the visual impression of a seascape, but *Ultramarine,* as a title, expresses much more. The direct Latin meaning becomes "beyond the sea" in English. But "ultra" has another shade of meaning, that of "more than." The book, then, is going "beyond the sea" to far countries to express "more than" what lies within sight on the sea. But "ultramarine" means still more than this. It is the name of a blue pigment made by pulverizing lapis lazuli. Brought to Rome from far countries, this pigment was something very beautiful from beyond the sea. The choice of this title for his book suggests a poetic awareness in the young writer.

The book, however, is not poetic, nor is it meant to be. It is the story of a boy making his entry into the world of men. The environment and many of the details are based on Lowry's own sea and shore experiences. He wisely used the material that he knew, but he colored it with imagination. He asked himself, "How would this boy, having this background and this character, react when placed in these circumstances?" Criticism has been offered that the protagonist is a somewhat unlikely fellow acting and reacting in a somewhat strange way. But Dana Hilliot, placed in an entirely different milieu from that in which he grew up and facing a challenge of remaining faithful to his girl and to the standards of conduct instilled into him by his training, is not so atypical as one might think. He is youth on the edge of awareness. In many ways he is Romeo in love with love, just as callow and inexperienced; he is the anti-hero, at times comic, at times pathetic. Dana's girl is not the quick-witted, resourceful, strong-willed Juliet. But she is the girl who has captured his imagination and, for the time being, at least, his heart.

Dana Hilliot is a schoolboy living by choice among rough men with the intention of learning about life from them. But these men do not prove to be the simple, strong, direct men that Dana had expected. He had dreamed of Rousseauistic "natural" men. These men have set ridiculous standards as their test of manhood. Dana is looked on with suspicion; he belongs to the world of the ship-owners, he is a rich man's son, he is doing an honest man out of a job by taking one that he does not need, he has taken his job for experience and not to earn his daily bread. In spite of the fact that the boy can outdrink the best of them he is an outcast because, faithful to his promise to Janet, he refuses to enjoy the fleshpots of the East.

In a way, the crew members are like schoolboys of the world Dana has just left. They show the same unreasoning prejudices that schoolboys show when they band together against a newcomer who has roused their animosity or whom they wish to test. Their dislike of Dana suddenly fades away in the shame they all feel in not rescuing Norman's pigeon, a "mickey" in their jargon. These men, who were to show Dana what life was like, show him instead that they are guided by the same snobbery, the same lack of understanding, the same selfishness that he had seen and hated in the middle-class environment from which he had hoped to escape. Whether intentional or accidental, this is clever anticlimax.

This is what Lowry is trying to tell his reader. How does he do it? He does it quite simply by the very thing that constitutes the book's originality, by taking the reader into the crew's quarters and letting him listen to their conversation. The book opens with rapid-fire question and answer, a full page of stichomythia. It gives an immediate sense of assembly-line efficiency and complete impersonality as the crew is signed on. This breaks off suddenly and the reader is plunged into Dana's thoughts after six weeks at sea. Another break into reality comes as the bosun calls the lad to the well deck to help prepare for docking. His clumsiness brings scornful dismissal, "you can go back and dream to your heart's content." He dreams bitterly,

No, there was precious little meaning left now in this life which so surprisingly had opened out before him. Nor could he see why he had ever been fool enough to set this seal upon such a wild self-dedication. No meaning at all, he thought, as he shook out some ash from his pipe. Not, at any rate, to himself, a man who believed himself to live in inverted, or introverted, commas; to a man who saw the whole damned business in a kind of benign stupor.

The phrase "to live in inverted, or introverted, commas" carries one back with surprised recognition to Lowry's schooldays and the story "The Blue Bonnet," with Macexe dying "just before the close of the inverted commas." It is the same mind at work.

There are incidental descriptions that have the ring of authentic observation. Dana's thoughts go back to his arrival on the ship; he saw:

> The two detectives on the *Oedipus Tyrannus,* the night watchman and the dirty firemen carrying wrenches; saw himself enter the forecastle and put his seabag in a bottom bunk before looking into the sailors' messroom; saw the light burning, and the shadows which galloped over the long cedarwood table with forms around it, riveted to bulkheads, saw the stove with a twisted chimney on which a dishcloth and a pair of dungarees were drying. A skylight opened out on the poop.

The same skylight gives him another viewpoint from which to observe the crew's activities later on. Hilliot has made up his mind to face Andy, whose taunting "Hurry up there, Miss Hilliot, seven bells gone half an hour ago, your ladyship" has become more than he can stand. In searching for him,

> Hilliot suddenly lifted the skylight by which he was standing, and looked down into the messroom of the sailors' forecastle: tobacco smoke curled up towards him, and there was a fresh smell of soap and water. It was as if he had lifted the lid of a box of toys.

He then picks out individuals in the group, each caught as if photographed in the action he was performing at the moment. It is a good description and is brought sharply into focus with a simple but incisive sentence, "It was as if he had lifted the lid of a box of toys."

Although the ship is a world apart, he places it neatly into its setting:

The ship rose slowly to the slow blue combers, a ton of spray was flung to leeward, and that other sea, the sky, smiled happily down on her, on seamen and fireman alike. . . . But the *Oedipus Tyrannus* poured out black smoke, mephitic and angry, from her one enormous funnel; its broad shadow slanted blackly along the sea to the horizon; it was the one black smudge on all that glad serenity.

With a sure writer's instinct he follows the cue and describes the engineroom, the place from which this "smudge" on the "glad serenity" originates:

Hilliot poked his head in through an iron engineroom entrance, and watched the engines, a maelstrom of noise which crashed on his brain; it was humiliating to watch the nicety with which lever weight and fulcrum worked, opening and closing their hidden mechanisms and functioning with such an incomprehensible exactness!

He walks along until he can see the stoker, "through a shower of sparks, like red blossoms . . . a firebright fiend." The introspective nature of the boy is well presented in scenes like this in which keen observation is linked with poetic expression.

It is also shown in his reminiscences of his girl Janet. She is the means by which he can justify himself to his own ego for his petty failures. When he is snubbed by the crew, is clumsy at his work or oppressed by the monotony of his life on board ship, he seeks release in daydreams about her. Like Romeo toward Rosaline, he thinks it is a young man's duty to be in love, and so is in love with love. Later, when he comes to see life and himself more maturely, he expresses clearly what Janet has been. In a letter which he does not intend to send her, he says:

I regard it all now with sanity and detachment . . . the relative ease and quickness with which I have shifted my balance towards Andy, after the interrogative stage of things, is partly occasioned by the fact that yourself acting as an inhibiting factor are at the same time a sublimatory factor. Although Andy beat me out in port, it ceases to bother me because first, there is yourself; secondly, being in love with you I have the universal experience of sublimated all-embracing love for mankind.

This is hardly the sort of thing one says in a love letter. He is quite obviously using the letter as a means whereby he can gain insight into his own situation and his response to it. Lowry uses

Janet all through the book in this way. She is the push button which releases the stream-of-consciousness, or the interior monologue which shows the reader the stage Dana Hilliot has now reached in his development. The letter, written but not sent, is a further application of this device. The two together help Lowry express Dana's thoughts and help to express them through a means other than simple introspection.

Lowry the craftsman has gained much in precision of expression. One recalls his early attempt to describe sound with a visual image, the voice that "looked like violets in a mud-bank." From time to time in *Ultramarine* he describes sounds much more happily by direct imitation, as in this short passage: "And in Norway itself, where they had first fallen in love, over beyond Sandvika, the goat bells going tinkle tonkle tankle tunk——" There is also the description of an echo which is neatly handled. The ship is approaching port as "the sun bled away behind chalk-white fields." "Then the *Oedipus Tyrannus*' siren roared, and the mountains and rice fields and the town roared back thunderously at the *Oedipus Tyrannus*."

In Chapter II, and from time to time in the rest of the novel, Lowry uses a device by which he often relates his characters to their environment. Dana walks from one part of the ship to another and the signs over the doors or on plates set into the walls flash into his consciousness as he goes along, *"Saloon. Purser. Third Engineer—Oedipus Tyrannus—Liverpool . . . Cammel Laird Shipbuilding Company, Birkenhead. Bosun. Carpenter. Cooks."* He uses the same link with reality in his description of the town when Dana goes on the prowl with Popplereuter. The headlines of a poster, signs on bars and stores, and the current offering of the theater blend into the atmosphere of the place.

A poster of the *Free Press* in English said:

MURDER OF BROTHER-IN-LAW'S CONCUBINE . . . *Bar. Boston Bar. Cafe Baikine. Bar and Cabaret. Trocadero. Satsuma Wares. Grand Revival—Richard Barthelmess in 'The Amateur Gentleman.' Mike Bar. Dancing. Norddeutscher Lloyd Steamships.*

It is a simple device but a most effective one.

The difference, in upbringing and education, between Dana and the crew is emphasized, not only by the way he speaks, but also by the literary allusions that pass through his mind. A passage of Greek on a page of sailor talk brings this difference sharply to mind. The same effect is obtained by the use of allusions to literary style, for Dana, planning to be a writer, is conscious of technique. One of the hands, describing an incident to another, finishes with the expression, "—so drunk that he tried to wrap the deck round him for a blanket." This releases Dana's thoughts in another direction:

> ("—a selection of the real language of men—" "—the language of these men—" "—I propose to myself to imitate and as far as possible to adopt the very language of these men—" "—but between the language of prose and that of metrical composition there neither is nor can be any essential difference—" *Lingua Communis*. . . .)

The incident is cleverly used and shows Lowry's sense of humor, for the conversation that preceded his digression was certainly not expressed in the language Wordsworth had in mind, nor was it the sort of anecdote he would have considered the subject of poetry.

Ultramarine was finished after nearly five years of work and was published in 1933 by Jonathan Cape of London. It had been accepted by the board of the university as his thesis; he had passed his examinations and, in the summer of 1932, he left Cambridge with third-class honors in the English tripos and his B.A. Parts of his novel had appeared in 1930, 1931, and 1933 and had received recognition by Edward J. O'Brien in *Best British Short Stories of 1931*; these were "Port Swettenham," which became Chapter 5 of *Ultramarine,* and "Seductio ad Absurdum," the earlier, shorter version of Chapter 4 which appeared also in *Experiment* under the title "Punctum Indifferens Skibet Gaar Videre." In 1933, Lowry made his first literary appearance in America with an expanded version of "Port Swettenham," Chapter 5 of the novel. It was given a 3-star listing by O'Brien in his *Best* (American) *Short Stories for 1934*. The young writer was beginning to receive recognition. The reviews of *Ultramarine* were, however, not particularly encouraging. J.E. Arrowsmith claimed that one would have to go through an experience "precisely similar" to that of Dana in order to understand the book—not a very cogent critique since it omits the part played by the reader's imagination in accepting all literature. Derek Verschoyle failed to understand what Lowry was trying to do. He found the writing "disastrously mannered," and accused the author of mixing a manner derived from *Ulysses* with the "psychology of the more analytical type of school story." He found that a mixture was not successful but arrived instead at effects "which are neither cumulative nor adequately complementary." A more hopeful note appears at the close of the review by V. S. Pritchett. After pointing to "strained self-consciousness" as the curse that lay upon the book and the "unimportant and insignificant schoolday memories" as flaws in its structure, he commented on Lowry's skill as a writer and concluded in these words: "When he has stopped straining eyes, ears and nerves and ceases to let the world hammer him so that he sees nothing but stars and fragments, he may do something good."

However, with the reissue of *Ultramarine* in 1962, a new approach was evident; the critics looked at it through *Under the Volcano*. David Dempsey considered it "a brilliant performance" in which the "autobiographical tendencies never crowd out the milieu about which Lowry is writing." He finds that in all his work Lowry "used the self primarily as a fulcrum to pry loose the reality that he found embedded around him." He goes on to outline the autobiographical elements and then deals with the style:

> Lowry was not interested here in the conventional structure of the novel, and he shifted between an intense verbal realism—a documentary approach that at times gives one a sense of reading the notebook itself—and a subjective monologue that provides the outlet for his poetic grasp of life. Life to Malcolm Lowry was language itself: he was a born writer who could not separate experience from its ultimate necessity for expression.

Critic after critic makes a brief comment on the style, especially in regard to Lowry's skill in handling multiple dialogue to give the impression, as Robert Lawrence expresses it, "of a babble of voices heard from a distance."

Although *Ultramarine* was the most significant work Lowry produced up to this time, it was not the only piece of work published. The short stories that later formed chapters of the novel, and their recognition of E. J. O'Brien, have already been mentioned. While at Cambridge he contributed "For Nordahl Grieg Ship's Fireman" to *Cambridge Poetry, 1930*. Two Norwegian firemen, sharing a watch, are conscious of the ship, "an iron moloch" that "visits lands of strange beauty/ Where broad leaves struggle against the sun." They think of the places they have visited and their thoughts return to the cruelty of the ship "When they remember this the ship is a moloch/ An iron monster that crushes seamen and firemen/ in its jaws; . . . There is no beauty about the ship." But one night all this is changed. They are standing near the hencoop and one of them notices that a hen has chicks. They wonder, "How *these* could emerge from the cruel naked iron and thrive,/ And they forget the murdering strength of the ship,/ How it slays like a lion."

This brings a flood of happy memories and, as "the ship staggers and wallows in the sea," they pity it because "One thinks that the poor lonely ship is still in its birth-agony,/ It is as though the very ship itself has given birth." It is a good poem. It shows that the young poet realized that a seemingly trivial incident could carry the burden of immediacy and that he has acquired simplicity of expression.

Lowry worked on other stories and poems at this time; a few he shelved with the intention of using them later, some he lost in the Dollarton fire, the rest he polished and revised, working at them continually until his death. Of this last group "Lunar Caustic" and some poems have been published posthumously.

"Hotel Room in Chartres" was published in 1934 and was given 2-star listing by E. J. O'Brien in his *Best* (American) *Short Stories for 1935*. It was probably written in France during Lowry's first marriage and has for subject the incompatibility, quarrel, and reconciliation of a young couple. He used this idea again in *Under the Volcano*, where he expressed the need for love and the difficulty of communicating with another even in marriage. Lowry had not yet learned to handle the deeper emotions with a sure and delicate touch. For this reason "Hotel Room" is flawed in execution. But it is affecting and indicates the growing power of the young writer.

"Economic Conference 1934" was written about this time but appeared in *Arena* in 1949. The Contributor Notes indicate that it is a passage from an unpublished prewar novel, but no records in the Lowry papers indicate which novel or what happened to this novel. Perhaps it would be more correct to say "a projected novel," since Lowry always had ideas for possible novels hovering in the background of the work then in progress. Mrs. Lowry believes this story was written at Cambridge and given to John Davenport, his friend and fellow undergraduate, who latter became the editor of *Arena* and who published the story, without Lowry's permission, after the success of *Under the Volcano*. It tells of an American, a writer on economics, stranded in London because of a forgotten checkbook, and befriended by a taximan. Liquor flows and the two solve the economic problems of the world in hazy, disconnected dialogue in which flashes of brilliance occur. The situation is well handled and the befogged world of the alcoholic is presented with deft touches and a surety in obtaining effects that indicate steady development in technique.

Two unpublished short stories from this period are in the Lowry Collection. "Enter One in Sumptuous Armour" was probably written about 1930. There are working notes with it that belong to a much later date. It deals with the induction of a newcomer into the public-school world. The subject matter and treatment suggest that the experience described or the idea from which it evolved —they are often identical with Lowry—might be linked with The Leys. The style is more mature than that of the school writing, which would indicate that if the idea came early the version that exists developed later.

Also in manuscript in the collection is "June 30th, 1934," which uses the journey device for closing the characters off from intrusion, and two incomplete drafts of "In the Black Hills," which seemingly date from Lowry's first stay in Los Angeles.

Lowry's major literary efforts, however, during the period preceding *Under the Volcano* were the dramatic version of Grieg's *The Ship Sails On,* the novel "In Ballast to the White Sea" and the novella "Lunar Caustic." The first two were never completed, and the working drafts and notes were either lost completely in the fire or were depleted to such an extent that he could not develop them further. The novella "Lunar Caustic" was in progress to the day of his death. A French version, "Le Caustic Lunaire," translated by Michele d'Astorg and Clarisse Francillon, was serialized in *Esprit* in 1956. The papers in the Collection give some idea of the amount of work Lowry put into this novella. Of the first version, "The Last Address," 385 pages of manuscript exist. This was reworked into the second version, "Swinging the Maelstrom," of which 135 pages are extant. The final version, "Lunar Caustic," has shaped up to twenty-four finished pages and notes for the completed manuscript. Edited by Mrs. Lowry and Earle Birney, the final version appeared in fifty-four pages of *The Paris Review*.

In his introduction, "Malcolm Lowry and the Outer Circle of Hell," which prefaces the novella, Conrad Knickerbocker says that

> at one point in the mid-1930's, an early draft, under the title, "The Last Address," was accepted by Whit Burnett for *Story* magazine,

but Lowry called it back. He permitted a French translation of the first version . . . only because, he explained, he was afraid of losing the manuscripts, something that had happened to him more than once.

The pages of this manuscript are very interesting to anyone studying Lowry's work habits as an approach to his style. Fifteen and more versions of some sentences, varying only by a word or a short phrase, show the meticulous care with which Lowry shaped and polished his work into its final form. This novella cannot be judged as part of the journeyman's development, since its progress extends far into the period of mastery that has been reached by the finished writer. The involved, convoluted style makes the story of an alcoholic's commitment to Bellevue Hospital twist and spiral in a superb representation of the tortured mental process of the protagonist. It is a terrible novella, harsh and cruel, but one that presents the alcoholic's problem with a full understanding of the meaning of despair.

During these years of development Lowry released a few poems for publication. One of the earliest of these is a sonnet based on a news item telling of a sealed bottle containing a message for those at home found by a fisherman in the North Atlantic. The original letter was written in Norwegian and Lowry put it into poetic form:

> While we sail and laugh, joke and fight, comes death
> And it is the end. A man toils on board;
> His life blows away like a gust of breath:
> Who will know his dreams now when the sea roared?
> I loved you, my dear, but now I am dead,
> So take somebody else and forget me.
> My brothers, I was foolish, as you said:
> So are most who place their fate in the sea.
> Many tears have you shed for me in vain.
> Take my pay, Mother, Father; I have come
> A long way to die in the blood and rain.
> Buy me some earth in the graveyard at home.
> Good-bye. Please remember me with these words
> To the green meadows and the blue fjords.

This was one of Lowry's favorites among his poems.

"Sestina in a Cantina," a double sestina written at Dollarton, appeared in *Canadian Poetry Magazine* in 1947. The difficult poetic form is well sustained and has some challenging lines, from the simple question "How long since you have really seen a sunset?" to the philosophical comment "The mind has ways of keeping us in prison." The poem closes with the words of those driven from the tavern at daybreak, "And now the dawning drives us from our prison/ Into the dawn like sunset, into the ocean,/ Bereaving him of horrors, but leaving him his mirrors." The drunkard, driven by guilt or misunderstanding, is a subject that recurs in Lowry's work. The idea of a multiplication of images in a mirror is one that he tried many times to express to his satisfaction. In the rough draft of "Elephant and Colosseum" eighteen versions of a sentence expressing this idea indicate how he struggled with it.

Another poem, "Salmon Drowns Eagle," published in *Contemporary Verse* in 1947, has become well known and is included in *The Oxford Book of Canadian Verse*. It is based on a story told Lowry by "Old Sam," a Dollarton squatter. The tone is lightly contemptuous as the eagle expresses her dislike of the crows that swoop in to share in her catch. But the salmon is not dead. When the eagle tries to rest, the salmon threshes and turns and finally pulls the eagle under the water. Lowry's closing comment is typical: "It appears,/ In the mundial popular thunder,/ And moral to this dins in drowned ears."

There is a considerable amount of poetry that belongs to this period, but, since it was not published until much later, most of it posthumously, the form in which it existed at this time is difficult to determine. The rest of his poetry will be dealt with at the end of the next section.

From this study of Lowry as a journeyman the indications of his growth and development are evident. He has gained, through sympathy and understanding toward others, a greater awareness of the beauties as well as the sufferings that are experienced as life goes on. He has gained immeasurably in his ability to express the ideas that clamored for expression. In an early letter to Conrad Aiken he says,

> I have made up my mind about only one point in this business of living which is that I must, and as soon as possible, identify a finer scene: I must in other words give an imaginary scene identity through the immediate sensation of actual experience.

Although he makes fun of himself in the sentences that follow, one has the impression that he is using understatement to cloak his real feelings on the subject. His life shows that he did try to "identify a finer scene." He drained experience to the dregs, then fought his way back to the expression of what he knew of life and of himself. When he came to write in this way he had finished his period of training. He was now ready for his masterpiece.

C. The Master

In a letter to Harold Matson, their literary agent, Mrs. Lowry offers a defense of her husband's novel that is of value to any study of his work. It is of biographical interest also, since it is not often that a wife can be vocal to this extent and under these circumstances. She presents her opinion of the novel:

> One possibly expects good books, even first-rate ones, to come one's way occasionally, but one does not expect one of the caliber of the *Volcano,* and why should one, for they come, if they come, very rarely indeed. I tell you without hesitation that the *Volcano* is such a book: one which will stand comparison with the past as well as the future.

Then she points out the faults that she sees in the book:

> I am not blind to Malcolm's faults as a writer. His astonishing awareness of the thickness of life, of the layers, the depths, the abysses, interlocking and interrelated, causes him to write a symphony where anyone else would have written a sonata or at most a concerto, and this makes his work sometimes appear dispersed, whereas actually the form and context have arisen so inextricably one from the other that they cannot be dissociated. Then too he is cramped, for instance, to some extent as a novelist by the subjective equipment of a poet, so that I doubt if he could ever be a great novelist of 'character'.

She goes on to discuss the book and the indifferent acceptance of most masterpieces when they first appeared, and challenges him to find a publisher:

> In this book you have the opportunity of handling a work that is not merely a 'good book' or even merely a first-rate one, but, it is at least arguable, is a classic of some sort, every bit as much as

Moby Dick or what not, a milestone, if you like, and it is on this basis and no other that it must be dealt with, for, seeing its faults as we do and recognizing them, it has found its form, it is complete, Malcolm has found his style and come to maturity as an artist with it: it is finished . . . only a person whose whole existence *is* his work, who has dominated and disciplined the volcano within him, at what a cost of suffering even I do not wholly understand, could have written such a book.

This is the earliest critical comment on *Under the Volcano* in its final form, the fourth version. It accepts the fact that the book has faults, looks at those faults with observant and understanding eyes, then looks beyond the faults to the book's unique character and makes the judgment that this book will last because it offers something that no other book has given, or could give. Every quality that had formed his earlier work is here, intensified and perfected. Many qualities not apparent before are present now because, as his wife has said, he has become aware of "the thickness of life, of the layers, the depths, the abysses, interlocking and interrelated," and he has now found the means to express this.

The book is cosmic in scope, the whole world is its locale. Lowry has established this with the first paragraph. He has universalized the opening of the novel by traveling over the globe locating points on the same latitude as Cuernavaca, his "Quauhnahuac." This is the seaman's approach, the concept of wide horizons. Although the action is limited to a small area, a few square miles, and a brief time, one day recalled a year later, it ranges from England to India, Normandy to Mexico, Spain to Canada and throughout the conscious lives of the characters as their thoughts move forward and backward to weave the texture of the novel.

The range is even beyond what is normally understood by "the world." The title means more than at the foot of or in the shadow of the volcano. The significance is "under" in the Dantean sense, that is, into the depths by trial and ordeal to purification and understanding and love. Lowry thought of his projected novel sequence as a modern *Divine Comedy,* and this gives cosmic scope or dimension to the concept of this book. There is a range too beyond the sea—the "ultramarine" idea—and even beneath sea. The Consul says to the doctor, "Do you know, companero, I sometimes have the feeling that it's actually sinking, like Atlantis, beneath my feet. Down, down to the frightful 'poulps.' Meropis of Theopompus . . .

And the *ignivome* mountain." The depth is intensified by the word "poulps," whose source is Jules Verne's *20,000 Leagues Under the Sea*. The cosmic dimension also stretches up "through eddies of stars scattering aloft with ever wider circlings like rings on water, . . . towards Orion, the Pleiades" as Yvonne passes from consciousness to death. Depth appears again as the Consul imagines himself falling, from the summit he has somehow reached, "into the Volcano . . . the world itself was bursting" as he too met death. These two characters are cosmic in that they represent Everyman and Everywoman, the whole human race, all who cannot, dare not, live without love.

Modes of expression that had been considered flaws in his earlier work now play an integral part in the style. One remembers the "Pantagruelian kick" and "Pericles" in his attempt to bring a fresh approach to sports reporting. One also recalls the literary allusions which, as half-digested scraps from his schooldays, popped into the mind of Dana Hilliot and, although quite in keeping with his character, fitted, at times, rather oddly into the setting aboard ship. This was an attempt at contrast, especially in characterization, but it did not always succeed. Now, at last, in the *Volcano* Lowry is free to draw on his vast store of knowledge and weave it into the texture of his prose to the delight of his reader. It is true that all readers do not enjoy this feature to the full. There is the reader for whom the story only is of interest. He reads at one level. But there are many, many more readers to whom the allusions give a shock of recognition and a delighted enjoyment at their fresh application.

The book can, indeed, be read on many levels. One is first aware of the human interest when faced with these people, in this place, facing these problems. Alcoholism is a disease that reaches far into our society today. There is some basis of truth in Hugh's cynical remark, "Good God, if our civilization were to sober up for a couple of days it'd die of remorse on the third." But Lowry gives it another dimension. Through this weakness the Consul, a kindly, friendly, even lovable man, is shut out from others, barred from loving as he should, driven from the Garden of Eden, or enclosed within it according to his own idea of the punishment of Adam. It is his tragic flaw.

The novel can also be approached from the historical level. The aura of world conditions permeates the story; various classes of society and their impact on one another from the turn of the century to the Day of the Dead, 1939, blend into the history of Mexico to

form the milieu in which the characters move and act. The history
impinges on politics; political factions in Spain and in Mexico forge
the trap in which the Consul is finally caught. There is the level of
mystery, natural and occult. The Consul's father has disappeared
in the Himalayas, the Consul has been involved in the *Samaritan*
incident, Hugh moves in espionage entanglements as a gunrunner
for the Spanish Loyalists. The Consul, supposedly writing a book
on the subject, is interested in mystical phenomena, the cabala, and
alchemy to the point that Hugh suggests jokingly to Yvonne,
"Maybe he's a black magician!" The book can also be enjoyed for
its humor and for the artistry with which it is presented, but these
require fuller treatment.

Lowry's early style had aroused indignant comment on his tricks
with punctuation. He was criticized by the schoolboy readers of *The
Leys Fortnightly* for the use of dots, dashes, and asterisks. In *Ultramarine* he continued to use dots and dashes. From the dashes he
evolved the trick of expressing a silent reaction as if it were spoken;
this is done with a dash enclosed in quotation marks, "—", as in
this conversation:

> "Well, there you are, you see! Well, I must be getting. Coming
> along ashore tonight?"
> "I'll say not. Cheerio."
> "—"

He uses the same device in the *Volcano* but intensifies it:

> . . . The Englishman switched his engine off. "I say, haven't I
> seen you before or something."
> "—"
> "—"

For more than a page, as Lowry describes the early-morning walk
to the house after Yvonne's return, her only replies, except one, to
the Consul's running commentary are in this form. It has become
a very useful tool to express briefly what would otherwise be difficult to express.

Lowry used advertisements and street signs in his early writing
as links with the outside world during a journey or, as in *Ultramarine,* to give the atmosphere of the city. Now he uses them to
express the intrusion of the business world into the privacy of the
individual, or to show a state of mind; fuzzy from alcohol in the
Consul's case, anguished and desperate in Yvonne's. When Yvonne

thinks of her career as an actress she is tortured by her sense of failure:

> For that matter what was she if not that now (if greatly directed) as she walked or drove furiously through her anguish and all the red lights, seeing, as might the Consul, the sign in the Town House window 'Informal Dancing in the Zebra Room' turn 'Infernal'— or 'Notice to Destroy Weeds' become 'Notice to Newlyweds'.

Lowry's tongue-in-cheek understatement in his school writing has now developed into a stylistic device. He uses it here to describe the Consul's befogged mind:

> "All right, Geoffrey: suppose we forget it until you're feeling better: we can cope with it in a day or two, when you're sober."
> "But good lord!"
> The Consul sat perfectly still staring at the floor while the enormity of the insult passed into his soul. As if, as if, he were not sober now! Yet there was some elusive subtlety in the impeachment that still escaped him. For he was not sober. No, he was not, not at this very moment he wasn't! But what had that to do with a minute before, or half an hour ago?

He continues in this vein and comes eventually to the inspired remark, "Ah, a woman could not know the perils, the complications, yes, the *importance* of a drunkard's life!"

In the letter to Harold Matson cited above, Mrs. Lowry says that because Malcolm has "the subjective equipment of a poet" she doubts "if he could ever be a great novelist of 'character'." In this novel there is little personal description, and somehow, as in the morality plays, none is needed; the depths of the soul are presented and the reader is left to fill in the physical details for himself. Fairly late in the novel Yvonne describes herself, the glamorous Hollywood actress, but the reader wonders to what extent the portrayal is colored by her imagination. The picture of the Consul as he left for the afternoon outing is sharply in focus and it also has connotations of character portrayal. Dressed in his freshly pressed shirt and tweed suit, he "appears fresh and lively" and "dispossessed of any air of dissipation whatsoever."

Size is presented indirectly, as in this passage showing the Consul's shock as he realizes that his wife has come back: "Still holding the time-table the Consul built himself to his feet as she came forward." There is the even more clever comment on size, this time direct, for the purpose of deflation as he gives Hugh's reaction, " 'My God! Horses,' Hugh said, glancing and stretching himself to his full mental height of six feet two (he was five feet eleven)." What a complete insight is given in that remark!

Character is betrayed too by reactions to situations and to one another. As they near Laruelle's house where she had betrayed her marriage, Yvonne's detailed comment on the postman makes Hugh wonder, "Why are you so voluble?" Later in the day the alcoholic fumes lift for a moment and the Consul sees Yvonne: "The mist had cleared, but Yvonne's eyes were full of tears, and she was pale." But he cannot understand her problem, nor can he solve his own. When they are having dinner he comes close to it for a moment:

> And then, for the second time that day, their eyes, in a long look, a long look of longing. Behind her eyes, beyond her, the Consul, an instant, saw Granada, and the train waltzing from Algeciras over the plains of Andalusia, *chufferty pupperty, chufferty pupperty, . . .*

He thinks over pleasant memories until a realization of the barrier between them sweeps down on him: "How many bottles since then? In how many glasses, how many bottles had he hidden himself, since then alone?" Then he sees the glasses, "a babel of glasses," and hears as well as sees the long procession of bottles of every kind, all the drinks of all the world. He sat very still and asked himself,

> How indeed could he hope to find himself to begin again when, somewhere, perhaps, in one of those lost or broken bottles, in one of those glasses, lay, for ever, the solitary clue to his identity? How could he go back and look now, scrabble among the broken glass, under the eternal bars, under the oceans?

No, Lowry is not a great novelist of "character." He lets his reader round the character out for himself. He does more than paint characters. With all the power that can be found in Greek tragedy he presents what lies behind the *dramatis personae*.

In her letter to Harold Matson, Mrs. Lowry draws his attention to another aspect of the novel when she says, "it is always dynamic and frequently hilariously funny, (it is, in fact, on one plane a comedy, a sort of cosmic jape if you like)." Again she is right. The obviously comic scenes when the Consul falls in the Calle Nicaragua, when he talks with Mr. Quincey, when he takes refuge in the Infernal Machine to escape the children who later befriend him, when he finishes off all the drinks in Laruelle's house, when he reads the menu and when he struggles through the sense of the tourist folder while in the toilet, are all funny, "a sort of cosmic jape." But there are many other examples of humor that help to give the book its individuality. The Consul's distorted world which he views with alcoholic solemnity is serio-comic, and so are the small, rather absentminded lapses which bring him up with a shock from time to time. As the Consul and Yvonne are filling in time with pointless conversation, the Consul "struck a match against their old jest" to light the cigarette "he had somehow failed to place between his lips: after a little, finding himself with a dead match, he put it in his pocket." Later the Consul begins to get ready for their outing at Tomalin:

> First to wash. Sweating and trembling again, he took off his coat and shirt. He had turned on the water in the basin. Yet for some obscure reason he was standing under the shower, waiting in an agony for the shock of cold water that never came. And he was still wearing his trousers.

A laugh at the Consul's expense is usually tinged with pity.

At times the humor lies in the aptness of a phrase, the mistranslation of an expression, the distortion of a literary allusion or in an error in quotation. These quips and jests are points of light gleaming, at the most unexpected moments, in the fabric of the novel. "Come, *amigo,* throw away your mind." "And flood: the drains of Quauhnahuac visited us and left us with something that smelt like the Cosmic Egg till recently." "Intercepting Concepta . . . with the breakfast tray, the Consul, innocently as a man who has committed a murder while dummy at bridge, entered Yvonne's room." "He was not the person to be seen reeling about in the street. True he might lie down in the street, if needed be, like a gentleman, but he would not reel." "Guanajuato is sited in a beautiful circus of steepy hills." "I should have become a sort of Donne of the fairways at least. Poet of the unreplaced turf." One could multiply examples indefinitely.

The writer who, as a schoolboy, described a ball as having "scarfed itself" around a circle did not lose his gift for the apt phrase. The lurid sunset is contrasted with the quietness of the town, in the opening lines:

Slightly to the right and below them, below the gigantic red evening, whose reflection bled away in the deserted swimming pools scattered everywhere like so many mirages, lay the peace and sweetness of the town.

The next page has a biting comment:

Though tragedy was in the process of becoming unreal and meaningless it seemed one was still permitted to remember the days when an individual life held some value and was not a mere misprint in a communiqué.

As the darkness came down "there was a savage scribble of lightning over the hotel opposite the cinema, followed by another peal of thunder."

The same precision of expression is evident in the description of animals and insects. In his garden the Consul notices "huge butterflies, whose precise stitched markings reminded one of the blouses in the market," and in the bathroom he watches

The insects which lay at different angles from one another on the wall, like ships out in the roadstead. . . . A large cricket, with polished fuselage, clung to the curtain. . . . He turned, expecting the caterpillar to be much nearer, but it too had turned, just slightly shifting its moorings.

But, once again, examples could be multiplied indefinitely.

In the development of the plot Lowry does not play tricks on his reader. Everything that contributes to the climax is introduced early into the novel and carried along with the action. The net in which the Consul is entangled is established from the first page: "Quauhnahuac possesses eighteen churches and fifty-seven cantinas." The barranca is a "dormitory for vultures and city Moloch" and, on the bridge which crossed it, Laruelle recalls his holidays with Geoffrey Firmin when they were boys. His reverie is interrupted by a horse, guided crazily by a drunken rider. The prison watchtowers and their police guards dominate the landscape and make their presence known from time to time with the rattle of their target practice. A powerful use of foreshadowing is in the closing sentence of Chapter II: "A hideous pariah dog followed them in." Was it the same dog that followed the Consul into the barranca?

These properties for the last act of the tragedy are not just introduced and then tossed aside until they are needed for the climax and the conclusion. They move in and out of the action and contribute to the development of the plot. The barranca is crossed and recrossed by the characters, or they walk beside it and look into its depths noticing the rubbish that has been tossed into it. Hugh and Yvonne have an idyllic ride through the countryside with the foals following their mares. The Indian rides back and forth on his horse that is branded with the number seven. Hugh and Yvonne notice him and he even intrudes into the befogged consciousness of the Consul as he inspects the garden, once an Eden, now a jungle. The black spectacled men in the streets hint that the Consul is under surveillance. When the police are mentioned in connection with the dying Indian, they are made to appear ruthless enforcers of pitiless laws.

The same meticulous care has gone into the use of symbols. Almost everything in the novel can be construed into a symbol if one is so inclined. The properties mentioned earlier are symbolic, especially the barranca and the dog. There are, however, two symbols that are particularly important to this study of Lowry's artistry: The garden and the wheel. The Consul's garden, now fallen from its pristine state, is a symbol of the Consul's condition. It abuts on the public garden with its sign, which he constantly misreads. "See to it that your children do not destroy it" becomes a warning of eviction to him, giving him a sense of frustration. These small parks are being set up everywhere by the government, so the Consul is conscious of them at every turn; he even watches the workmen putting up the signs, knowing beforehand what they will say. This is linked with the inscription of Laruelle's house, "No se puede vivir sin amar"—"One cannot live without love." This is the real problem, the real reason for the Consul's eviction from the Garden of Eden; it is also the reason for the existence of the political system by which he is finally trapped.

More powerful than the garden symbol is the wheel. It is more than a symbol; it is the pattern on which the novel is constructed. Cyclic movement fascinated Lowry. The wheel, the eddy, the maelstrom, the spiral flight of birds are patterns that he describes time after time in his works. Sometimes it is factual description, often it is a simile or a metaphor, occasionally it is a symbol that finds expression in this way. Lowry planned the book on a cyclic pattern; when one reaches the end one is impelled to turn back to the beginning and reread at least the first chapter. The wheel is in the closing sentence of Chapter I, "Over the town, in the dark tempestuous night, backwards revolved the luminous wheel." In the letter to Jonathan Cape in which he defends his book, Lowry traces the wheel pattern in all its intricate manifestations, in chapter after chapter as he criticizes his own work. . . . To him "this sublime celestial machinery" suggested movement into infinity as well as man's eternal quest. The scope of his thought becomes clear from this passage:

> And the earth itself still turning on its axis and revolving around that sun, the sun revolving around the luminous wheel of this galaxy, the countless unmeasured jewelled wheels of countless unmeasured galaxies turning, turning, majestically, into infinity, into eternity, through all of which all life ran on—all this, long after she herself was dead, men would still be reading in the night sky and as the earth turned through those distant seasons, and they watched the constellations still rising, culminating, setting, to rise again—Aries, Taurus, Gemini, the Crab, Leo, Virgo, the Scales and the Scorpion, Capricorn the Sea-goat and Aquarius the Water Bearer, Pisces, and once more, triumphantly, Aries!—would they not, too, still be asking the hopeless eternal question: to what end?

The wheel, especially the luminous wheel, is the pattern of Lowry's thought. To him it is the pattern of life itself and all human relationship.

In this novel Lowry uses cinematic technique to develop his plot by giving continuity to the action. The opening lines give a cosmic view as if the world were in focus from outer space. This gradually sharpens as detail after detail is supplied until the hotel, the tennis courts and finally the two men are centered on the screen. Wide vistas are followed by close-ups as one scene after the other is presented. The presentation of these different perspectives is cleverly handled. Hugh and Yvonne walk, then ride, and from their viewpoint the Consul's white house gleams out against the shrubbery on the hillside. Signs and shop windows give the sense of movement as the Consul and Yvonne walk along the street. Glimpses of the scenery alternate with close-ups of the passengers during the bus ride. Laruelle's farewell walk through the town is a means of introducing the reader to the area in which the first major scenes are laid. This following of one character showing him in his environment then fading into a presentation of his thoughts is definitely cinematic and is handled with consummate skill. One character after another is treated in this way until the reader feels that Laruelle has kept his promise and had made his film which is unrolling before him. One does not just read this book; one watches it unfold.

A final characteristic of Lowry's writing in his great novel must be noted. This is the use of delicately handled descriptions, particularly those that are idyllic. The little descriptions are nearly all authentic pieces of local color, the sort of thing the cameraman would catch in a close-up as it passed by. The Consul had spoken of a corpse as Yvonne stood and watched him before he knew she had returned. When they were walking towards home,

> It came sailing out of nowhere, the child's funeral, the tiny lace-covered coffin followed by the band: two saxophones, bass guitar, a fiddle, playing of all things "La Cucaracha," the women behind, very solemn, while several paces back a few hangers-on were joking, straggling along in the dust almost at a run.

As a touch of local color this little scene is perfect.

Late in the afternoon the sun is getting low in the sky and shadows are lengthening as the group moves toward the Salon Ofelia.

> A hot thundery wind launched itself at them, spent itself, and somewhere a bell beat out wild tripthongs. Their shadows crawled before them in the dust, slid down white thirsty walls of houses, were caught violently for a moment in an elliptical shade, the turning wrenched wheel of a boy's bicycle. The spoked shadow of the wheel, enormous, insolent, swept away.

This description is imagination coloring observation and it shows the real artist at work.

Chapter IX closes with another vignette that links close observation with skillful description:

> "Now their own shadows fell full across the square to the raised twin doors of the tavern, Todos Contentos y Yo También: under the doors they noticed what looked like the bottom of a crutch, someone leaving. The crutch didn't move; its owner was having an argument at the door, a last drink perhaps. Then it disappeared: one door of the cantina was propped back, something emerged.
>
> Bent double, groaning with the weight, an old lame Indian was carrying on his back, by means of a strap looped over his forehead, another poor Indian, yet older and more decrepit than himself. He carried the older man and his crutches, trembling in every limb under this weight of the past, he carried both their burdens.
>
> They all stood watching the Indian as he disappeared with the

old man around a bend of the road, into the evening, shuffling
through the grey white dust in his poor sandals . . .

That is not just a description of the scene; it is a statement of the
humanity of the man who wrote it.

Except for a few descriptions of the Mexican scene, for example,
the town at sunset and early evening as Laruelle walked through it,
the countryside as Hugh and Yvonne saw it on their walk and ride
together, and the descriptions of the two volcanoes that link the
landscape with the cloud-filled sky, the idyllic passages are descriptions of the area around Dollarton, now Cates Park, that was home
and Eden to the Lowrys for fourteen years. Indeed, it would be
almost more correct to say seventeen years; during the last three
years of exile he hoped some day to go back to the place where he
had been so happy. The dream of this haven first slips into the novel
in the Consul's letter to Yvonne which M. Laruelle finds in the
book of Elizabethan plays. Dreaming of possible happiness with his
wife, the Consul writes:

> I seem to see us living in some northern country, of mountains
> and hills and blue water; our house is built on an inlet and one
> evening we are standing, happy in one another, on the balcony of
> this house, looking over the water. There are sawmills half hidden
> by trees beyond and under the hills on the other side of the inlet,
> what looks like an oil refinery, only softened and rendered beautiful
> by distance.
>
> It is a light blue moonless summer evening, . . . from beyond
> along the coast comes the gathering thunder of a long many-engined
> freight train, thunder because though we are separated by this wide
> strip of water from it, the train is rolling eastward and the changing
> wind veers for the moment from an easterly quarter, . . . and then
> all at once a fishing-boat with tall gear comes running round the
> point like a white giraffe, very swift and stately, leaving directly
> behind it a long silver scalloped rim of wake, not visibly moving
> inshore, but now stealing ponderously beachward towards us, this
> scrolled silver rim of wash striking the shore first in the distance,
> then spreading all along the curve of beach, its growing thunder
> and commotion now joined to the diminishing thunder of the train,
> and now breaking reboant on our beach, while the floats, for there
> are timber diving floats, are swayed together, everything jostled and
> beautifully ruffled and stirred and tormented in this rolling sleeked
> silver, then little by little calm again, . . . And as we stand looking

all at once comes the wash of another unseen ship, like a great wheel, the vast spokes of the wheel whirling across the bay.

The dream of the shack by the sea is presented by Hugh when he rides with Yvonne. She wants to get the Consul away from Mexico, preferably to a farm in Canada. Hugh realizes that the Consul will never fit into that environment, so he suggests a squatter's cottage with foreshore rights near Vancouver. The idea appeals to Yvonne and from then on it slips into the novel whenever she has a moment to dream. Hugh presents his idea:

> I can see your shack now. It's between the forest and the sea and you've got a pier going down to the water over rough stones, you know, covered with barnacles and sea anemones and starfish. You'll have to go through the woods to the store. . . . The woods will be wet. And occasionally a tree will come crashing down. And sometimes there will be a fog and that fog will freeze. Then your whole forest will become a crystal forest. The ice crystals on the twigs will grow like leaves. Then pretty soon you'll be seeing the jack-in-the-pulpits and then it will be spring.

This is Roche Point in all its pristine beauty as the Lowrys knew it, the place where *Under the Volcano* was written.

As she dreams of this Eden, Yvonne adds details, "salmonberries and thimbleberries and wild blackberry bushes that on bright winter nights of frost reflected a million moons;" behind the house she sees a "dogwood tree that bloomed twice in the year with white stars." Womanlike, she furnishes the house down to the lamps and the bright Indian blankets. She imagines the

> millweel reflections of sunlight on water . . . sliding down the front of their house, sliding, sliding, over the windows, the walls, the reflections that, above and behind the house, turned the pine boughs into green chenille.

But the transience of life, the cycles of change that make one wonder about its purpose—the *cui bono*?—was always present in Lowry's mind. This happiness is not to be for the Consul and Yvonne. In her next dream she sees the house from different viewpoints, from above, in the forest, from the beach, from the sea. Then she suddenly asks herself, "Why was it though, that right in the centre of her brain, there should be a figure of a woman having hysterics, jerking like a puppet and banging her fists upon the ground?" These are prophetic words. As she dies Yvonne has another dream of the house, but this time it is on fire. One after the other the things she had put into the house or around it are destroyed:

> Geoffrey's old chair was burning, his desk, and now his book, his book was burning, the pages were burning, burning, burning, whirling up from the fire they were scattered, burning, along the beach, and now it was growing darker and the tide coming in, the tide washed under the ruined house, the pleasure boats that had ferried song upstream sailed home silently over the dark waters of Eridanus. Their house was dying, only an agony went there now.

The house was dying, the dream had faded, the dreamer was dead. These lyrical passages which have served their purpose in giving beauty and authenticity to the novel are factual. Lowry has used his own experience of the beauty of this place he loved so dearly and the traumatic shock of its loss through fire to present something he otherwise might not have been able to say. The artist is at work; from the warp of reality and the weft of vision he has presented a world that is wholly his own.

So far as style is concerned, *Under the Volcano* represents the highest level of Lowry's achievement. When Mrs. Lowry wrote, "Malcolm has found his style and come to maturity as an artist with it," she stated an undeniable fact. Everything else he wrote from then on was determined or measured by this achievement. The title *Under the Volcano* was even more significant than Lowry thought. He became Vulcan shaping his thoughts into swords and plowshares through the medium of words. . . .

Many of the ideas embedded in the *Volcano* are developed elsewhere as poems. He wrote a considerable amount of poetry which he was reluctant to release for publication. In the introduction to *Selected Poems of Malcolm Lowry,* Earle Birney suggests that this reluctance stemmed from the fact that "his verse was so innocent of defense." No doubt this is true. Many of his poems are intensely personal. Some of them speak surprisingly of the hatred that often engulfed him. In the light of the *Letters* this is rather different from what one would expect; he does not sound like a person driven by hatred. Were the poems and his drinking the outlet for it?

In reading some of the poems one notices the similarity, in subject matter and expression, to thoughts or incidents in *Under the Volcano*. Perhaps through the poem he was able to effect a crystallization of an idea that made it possible for him to give the prose expression the validity it needed and which he could not otherwise have achieved.

Lowry was always fond of seagulls. Simple line drawings of them decorate letters and manuscripts when he is in a happy mood. There are countless references to them from his earliest writing; like the wheel they form a recurrent pattern. Only one who knows the gull and its habits could have written this poem, especially its first three lines:

THE GLAUCOUS-WINGED GULL

> The hook-nosed angel that walks like a sailor,
> Pure scavenger of the empyrean,
> Hunter of edible stars, and sage
> Catsbane and defiler of the porch,
> Dead sailor, finial, and image
> Of freedom in morning blue, and strange torch
> At twilight, stranger world of love
> Old haunter of the Maure tania,
> Snowblinded once, I saved. And hove
> Out of the rainbarrel, back at heaven—
> A memory stronger than childhood's even
> Or freighters rolling to Roumania.

This poem takes on an added dimension when one compares it with the passage in *Under the Volcano* in which Hugh is justifying himself to his conscience:

> No: I am much afraid there is little enough in your past, which will come to your aid against the future. Not even the seagull? said Hugh. . . .
> The seagull—pure scavenger of the empyrean, hunter of edible stars—I rescued that day as a boy when it was caught in a fence on the cliffside and was beating itself to death, blinded by snow, and though it attacked me, I drew it out unharmed, with one hand by its feet, and for one magnificent moment held it up in the sunlight, before it soared away on angelic winds over the freezing estuary?

The two are not exactly alike in detail but some experience seems to have sparked the description. If Lowry did rescue a seagull what a sense of power this would have given him in that "magnificent

moment" and what a surge of happiness would have accompanied
the memory ever after.

The loss of their house by fire is also expressed in a poem which
has its echoes in the novel:

A LAMENT—JUNE 1944

Our house is dead
It burned to the ground
On a morning in June
With a wind from the Sound.
The fire that fed
On our marriage bed
Left a bottle of gin.
Black under the moon
Our house is dead.
We shall build it again
But our home is gone.
And the world burns on.

This is very close to Yvonne's last dream as she loses consciousness; the dream that closes with the tragic line, "Their house was
dying, only an agony went there now."

The passage quoted earlier in which, in her imagination, Yvonne
sees the light reflected from the water and playing on the walls is
almost identical with the poem "Indian Arm," which begins, "Mill-
wheel reflections of sun on water/ And the spokes of light wheeling
on the shacks." It closes with these lines which echo the picture in
Under the Volcano:

Softly renews the round of the mill-wheel
Sun reflections winding longer shadows
And turns the pine bough into green chenille.

After the moonlight walks over windows
Mill-wheel reflections of moonlight later
On water embroider waving windows . . .

Lowry wrote many poems about ships and the sea, the forest, and
the happiness of life at Dollarton. He also wrote about death and
remorse. These subjects are used so often and so powerfully that
one recognizes in them a preoccupation that is almost an obsession.
Some of these poems are not only very powerful, but also very
beautiful. This is one of the finest:

SUNRISE

Sober I rode into the brand new dawn,
With steady hand grasping the single rein,
New-shod new-shrived and all but newly born
Over the smiling grandiloquent plain.

Surcingleless as heaven ran my steed
And true to heaven rose my simple song,
Ah, the years behind seemed lost, and lost the deed,
As pommel and stirrups unheeded I cantered along.

—But what cactuses are these on every hand,
Wild dogs and spectres, all enveloping?
And came again into that evening land,

Galloping, galloping, galloping—

Bound to that unrelenting fatuous horse
Whose eyes are lidless and whose name, remorse.

Man's cruelty troubled him greatly and it is often expressed in,
or linked with, poems about death. Surprisingly he uses the vil-
lanelle, usually the vehicle for a happy subject, to express sorrow
in "Death of a Oaxaquenian," which begins, "So huge is God's des-
pair/ In the wild cactus plain/ I heard Him weeping there."

Lowry could also write whimsical poetry when he chose, and his
sense of humor flashes out from time to time in the turn of a phrase,
as in this which is half serious, half comic:

THE UNBORN

He wrote for the dead, but the ubiquitous dead
Liked their own wisdom, and preferred their bed;

He wrote for the blind, yet the polygonous blind
Had richer, thicker things just then in mind;

He wrote for the dumb, but the golden-voiced dumb
Were singing their own songs and could not come;

So he wrote for the unborn, since surely, it is said,
At least they're neither dumb, nor blind, nor dead.

In the Lowry papers there are many pages of partly finished
poems, some of them barely started. This problem of creating the

poem and shaping it to its perfect form is the theme of "One Flying Line," from which these few lines have been extracted:

> Phrases rejected for a trochee's sake
> bobbing like corks on margins of volumes
> may mark depths where the caught iambic glitters:
> or one flying line among such fragments
> soar on forever like the Bird of Paradise.

His poetry often does just that, utters a "flying line" that soars. Describing, in "Iron Cities," a busy harbor with ships moving back and forth, he says, "The ferry utters/ A last white phrase." What a perfect picture of the moment when the boat speaks with its steam whistle! The ship's stoker must be behind this metaphor for lightning: "And lightning scrapes blue shovels against coal." Perhaps the loveliest of these single lines is this one, which is a little poem in itself: "The meadows wait for rainbows to say God."

All Lowry's themes, his loves and his hates, are gathered into this short poem, which will serve as a final example:

FOR THE LOVE OF DYING

> The tortures of hell are stern, their fires burn fiercely.
> Yet vultures turn against the air more beautifully
> than seagulls float downwind in cool sunlight,
> or fans in asylums spin a loom of fate
> for hope which never ventured up so high
> as life's deception, astride the vulture's flight.
> If death can fly, just for the love of flying,
> What might not life do, for the love of dying?

The themes and techniques that Lowry had learned and applied in his novel and in his poetry were used also in his short stories. Some of his stories are still being edited with the hope that they will be published. The most widely known have been released in the collection *Hear Us O Lord from Heaven Thy Dwelling Place*. There are seven stories in the book, including the two which have been most frequently anthologized, "The Bravest Boat" and "The Forest Path to the Spring."

Lowry seems to have been particularly happy in the short story, although the mass of notes and rewritten versions in the Collection suggests than he often had to wrestle with his theme to make it take form. The great perfection of some sentences is, in itself, a comment on the author's clarity in seeing as well as his ability in expressing. "The Bravest Boat" opens with this sentence: "It was a day of spindrift and blowing sea-foam, with black clouds presaging rain driven over the mountains from the sea by a wild March wind." Point after point is noted in the landscape as he builds up a picture of the mountains and sea, clouds and trees that is alive with movement and color. The seagulls are there, "The angelic wings of the seagulls circling over the tree tops shone very white against the black sky." But the eye travels beyond them, up into the sky beyond the mountain tops, "And highest of all an eagle, with the poise of a skier, shot endlessly down the world." The beautiful prose should not be fragmented in this way, even though these sentences are so well worth nothing. The people in the story are Astrid and Sigurd. They are also Margerie and Malcolm Lowry, for the autobiographical note comes in very simply as the two protagonists walk along the beach with its welter of driftwood swinging at the tideline. When they come upon "a few bits of lumber almost ready to burn" thinking that someone might take them home, "automatically they threw them up beyond the sea's reach for some passing soul, remembering their own winters of need."

The next story in the collection is "Through the Panama." To the accompaniment of the ship's engines beating out "Frère Jacques" the Wildernesses, Sigbjorn and Primrose, sail on the freighter *S.S. Diderot* for Rotterdam. This story is taken from Sigbjorn's notebook, but he becomes Martin in the story that is told. Again, the protagonists are really Margerie and Malcolm Lowry, who sailed to France, in November, 1947, on the *S.S. Brest*. The story is not only an account of the voyage but also a commentary on what Lowry had been reading at the time. Newspaper clippings and guide books are incorporated into the text or used, along with the glosses from Coleridge's "The Rime of the Ancient Mariner," as a running marginal commentary. Martin is a writer. This gives Lowry freedom for the distorted literary quotations and references that he liked to use, for example "I am the chief steward of my fate, I am the fireman of my soul," and "My faithful general Phenobarbus, treacherous to the last." The ship runs into storms; at times the protagonist dreams of home: "Thousands of white gulls. The crew feeding them. Will our gulls starve without us?"

There are deliberate repetitions and echoes of earlier works in this story. These are meant to establish the fact that this man is the same author who wrote the earlier passages. In this story Lowry tried out an interesting experiment in short-story technique. The marginal glosses make a running commentary on the ideas in the story itself, or present the same ideas from a different viewpoint. It is like the photographing of the same scene with two cameras set a few feet apart to obtain a stereoscopic or three-dimensional, effect. In this way Lowry uses cinematic technique to give multilevel presentation a startlingly new impact.

The next story in the collection, "Strange Comfort Afforded by the Profession," is also built up from a notebook belonging to Sigbjorn. The letter he uses is almost a replica of the draft of one Lowry wrote to the person in charge of his trust fund. With this story and its autobiographical twist, the previous account of the sea voyage is so closely related that one relizes that Lowry is attempting to write a novel by presenting a series of related short stories. Glimpses of the Keats and Shelley memorials in Rome are given in such a way that the reader feels that cults are often nothing more than the indulgence of sentimentality. This feeling becomes stronger when the author presents the notes of his visit to Poe's shrine in Richmond. He draws the parallel with his own life and shows that an author is one who needs tangible help and understanding during life more than he needs memorial rooms or shrines when he is dead.

"Elephant and Colosseum" is also about a writer, this time on a visit to Rome from America. In youth he had shipped on a freighter as cabin boy and had been appointed caretaker of the animal cargo the ship was bringing back to the zoos. There are echoes of this in *Ultramarine*. Kennish Drumgold Cosnahan, a native Manxman, allows his mind to wander over the whole range of Lowry thought including the occult. The Collection indicates how much work goes into a Lowry story and especially how much went into this one. The 654 pages of manuscript and the working notes make a pile eight inches high. From this Lowry distilled the 58 pages of the finished, published version. The beautiful Lowry style is the product of heartbreaking labor.

"Present Estate of Pompeii" presents another view of the writer's mind, as its protagonist, Roderick McGregor Fairhaven, is also an author. He is more than this. He comes from the same place as the Wildernesses, knows them well, so well, in fact, that he quotes Wilderness as several of his ideas fit into the experience the Fairhavens are having, as they view the remains of Pompeii. In this story the theme of eviction is strong and the passages describing Eridanus are particularly evocative and nostalgic. The reader becomes aware of the intensity of suffering when one is wrenched unwillingly from the place that has been a haven of peace.

With "Gin and Goldenrod" the protagonists are back at Eridanus and are, once again, Primrose and Sigbjorn Wilderness. The threat of eviction hovers in the background, expressed mainly by the signs on the office of the real estate development company, the scars on the landscape where new roads have gone through, the felled trees, and the ugly new houses. The story is a vignette which brings more sharply into focus the people who have been moving through the book. The reader gets a glimpse into their lives that reveals a good deal about their characters. The same pattern of drinking that marked "Through the Panama" forms the background of the situation in which the protagonists are placed. One never escapes from it for very long in Lowry's work. The reader sees clearly that civilization is moving into the forest and destroying their Eden. There is a very definite sense that the way of life that had meant so much to these two people is now over. They will never find it again.

The last story, "The Forest Path to the Spring," is the most beautiful thing Lowry has written. It was intended as the closing section of his novel sequence and would, indeed, have formed a fitting conclusion to the saga. Dedicated "to Margerie, my wife," it is an eloquent tribute to all that she meant to him. It shows, as nothing else could, what the peace and beauty of his simple home at Dollarton meant to him and the part this environment played in his fulfillment as a writer.

The protagonist in this story is a musician, one who plans to write a great symphony, but so far is tortured with contradictions and perplexities. He comes upon the dedication which he had written years before and which was all that was left of the work, the rest having been destroyed by fire. If the one word "notes" is changed from a musical to a literary connotation, the words will serve as Lowry's own statement of purpose:

> Dear Lord God, I earnestly pray you to help me order this work, ugly chaotic and sinful though it may be, in a manner that is acceptable in Thy sight; thus, so it seems to my imperfect and disordered brain, at the same time fulfilling the highest canons of art, yet breaking new ground and, where necessary, old rules. It must be tumultuous, stormy, full of thunder, the exhilarating Word of God must sound through it, pronouncing hope for man, yet it also must be balanced, grave, full of tenderness and compassion, and

concepts, but let me be truly Thy servant in making this a great
and beautiful thing, and if my motives are obscure, and the notes
scattered and often meaningless, please help me to order it, or I am
lost. . . .

The whole Dollarton setting is found in this story: the untouched
forest, the spring, the beach, the distant oil refinery, the lighthouses,
Deep Cove, Burrard Inlet and its northern branch familiarly called
Indian Arm. The fishermen who were the Lowrys' only neighbors
during the winter and the summer visitors who were their friends
are there. They do the things such people would do and they talk
about the things that would interest them and Lowry gives it the air
of authenticity by the sureness and beauty of his prose. The writing
is not "fine writing" in the derogatory sense; it is fine writing in
which every art is employed to show forth with truth the thing one
loves.

There are many "flying lines" and gems of description. He gives
a glimpse of the view from the path:

> Often all you could see in the whole world of the dawn was a huge
> sun with two pines silhouetted in it, like a great blaze behind a
> Gothic cathedral. And at night the same pines would write a
> Chinese poem on the moon.

Freighters come into view or anchor in the roadstead: "Sometimes
too, on the seaboard of the night, a ship would stand drawn, like
a jeweled dagger, from the dark scabbard of the town." When the
mist was thick they heard "the thrilling diatonic notes of a foghorn
in the mist, as if some great symphony had just begun its opening
chords." A beacon was visible to the south,

> It was a whitewashed concrete structure, thin as a match, like a
> magic lighthouse, without a keeper, but oddly like a human being
> itself, standing lonely on its cairn with its ruby lamp for a head and
> its generator strapped to its back like a pack; wild roses in early
> summer blew on the bank beside it, and when the evening star
> came out, sure enough, it began its beneficent signaling too.

Lowry delighted in the wildlife around him and wrote many
delightful passages about the animals, the birds, and the sea creatures he was constantly observing.

> That night there were two evening herons in the moon at high tide,
> the herons projected large and primeval before it, the one flapping

high, blocking a moment the moon itself, the other, engines switched
off, gliding low an inch above the moonstruck swelling water to
land noiselessly on the float: a *squark* when they met, the one waiting for the other, and then flying off together.

Literary allusions are part of the texture, but there is one that is
particularly interesting. The couple had gone by boat up the inlet
and were impressed by the beauty of the mountains that could be
seen in the distance. Then they had a significant experience.

> As we rowed along the shore in the warm late afternoon light these
> great peaks were reflected in and shadowed the flowing water, and
> seemed to move along with us, so that my wife spoke of Words-
> worth's famous peak, that strode after him; this was something
> similar, she said, though very different, because there was nothing
> threatening about this apparent movement; these peaks that followed
> us were, rather, guardians. Many times were we to see this phenome-
> non, as of a whole mountainside or ridge of pines detaching them-
> selves and moving as we rowed, but never did it, or they seem
> "after" us: it seemed a reminder of duality, of opposing motions
> born of the motion of the earth, a symbol even while an illusion,
> of nature's intolerance of inertia.

Sigbjorn is tortured by hates and fears that surge into his soul.
He is unable to explain their cause or to understand them. Finally,
as the peace of the place calms and strengthens him, he conquers
these fears. Part of this new strength comes from his wife's belief
in him, part of it from his love for her. He comments on this, "I
reflected how little I had known of the depths and tides of a woman
until now, her tenderness, her compassion, her capacity for delight,
her wistfulness, her joy and strength, and her beauty, that happened
through my wild luck to be the beauty of my wife." From this love
and this peace comes a greater understanding of life and of what
will satisfy man's hunger for beauty:

> And suddenly, as I helped my wife out and tied up the boat,
> I was overwhelmed with a kind of love. Standing there, in defiance
> of eternity, and yet as if in humble answer to it, with their weath-
> ered sidings as much a part of the natural surroundings as a Shinto
> temple is of the Japanese landscape, why had these shacks come to
> represent something to me of an indefinable goodness, even a kind
> of greatness?

It is not surprising that *Hear Us O Lord from Heaven Thy Dwelling Place* won the Governor-General's Award for fiction in 1962. This was the first time the award was made posthumously.

Lowry wrote other stories at this time, notably "The Element Follows You Around, Sir!" which grew into . . . *October Ferry to Gabriola*. He wrote book reviews, notably one on *Turvey*, the novel of his friend Earle Birney. He wrote a charming article on Mexico, "The Garden of Etla," which talks about the friend in whose memory he wrote . . . *Dark as the Grave Wherein My Friend Is Laid*. . . . He wrote *La Mordida*, a novel about the Lowrys' experience with the Mexican police, and this . . . is in the process of being edited with a view of publication in the near future. But, all this time, and right to the end of his life, he wrote letters; charming, indignant, desperate, beseeching, humorous, friendly letters that show the man better than anything else ever could.

To the student of Lowry's style, however, these letters have a particular value. They reveal his thoughts on the subject of style, the way in which the artist expresses what he has to say, what he thought was important for a writer to know. *Under the Volcano* marked the peak in his stylistic development. Mrs. Lowry said truly, "Malcolm has found his style." Everything he wrote before this was a preparation for it; everything he wrote after had been shaped or "informed" by it. . . .

PART FOUR

_____

Some of the
Last Stories

Under the Volcano

I

As they walked up the Calle Nicaragua toward the bus stop Hugh and Yvonne turned to watch the marmalade-colored birds trapezing in the vines. But her father, afflicted by their raucous cries, strode on austerely through the blue, hot November afternoon.

The bus was not very full at first and soon was rolling like a ship in a heavy sea.

Now out of one window, now out of another, they could see the great mountain, Popocatepetl, round whose base clouds curled like smoke drawn from a train.

They passed tall, hexagonal stands with advertisements for the Morelos Cinema: Los Manos de Orlac: con Peter Lorre. Elsewhere, as they clattered through the little town, they noticed posters of the same film, showing a murderer's hands laced with blood.

"Like Paris," Yvonne said to Hugh, pointing to the kiosks, "Kub, Oxygénée, do you remember?"

Hugh nodded, stammering out something, and the careening of the bus made him swallow every syllable.

". . . Do you remember Peter Lorre in 'M'?"

But they had to give it up. The patient floor boards were creaking too loudly. They were passing the undertakers: *Inhumaciones*. A parrot, head cocked, eyed them from its perch at the entrance. Quo Vadis? asked a notice above it.

"Marvelous," the Consul said.

At the market they stopped for Indian women with baskets of poultry. They had strong faces, the color of dark earthernware. There was a massiveness in their movements as they settled themselves. Two or three had cigarette stubs behind their ears, another

[1] This original short story developed into Chapter VIII of the now famous novel *Under the Volcano*.

chewed an old pipe. Their good humoured faces of old idols were wrinkled with sun but they did not smile.

Then someone laughed, the faces of the others slowly cracked into mirth, the camion was welding the old women into a community. Two even managed to hold an anxious conversation in spite of the racket.

The Consul, nodding to them politely, wished he too were going home. And he wondered who had suggested making this ghastly trip to the fiesta at Chapultepec when their car was laid up and there were no taxis to be had! The effort of going without a drink for a day, even for the benefit of his daughter and her young man who had arrived that morning from Acapulco, was far greater than he had expected. Perhaps it was not the effort of merely being sober that told so much as that of coping with the legacy of impending doom recent unprecedented bouts had left him. When Yvonne pointed out Popocatepetl to him for the fifth time he smiled wanly. Chimborozo, Cotopaxi—and there it was! To the Consul the volcano had taken on a sinister aspect: like a sort of Moby Dick, it had the air of beckoning them on, as it swung from one side of the horizon to the other, to some disaster, unique and immedicable.

The bus lurched away from the mercado where the clock on the main building sheltering the stalls stood at seven minutes past two —it had just struck eleven, the Consul's watch said a quarter to four—then bumped down a steep cobbled incline and began to cross a little bridge over a ravine.

Was this the same arras, Yvonne wondered, that cut through her father's garden? The Consul was indicating that it was. The bottom was immensely far below, one looked down at it as from the main-truck of a sailing ship, though dense foliage and wide leaves partly concealed the real treachery of the drop. Its steep banks were piled with refuse, which even hung on the foliage; from the precipitous slope beyond the bridge, turning round, Yvonne could see a dead dog right down at the bottom, with white bones showing through, nuzzling the refuse.

"How's the rajah hangover, Dad?" she asked, smiling.

" 'Taut over chaos,' " the Consul gritted his teeth, " 'crammed with serried masks.' "

"Just a little longer."

"No. I shall *never* drink again. Nevermore."

The bus went on. Halfway up the slope, beyond the ravine, outside a gaudily decorated little cantina named the El Amore de los

Amores, waited a man in a blue suit, swaying gently and eating a melon.

As they approached, the Consul thought he recognized him as the part owner of the cantina, which was not, however, on his beat: from the interior came the sound of drunken singing.

When the bus stopped, the Consul thirstily caught sight, over the jalousied doors, of a bartender leaning over the bar and talking with intensity to a number of roaring policemen.

The camion throbbed away to itself while the driver went into the cantina. He emerged almost immediately to hurl himself back on his vehicle. Then with an amused glance at the man in the blue suit, whom he apparently knew, he jammed the bus into gear and drove away.

The Consul watched the man, fascinated. The latter was very drunk indeed, and he felt a queer envy of him, albeit it was perhaps a stir of fellowship. As the bus drew in sight of the brewery, the Cerveceria de Quahnahuac, the Consul, his too sober gaze on the other's large, trembling hands, thrust his own hands into his pocket guiltily, but he had found the word wanted to describe him: pelado.

Pelados, he thought, the peeled ones, were those who did not have to be rich to prey on the really poor. They were also those half-breed politicians who work like slaves to get into office for one year, just one year, in which year they hope to put by enough to forswear work for the rest of their lives. Pelado—it was an ambiguous word, to be sure! The Consul chuckled. A Spaniard whom he despised, used, and filled with—ah—'poisonous' liquor. While to that Indian it might mean the Spaniard, or, employed by either with an amiable contempt, simply anyone who made a show of himself.

But whatever it might or might not mean, the Consul judged, his eyes still fixed on his man with the blue suit, it was fair to consider that the word could have been distilled only from such a venture as the Conquest, suggesting as it did on the one hand exploiter, and on the other, thief: and neither was it difficult to understand why it had come in time to describe the invaders as well as their victims. Interchangeable ever were the terms of abuse with which the aggressor publicly discredited those about to be ravaged!

The pelado then, who for a time had been talking thickly to himself, was now sunk in stupor. There was no conductor this trip, fares were paid to the driver on getting off, none bothered him. The dusty blue suit with its coat, tight at the waist but open, the broad trousers, pointed shoes shined that morning and soiled with the saloon's sawdust, indicated a confusion in his mind the Consul well understood: who shall I be today, Jekyll or Hyde? His purple shirt, open at the neck and showing a crucifix, had been torn and was partially hanging out over the top of his trousers. For some reason he wore two hats, a kind of cheap Homburg fitting neatly over the broad crown of his sombrero.

Soon they were passing the Hotel Casino de la Selva and they stopped once more. Colts with glossy coats were rolling on a slope. The Consul recognized Dr. Vigil's back moving among the trees on the tennis court; it was as if he were dancing a grotesque dance all by himself there.

Presently they were getting out into the country. At first there were rough stone walls on either side: then, after crossing the narrow gauge railway, where the Pearce oil tanks were pillowed along the embankment against the trees, leafy hedges full of bright wild-flowers with deep royal blue bells. Green and white clothing hung on the cornstalks outside the low, grass-roofed houses. Now the bright blue flowers grew right into the trees, already snowy with blooms, and all this beauty the Consul noted with horror.

The road became smoother for a time so that it was possible for Hugh and Yvonne to talk: then, just as Hugh was saying something about the 'convolvuli,' it grew much worse again.

"It's like a canterbury bell," the Consul was trying to say, only the camion bumped over a pothole at that moment and it was as if the jolt had thrown his soul up into his teeth. He steadied himself on the seat and the wood sent a piercing pain through his body. His knees knocked together. With Popocatepetl always following or preceding them they jogged into very rough country indeed. The Consul felt that his head had become an open basket swarming with crabs. Now it was the ravine that was haunting him, creeping after them with a gruesome patience, he thought, winding always around the road on one side or the other. The crabs were at the back of his eyes, yet he forced himself to be hearty.

"Where's old Popeye gone to now?" he would exclaim as the volcano slid out of sight past the window to the left, for though he was afraid of it, he felt somehow better when it was there.

"This is like driving over the moon," Hugh tried to whisper to Yvonne, but ended up by shouting.

"Maybe all covered with spinach!" Yvonne was answering her father.

"Right down Archimedes this time! Look out!"

Then for a while they were passing through flat, wooded country with no volcano in sight, nothing to be seen but pines, stones, fircones, black earth. But when they looked more closely they noticed that the stones were volcanic, the earth was parched looking, that everywhere were attestations to Popocatepetl's presence and antiquity.

After, the mountain itself would stride into view again, magnificent, or appearing sad, slate-grey as despair, poised over his sleeping woman, Ixtaccihuatl, now permanently contiguous, which perhaps accounted for it, the Consul decided, feeling that Popo had also an annoying quality of looking as though it knew people expected it to be about to do, or mean, something—as if to be the most beautiful mountain in the world were not enough.

Gazing around the camion, which was somewhat fuller, Hugh took stock of his surroundings. He noticed the drunk, the old women, the men in their white trousers with purple shirts, and now the men in black trousers with their white Sunday shirts—for it was a holiday—and one or two younger women in mourning. He attempted to take an interest in the poultry. The hens and cocks and turkeys imprisoned in their baskets, and those that were still loose, had all alike submitted. With only an occasional flutter to show they were alive they crouched passively under the seats, their emphatic spindly claws bound with cord. Two pullets lay, frightened and quivering, between the handbrake and the clutch, their wings linked, it seemed, with the levers. Hugh was bored with all this finally. The thought of Yvonne sagged down his mind, shook his brain, permeating the camion, the very day itself, with nervous passion.

He turned away from her nearness and looked out, only to see her clear profile and sleeked fair hair sailing along reflected in the window.

The Consul was suffering more and more intensely. Each object on which his glance fell appeared touched with a cruel, supersensual significance. He knew the very wood of the seat to be capable of hurting his hands. And the words which ran across the entire breadth of the bus over the windscreen: *su salva estará a salvo no escapiendo en el interior de éste vehículo*: the driver's round mirror, the legend above it, *Cooperación de la Crux Roja,* beside which hung three postcards of the Virgin Mary and a fire-extinguisher, the two slim vases of marguerites fixed over the dashboard, the dungaree jacket and whiskbroom under the seat opposite where the pelado was sitting, all seemed to him actually to be alive, to be participating, with evil animation, in their journey.

And the pelado? The shaking of the camion was making it difficult for him to remain seated. With his eyes shut, and swaying from side to side, he was trying to tuck his shirt in. Now he was methodically buttoning his coat on the wrong buttons. The Consul smiled, knowing how meticulous one could be when drunk: clothes mysteriously hung up, cars driven by a seventh sense, police eluded by an eighth. Now the pelado had found room to lie down full length on the seat. And all this had been superbly accomplished without once opening his eyes!

Stretched out—a corpse—he still preserved the appearance of being uncannily aware of all that was going on. In spite of his stupor, he was a man on his guard; half a melon slipped out of his hand, the segments full of seeds like raisins rolled to and fro on the seat, yet with eyeless sight those dead eyes saw it: his crucifix was slipping off, but he was conscious of it: the Homburg fell from his sombrero, slipped to the floor, and though making no attempt to pick it up, he obviously knew it was there. He was guarding himself against theft while gathering strength for more debauchery. In order to get into somebody else's cantina he might have to walk straight. His prescience was worthy of admiration.

Yvonne was enjoying herself. For the time being she was freed by the fact of Hugh's presence from the tyranny of thinking exclusively about him. The camion was traveling very much faster, rolling, swaying, jumping; the men were smiling and nodding, two boys, hanging at the back of the bus were whistling; and the bright shirts, the brighter serpentine confetti of tickets, red, yellow, green, blue, dangling from a loop on the ceiling, all contributed a certain sense of gaiety to their trip. They might have been going to a wedding.

But when the boys dropped off some of this gaiety departed. That predominance of purple in the men's shirts gave a disquieting glare to the day. There seemed something brutal to her too about those candelabra cactus swinging by. And about those other cactus, further away, like an army advancing uphill under machine-gun fire. All at once there was nothing to see outside but a ruined church full of pumpkins, caves for doors, windows bearded with grass. The exterior was blackened as by fire and it had an air of being damned. It was as though Hugh had left her again, and the pain of him slid back into her heart, momentarily possessing her.

Buses bobbed by in the other direction: buses to Tetecala, to Jujuta; buses to Xiutepec, to Xochitepec, to Xochitepec—

At a great pace they swerved into a side road. Popocatepetl appeared, off to the right, with one side beautifully curved as a woman's breast, the other jagged and ferocious. The drifted clouds were massing, high-piled, behind it.

Everyone felt at last that they were really going somewhere: they had become self-enclosed, abandoned to the tumultuous will of the vehicle.

They thundered on, passing little pigs trotting along the road, an Indian screening sand. Advertisements on ruined walls swam by. Atchis! Instantia! Resfria dos Dolores. Cafiaspirina. Rechaches Imitaciones. Las Manos de Orlac: con Peter Lorre.

When there was a bad patch the bus rattled ominously and sometimes they ran off the road. But its determination outweighted these waverings: all were pleased to have transferred their responsibilties to it, and to be lulled into a state from which it would be pain to awaken.

As a partner in this, it was with a freezing, detached calm that the Consul found himself able to think, as they bucked and bounded over an interminable series of teeth-rattling potholes, even of the terrible night which doubtless waited him, of his room shaking with daemonic ochestras, of the snatches of fearful sleep, interrupted by imaginary voices outside which were dogs barking, or by his own name being continually repeated with scorn by imaginary parties arriving.

The camion pitched and rolled on.

They spelt out the word *Desviación* but made the detour too quickly with a yelping of tires and brakes. As they swerved into alignment once more the Consul noticed a man apparently lying fast asleep under the hedge by the right side of the road.

Both Hugh and Yvonne appeared oblivious to this. Nor did it seem likely to the Consul that in this country anyone else was going to think it extraordinary a man should choose to sleep in the sun by the side of the road, or even in the middle of the road.

The Consul looked back again. No mistake. The man, receding quickly now, lay with his hat over his eyes, his arms stretched out toward a wayside cross. Now they were passing a riderless horse, munching the hedge.

The Consul leaned forward to call out but hesitated. What if it were simply an hallucination? This might prove very embarrassing. However he did call out, tapping the driver on the shoulder; almost at the same moment the bus leaped to a standstill.

Guiding the whining vehicle swiftly, steering an erratic course with one hand, the driver, who was craning right out of his seat watching the corners behind and before with quick yet reluctant turns of the head, reversed along the dusty detour.

There was the friendly, overpowering smell of exhaust gases tempered with the hot smell of tar from the repairs, though no one was at work on the road, everybody having knocked off, and there was nothing to be seen there, just the soft indigo carpet sparkling and sweating by itself. But a little further back, to one side by the hedge, was a stone cross and beneath it were a milk bottle, a funnel, a sock and part of an old suitcase.

Now they could see the man quite plainly, lying with his arms stretched out toward this wayside cross.

II

As the bus jerked to another stop the pelado almost slid from his seat to the floor but, managing to recover himself, not only reached his feet and an equilibrium he contrived remarkably to maintain, but in doing so had arrived half way to the door in one strong movement, crucifix fallen safely into place around his neck, hats in one hand, melon in the other. He nodded gravely and with a look that might have withered at its inception any thought of stealing them, placed the hats carefully on a vacant seat near the door, and with exaggerated care let himself down to the road. His eyes were still only half-open, preserving that dead glaze, yet there could be no doubt he had taken in the whole situation. Throwing away the melon he walked over toward the man in the road. Even though he stepped as if over imaginary obstacles his course was straight and he held himself erect.

Yvonne, Hugh, the Consul, and two of the passengers followed him. None of the old women had moved from their seats.

Half way across the road Yvonne gave a nervous cry, turning on her heel abruptly. Hugh gripped her arm.

"Are you all right?"

"Yes," she said, freeing herself, "Go on. It's just that I can't stand the sight of blood, damn it."

She was climbing back into the camion as Hugh came up with the Consul and the two passengers.

The pelado was swaying gently over the recumbent man.

Although the latter's face was covered by his hat it could be seen that he was an Indian of the peon class. There seemed no doubt that he was dying. His chest heaved like a spent swimmer's, his stomach contracted and dilated rapidly, yet there was no sign of blood. One clenched fist spastically thumped the dust.

The two foreigners stood there helplessly, each waiting for the other to remove the peon's hat, to expose the wound they all felt must be there, each checked from some such action by a common reluctance, an obscure courtesy. Each knew the other was also thinking it would be, naturally, even better still should the pelado or one of the passengers examine the man. But as nobody made any move Hugh became impatient. He shifted from foot to foot. He looked at the Consul with supplication. The Consul had been here long enough to know what could be done; moreover he was the one among them most nearly representing authority. But the Consul, who was trying to prevent himself saying, "Go ahead, after all, Spain invaded Mexico first," made no move either. At last Hugh could stand it no longer. Stepping forward impulsively he made to bend over the peon when one of the passengers plucked at his sleeve.

"Mistair, have you throw away your cigarette?"

"What!" Hugh turned around, astonished.

"I don't know," said the Consul. "Forest fires, probably."

"Better throw your cigarette, Senor. They have prohibidated it."

Hugh dropped his cigarette and stamped it out, bewildered and irritated. He was about to bend over the man once more when the passenger plucked his sleeve again. Hugh straightened up.

"They have prohibidated it, Senor," the other said politely, tapping his nose. He gave an odd little laugh. "Positivemente!"

"I no comprendo, gnadige Senor." Hugh tried desperately to produce some Spanish.

"He means you can't touch this chap because you'd be an accessory after the fact," nodded the Consul, beginning to sweat and wishing profoundly he could get as far away from this scene as possible, if necessary even by means of the peon's horse, to somewhere where great gourds of mescal crouched. "Leave well enough alone is not only the watchword, Hugh, it's the law."

The man's breathing and thumping was like the sea dragging itself down a stone beach.

Then the pelado went down on one knee and whipped off the dying man's hat.

They all peered over, seeing the terrible wound in the side of his head, the blood from which had almost coagulated, and before they stood back, before the pelado replaced the hat and, drawing himself erect, made a hopeless gesture with hands blotched with half dried blood, they caught a glimpse of a sum of money, four or five silver pesos and a handful of centavos, which had been placed neatly under the man's collar, by which it was partly obscured.

"But we can't let the poor fellow die," Hugh said despairingly, looking after the pelado as he returned to the bus, and then down once more at this life gasping away from them all. "We'll have to get a doctor."

This time from the camion, the pelado again made that gesture of hopelessness, which might have been also a gesture of sympathy.

The Consul was relieved to see that by now their presence had exampled approach to the extent that two peasants, hitherto unnoticed, had come up to the dying man, while another passenger was also standing beside the body.

"Pobrecito," said one.

"Chingarn," muttered the other.

And gradually the others took up these remarks as a kind of refrain, a quiet seething of futility, of whispers, in which the dust, the heat, the bus with its load of immobile old women and doomed poultry, even the terrible beauty and mystery of the country itself, seemed to be conspiring: while only these two words, the one of tender compassion, the other of fiendish contempt, were audible above the thudding and the gasping, until the driver, as if satisfied that all was now as it should be, began impatiently blowing his horn.

A passenger shouted to him to shut up, but possibly thinking the admonition was in jesting approval, the driver continued to blow, punctuating the seething, which soon developed into a general argument in which suspicions and suggestions cancelled each other out, to a heckling accompaniment of contemptuous blasts.

Was it murder? Was it robbery? Or both? The peon had ridden from the market with more than that four or five pesos, possibly he'd been in possession of mucho dinero, so that a good way to avoid suspicion of theft was to leave a little of the money, as had been done. Perhaps it was not robbery at all; he had only been thrown from his horse? The horse had kicked him? Possible? Impossible! Had the police been called? An ambulance—the Crux Roja? Where was the nearest phone? One of them, now, should go for the police? But it was absurd to suppose they were not on their way. How could they be on their way when half of them were on strike? They would be on their way all right, though. An ambulance? But here it was impertinent of a gringo to interfere. Surely the Red Cross were perfectly capable of looking after such a matter themselves? But was there any truth in the rumor that the Servicio de Ambulante had been suspended? It was not a red but a green cross and their business began only when they were informed. Perhaps it was imprudent of a gringo to assume they hadn't been informed? A personal friend, Dr. Vigil, why not call him? He was playing tennis. Call the Casino de la Selva then? There was no phone; oh, there was one once but it had decomposed. Get another doctor, Dr. Gomez. Un hombre noble. Too far, and anyhow, probably he was out; well, perhaps he was back!

At last Hugh and the Consul became aware that they had reached an impasse upon which the driver's horn still made a most adequate comment. Neither could presume, from the appearance of it, that the peon's fate was not being taken care of in some way 'by one of his own kind.' Well, it certainly didn't look as though his own kind had been any too generous to him! On the contrary, the same person who placed him at the side of the road, who placed the money in the peon's collar, was probably even now going for help!

These sentiments got up and knocked each other down again and although their voices were not raised, although Hugh and the Consul were not quarrelling, it was as if they were actually knocking each other down physically and getting up again, each time more weary than the last time down, each time with a practical or psychic obstruction toward cooperating or even acting singly, the most potent and final of all of which obstructions being that it was not their business at all but somebody else's.

Yet on looking around them they realized that this too was only what the others were arguing. It is not my business, nor yours, they said as they shook their heads, but someone else's, their answers becoming more and more involved, more and more theoretical, so that finally the discussion began to take a political turn.

To the Consul, time suddenly seemed to be moving at different speeds: the speed at which the peon was dying contrasting oddly with that at which everyone was arriving at the conclusion it was impossible to make up their minds. Aware that the discussion was by no means closed and that the driver, who had stopped blowing his horn, and was conversing with some of the women over his shoulder, would not think of leaving without first taking their fares, the Consul excused himself to Hugh and walked over to the Indian's horse, which, with its bucket saddle and heavy iron sheathes for stirrups, was calmly chewing the 'convolvulus' in the hedge, looking as innocent as only one of its species can when suspected even wrongfully of throwing its rider or kicking a man to death. He examined it carefully, without touching it, noticing its wicked, friendly, plausible eyes, the sore on its hipbone, the number seven branded on its rump, as if for some clue to what had happened. Well, what *had* happened? Parable of a too late hour! More important, what was going to happen—to them all? What was going to happen to him was that he was going to have fifty-seven drinks at the earliest opportunity.

The bus was hooting with real finality now that two cars were held up behind it; and the Consul, observing that Hugh was standing on the step of one of them, walked back shaking his head as the camion came toward him to stop at a wider part of the road. The cars, wild with impatience, thrust past and Hugh dropped off the second one. Bearing tin plates under their numbers with the warning 'Diplomático' they disappeared ahead in a cloud of dust.

"It's the diplomatic thing, doubtless," said the Consul, with one foot on the step of the camion. "Come on, Hugh, there's nothing we can do."

The other passengers were getting on board and the Consul stood to one side to talk to Hugh. The periodicity of the honking now had become much slower. There was a bored, almost amused resignation in the sound.

"You'll only be hauled into gaol and entangled in red tape for God knows how long," the Consul persisted. "Come *on*, Hugh. What do you think you're going to do?"

"If I can't get a doctor here, God damn it, I'll take him to one."

"They won't let you on the bus."

"The hell they won't! Oh—here come the police," he added, as three smiling vigilantes came tramping through the dust at that moment, their holsters slapping their thighs.

"No, they're not," the Consul said unfortunately. "At least, they're just from the policía de seguridad, I think. They can't do anything much either, just tell you to go away or—"

Hugh began to expostulate with them while the Consul watched him from the step of the camion apprehensively. The driver was wearily honking. One of the policemen began to push Hugh toward the bus. Hugh pushed back. The policeman drew back his hand. Hugh raised his fist. The policeman dropped his hand and began to fumble with his holster.

"Come on Hugh, for God's sake," the Consul pleaded, grasping him again. "Do you want to land us all in the gaol? Yvonne—"

The policeman was still fumbling with his holster when suddenly Hugh's face collapsed like a heap of ashes, he let his hands fall limply to his sides, and with a scornful laugh boarded the bus, which was already moving away.

"Never mind, Hugh," said the Consul, on the step with him, a drop of sweat falling on his toe, "It would have been worse than the windmills."

"What windmills?" Hugh looked about him, startled.

"No, no," the Consul said, "I meant something else, only that Don Quixote wouldn't have hesitated that long."

And he began to laugh.

Hugh stood for a moment cursing under his breath and looking back at the scene, the peon's horse munching the hedge, the police enveloped in the dust, the peon far beyond thumping the road, and now, hovering high above all, what he hadn't noticed before, the obvious cartoon birds, the xopilotes, who wait only for the ratification of death.

III

The bus plunged on.

Yvonne was flaccid with shame and relief. She tried to catch Hugh's eyes but he crammed himself into his seat so furiously she was afraid to speak to him or even to touch him.

She sought some excuse for her own behavior in the thought of the silent, communal decision of the old women to have nothing to do with the whole affair. With what sodality, scenting danger, they had clenched their baskets of poultry to them, or peered around to identify their property! Then they had sat, as now, motionless. It was as if, for them, through the various tragedies of Mexican history, pity, the impulse to approach, and terror, the impulse to escape (as she had learned at college), had been reconciled finally by prudence, the conviction it is better to stay where you are.

And the other passengers? The men in their purple shirts who had a good look at what was going on but didn't get out either? Who wanted to be arrested as an accomplice, they seemed to be saying to her now. Frijoles for all; Tierra, Libertad, Justicia y Ley. Did all that mean anything? Quién sabe. They were not sure of anything save that it was foolish to get mixed up with the police, who had their own way of looking at the law.

Yvonne clutched Hugh's arm but he did not look at her. The camion rolled and swayed as before, some more boys jumped on the back of the bus; they began to whistle, the bright tickets winked with their bright colors and the men looked at each other with an air as of agreement that the bus was outdoing itself, it had never before gone so fast, which must be because it too knew today was a holiday.

Dust filtered in through the windows, a soft invasion of dissolution, filling the vehicle.

Then they were at Chapultepec.

The driver kept his hand on the screaming emergency brake as they circled down into the town, which was already invested with the Consul's abhorrence because of his past excesses there. Popocatepetl seemed impossibly close to them now, crouching over the jungle, which had begun to draw the evening over its knees.

For a moment there was a sort of twilight calm in the bus. The stars were out now: the Scorpion had come out of its hole and waited low on the horizon.

The Consul leaned forward and nudged Hugh: "Do you see what I see?" he asked him, inclining his head toward the pelado, who had been sitting bolt upright all this time, fidgeting with something on his lap, and wearing much the same expression as before, though he was evidently somewhat rested and sobered.

As the bus stopped in the square, pitching Hugh to his feet, he saw that the pelado clutched in his fist a sad, blood-stained pile of silver pesos and centavos, the dying man's money—

The passengers began to crowd out. Some of them looked at the pelado, incredulous but always preoccupied. Grinning round at them he perhaps half hoped that some comment would be made. But there was no comment.

The pelado paid his fare with part of the bloodstained money, and the driver accepted it. Then he went on taking the other fares.

The three of them stood in the warm evening in the little zócalo. The old women had disappeared: it was as if they had been sucked down into the earth.

From a street near by the crashing, plangent chords of a guitar sounded. And from further away came the bangs and cries of the fiesta.

Yvonne took Hugh's arm. As they walked away they saw the driver, now ostensibly knocked off for the day, and the pelado, stepping high and with a fatuous smile of triumph on his face, swagger into a pulqueria. The three stared after them and at the name of the saloon, after its doors had swung shut: the Todos-Contentos-y-yo-Tambien.

"Everybody happy," said the Consul, the certainty that he would drink a million tequilas between now and the end of his life stealing over him like a benison and postponing for the moment the necessity for the first one, "Including me."

A bell somewhere compounded sudden wild triphthongs.

They moved in the direction of the fiesta, their shadows falling across the square, bending upward on the door of the Todos-Contentos-y-yo-Tambien, below which the bottom of a crutch had appeared.

They lingered curiously, noticing that the crutch rested for some time where it was, its owner having an argument at the door, or a last drink perhaps.

Presently, the crutch disappeared, as if it had been hoisted away. The door of the Todos-Contentos-y-yo-Tambien, through which they could see the bus driver and the pelado getting their drinks, was propped back; they saw something emerge.

Bent double and groaning with the weight, an old, lame Indian was carrying out another Indian, yet older and more decrepit, on his back, by means of a strap clamped to his forehead. He carried the older man and his crutches—he carried both their burdens—

They all stood in the dusk watching the Indian as he disappeared with the old man around a bend in the road, shuffling through the grey white dust in his poor sandals.

Ghostkeeper [1]

Alternate titles:

Henrik Ghostkeeper
Lost and Found
I Walk in the Park
But Who Else Walks in the Park?
O.K. But What Does it Mean?
Wheels Within Wheels

"What time is it, Tommy?"

"I don't know, sweetheart, have you forgotten I haven't got my watch now?"

"Do you remember the time we took the alarm clock on the picnic?"

"We should have brought the alarm clock along with us on our walk today."

"I guess it's about three. It was about quarter to when we left the apartment."

"Anyhow, we'll be able to see the clocktower in town when we get round the other side of the park."

The two figures, the man and his wife, continued their walk in Stanley Park, in Vancouver, British Columbia. To their right, people were playing tennis, though it was winter; in fact, to be precise, it was February 5, 1952. There was a fine rough wind, steel blue sea, mountains of rough blue serge topped with snow in the distance. The path they followed had the delicious sense of an English public footpath. Beyond the tennis courts there were dark pines and weeping willows, like fountains of gold thread, when the sun struck them, or bronze harp strings when it didn't. Here at sea level the snow

[1] This is not a "finished" story, it is a first draft, with notes.

had melted from the ground and early snowdrops were showing faintly under the trees. First they descended to a path that followed the seashore almost on shorelevel, just under the high bank of the park. There was much driftwood on the beach, evidence of winter storms. One cedar snag seemed scooped out by the sea, as if some Indians had started to make a war canoe out of it.

A woman, skirt tucked up, was sitting on a rock in the sun and wind. Someone, ahead of them, where the beach was less cluttered with driftwood, was even swimming, then running up and down the beach in the below freezing temperature. (The point of all this is a certain duality of appearance in the picture: which balances the duality within of the theme, and of existence. The picture was wintry, but it is also summery. This is like a nightmare, but it is also extremely pleasant.)

Stepping over winterbournes the man and his wife had to go up on the embankment again. A hoodlum went screeching by in a car: *threat*. The beach reminded the man of his birthplace, New Brighton, England, (if this can be done, because one theme is, or should be, rebirth.) At frequent intervals steps descended to the beach and a little further on they went down to the beach again. Above the trees were waving: a soft roaring of trees. Motionless gulls hung in a mackerel sky. The sea now was deserted: one barge, and a far cold lighthouse. (Note: somewhere: his grandfather had been named Henrik Goodheart, had gone down with his ship, a kind of Carlsen.)

And down there now, close under the bank, beneath the softly roaring pines, they found the wrecked boat. But what kind of a boat? On closer inspection it scarcely looked like a boat at all. Nearer, it looked like a wrecked paddlebox. Yet clearly, it was some sort of boat. Very narrow in the beam, blunt-nosed and blunt-sterned, about 15 feet long, no paint left on it, salt-grey, battered, pock-marked, and it seemed about a hundred years old. It must have weighed God knows how much. However would they launch such a thing even to lee? A tremendous bilge keel, or bilge piece on both sides was what made one think of a paddlebox. But this boat was like a solid block, built into the sand, with sand instead of a bottom. A bolted stalwart formidable bottomless hulk, though externally solid and sturdy. On the starboard side at the bow something had been carved: No. 1. For 16 persons. A F 13/2/45, it looked like. And beneath this had been recently written in chalk: H. Ghostkeeper. At this point a wandering Englishman came up, he was wearing dark glasses and was blind, or nearly blind. Some such conversation as this ensues:

"What is it?"

"It's a lifeboat, I think."

"Is it a clinker boat?"

"What's that?"

"The one with the laps." He puts his hands on the boat. "No, it's a carvel. What length is it? Has it got davit hooks?"

"Where would they be?"

"Down in the deadwood at each end. In the forepost and in the stern posts, if it's a lifeboat there'll be some gudgeons. Generally female gudgeons are on the stern post."

"Why female?"

"Because it's a round hole. The males have a long pintle on them."

"These numbers—would they be the date?"

"No, that'll be cubic capacity."

"Queer it doesn't have a name. Or a port of register."

"Well, it's a lifeboat all right."

Or it strikes me as an alternative idea that the Englishman, instead of being blind, should recognize him, saying "Haven't I seen you somewhere before, seen your picture in the paper?" It would then devolve that Tom Goodheart's column: *I Walk in the Park* is the Englishman's favorite column and the exposition can be easily handled in this way. But in any event, just as he is leaving, they ask him the time and he says: "That's funny, I lost my watch yesterday."

When he has gone Goodheart makes an entry in his notebook: Coincidence of the Englishman not having a watch either. The wreck: symbol of something, perhaps bad omen. Or worse—presage of some catastrophe, or death of someone. Then he adds: trouble is, I can't describe it. Once I would have longed to, and gone to endless trouble to find out about the wreck. Now I don't want to bother. How shall I describe it?

(Point is, Goodheart is sick to death of the daily grind of 500 words, wants to get out of the city and live in the country and do some creative writing, but can never manage to save up the money.)

Mem: bottle like a grebe below in the bay: the bottle almost had the iridescence of a bird's plumage: ethereal, sea-green, bobbing, swimming.

Mem: also the little turnstones, turning stones.

Mem: Perhaps begin the whole story with a suggestion of the ghostly ballet going on behind the blurred bon-amied windows on the old pier used by the Civic Repertory Theatre. Windows like store windows on the disused pier, though it has never been turned properly into a theatre and hasn't been used as a pier for 20 years. Packing cases standing about. In the office a notice, a picture of George V and a crown: Keep Calm and Carry On. The hall-echoing sound of an ill-turned cottage piano. The dimly seen whirling figures and the dismal echoing and trampling of feet.

Now they pass a man reading a Spiritualist newspaper, with a headline saying: Policemen Pursue Poltergeist.

If not use Englishman, then at this point anyhow we must have exposition, perhaps in dialogue between the Goodhearts. Goodheart is a large, bearded man, and is a columnist on a city paper whose column is entitled "I Walk in the Park." This is full of human interest stories or observations about nature, etc. and is very popular. Goodheart is extremely familiar with this park since he does indeed "walk in the park," to get most of his stories. Goodheart is an Englishman who has emigrated to Canada, his wife is an American, who doesn't think much of Canada and reminds Goodheart on every occasion that he is English. His wife, who is sympathetic in every other respect, and perhaps in this too, has no idea how she wounds Goodheart by these remarks, for her romantic teleologies are the reverse of his and directed toward Europe: for her, England and Europe are romantic and exciting, while to him, the European, it is the frontier, the wild country that is exotic and romantic. Goodheart has been trying to interest an American publisher in a book of short stories to be based on his feuilletons and has finally succeeded. But now, contrarily enough, he suddenly finds he can't write anything, his consciousness is at an agonized standstill; he can hardly write his column. This is at the time of Canada's beginning post war boom and prosperity, when the Canadian dollar has passed the American dollar in foreign exchange and Americans are taking more interest in Canada. But it is partly this very "boom" which is distressing Goodheart.

Meantime my protagonists have climbed up on the embankment again. Down below the wild ducks are rising and falling on the waves. Mary Goodheart is delighted with the pretty ducks and points them out: "Oh look, darling, scaups, golden eyes, and there's

even a pair of buffleheads! Do look!" But Goodheart is obsessed
with a sense of tragedy about the lifeboat. It was a sort of nothing,
yet it seemed ominous. A sense of something obsolescent, dead.

On the park embankment they are in the forest, and follow a
narrow footpath between the huge trees. A few lone men pass
them, walking, each with a cloud of smoke blowing over his shoulder, like little lone steamboats. Vancouver is full of lonely men like
this and they all go walking along the beach or through the forest
in Stanley Park.

Now Tommy Goodheart makes another note in his notebook:

Not sure he has any emotion at all about the lifeboat. Perhaps all
he wanted to do was to describe it. Something like a sort of
velleity of meaning is trying to possess him. Perhaps he felt like the
lifeboat. Were they like the lifeboat? What was like the lifeboat?
Was it a symbol of something, or just a lifeboat? To hell with it
anyway. Then he added: It was important not to have any fraudulent
sincerity about the lifeboat . . . as that fake Barzun calls it.

Out of the sky came a hushed roaring which was the trees. Now
above them the half moon appeared, and Goodheart made another
entry:

The afternoon half moon like an abstracted reading nun.

Trying to find an image for this moon gave Goodheart so much
trouble that he couldn't bear to look at it, and he walked on looking
at his feet.

Another man passes with an easel: smell of paints.

Mem: Flying Saucers must come in here: perhaps they pass a
man sitting on a bench reading the newspaper: and read over his
shoulder, or Mary does: "Vincent Vallach, 1266 Harber Street,
was on Strawberry Hill at 10:10 p.m. on Friday night. He saw a
spot on the moon, but it started moving across the face of it, and
then vanished straight up in the sky, with several other small dots
following."

Mrs. Goodheart must be placed as a tiny, pretty woman, all but
hidden in your sweet spooky grey costume, Margie dear. She is a
very sympathetic character if sometimes tactless, the two have a
fine relationship, and she is very interested in nature, flowers, and
particularly seabirds and wild ducks.

"A penny for them," Mary said, taking Tom's arm and shaking
it gently.

"I'm a Canadian writer, and that's tough."

"Nonsense. You're not a Canadian."

An argument now devolves, as another Englishman goes past, coatless, red-faced, wearing a loud checked vest, on Canada's origins. Mrs. Goodheart is cynical.

"After they'd conquered it from the Indians, they colonized it to a large extent by emptying the jails in England, and picking up the riffraff from the streets and shipping them out, though no Canadian would admit it now."

"Admit it!" Goodheart choked, then said, after a pause. "And what about Virginia?"

"Oh, it's true, to some extent, in America, but not so much. I read that article too, where somebody was very clever debunking the F.F.V.'s. But it doesn't mean what he says is entirely true, any more than all Canadians are descended from convicts."

Goodheart stopped dead for a moment, then said: "Do you know, you hurt me. I'm English. I'm Canadian. But I'm not descended from a convict."

"Oh Tom, how could you be when you just emigrated—"

"—And if I were descended from a convict and had been shipped out here—and how could I help it if I were—I would resent it."

"So far as I can tell, most Canadians resent the English, no matter how sentimental they may be about England."

Goodheart tried to follow the logic of this, then said: "I know it doesn't mean anything to you, but to me being an Englishman is a serious matter."

"But you always say you're Canadian now—"

"This is absurd! But for me, it's tragic too."

"Ah, tragedy. Why must there always be tragedy?"

"What are we talking about? I'm not English. I'm not Canadian. I am a British Columbian. Ever since I was a kid and collected stamps I have been in love with British Columbia. It had it's own stamp once. And I made up my mind to come here, and here I am. I do not recognise confederation. I deplore American influence. But I also deplore Canadian influence. I am unique, the only British Columbian in British Columbia! Keep Calm and Carry on," he added.

They laughed and kissed. They had very tender feelings toward each other and did not pursue this ridiculous argument. He made another note as they walked along:

Perhaps moon is omen too.

They came to Siwash Rock: a lonely storm beaten pine tree in the rock, beards of grass. He feels an empathy for the lone tree.

Gulls are sailing high. Scoters and scaups in the water below. Higher up, on a topped pine, was a kind of tree house, a loggers' contraption or a look out perhaps.

"Shall we sit down?"

"For God's sake let us sit upon the ground—" Goodheart said.

But the seat was wet and they walked on. (Perhaps there is a crash, they look round, and the loggers' tree house has fallen bang on to the bench where they thought of sitting.)

Then they came to Prospect Point.

Latitude: 49° 18' 51"

Longitude: 123° 08' 24"

Above Sea Level: 220 ft.

—— Crown Mountain: 4,931 ft. 7 miles.

—— Goat Mountain: 4,587 ft. 6.75 miles.

—— Grouse Mountain: 3,974 ft. 5.08 miles.

—— Second Narrows: 5:45 miles.

Far below an oiltanker, seemingly as long as the park, is sailing by endlessly into Vancouver. With the scarlet and white paintwork all tiddley, her flags flying, it was like an entire promenade in summer in, say New Brighton, gliding by silently, bandstands, ham and egg walks, flagstaffs and all.

They walked on, through a neck of forest and out into a cleared space. A sign read: *Bears. Rose Garden. Pavilion. Garden of Remembrance. Children's Zoo.* Nearly all the trees in the park were topped, giving them a queer bisected look. A heron, antefiluvian, meditated aloft upon one topped tree. Mandarin ducks, as if constructed out of sheets of tin or metal, that fitted into one another, painted with gold, sat about on the grass. Peacocks drowsed in the trees. Squirrels ran about. Pigeons feeding from people's hands. A tame dove. A sense of something unearthly, heavenly here, like Paradise in a Flemish painting. Pilgrims wandering here and there among the trees.

Mem: Important: Use Margie's note here about the young Frenchman and his watch. (This note follows)

"—Pardon, but would you like to buy my watch?"

He was very young, 19 or 20, tall, thin, blond with hazel or yellow eyes and a meticulously shaven fresh bright face; his smile was clear as a child's except for a certain faint humorous wry curl at the corner of his rather wide but beautifully cut mouth, above a chin that was almost feminine but not weak. His gaze was direct, candid and sparkling. One liked this boy at once. He wore a belted tan raincoat, of a silky texture, that didn't look very warm. It was a cold frosty day with a rough cold wind, the already low sun was a freezing blurred orange and here, at the waterfront, the streets and the bay were dim and opalescent with cold evening mist. He pushed up his sleeve and showed us a beautiful and expensive gold Swiss watch. Malc, a bit taken aback between his desire to help, lack of money, and imaginative sensitiveness, gave me a swift, baffled, imploring blank look. I said quickly:

"I wish we could, but we're rather broke ourselves this week."

"Next week," said Malc, giving him a beautiful warm smile, which the boy returned, "we'll have some money, but by then, I—"

"Next week," the boy shrugged, "I cannot wait so—"

"Of course, you need it now."

"It is a good watch. I bought in Paris."

"You're French—"

"Oui."

"Le prochain demain—"

"Ah! Vous parlez Français!"

"Oui. Un peu."

"Ah—" His face glowed.

"We were in Paris—how long, Margie?"

"Four years ago. We were there over a year." An instant's silence, then:

"It is a good country, France."

"We love it."

"I am not long in Canada. I am—new."

"You are an immigrant, you are going to stay here, in Canada?" I said.

"Pardon?—Ah, oui. I am immigrant. I shall stay. I have been working in a camp, but is closed, when after the New Year I go back."

"Oh, a logging camp."

"Pardon?—Ah oui. They are logs. But I cannot get your insurance for not employment until I am 3 weeks not employed."

"What will you do?"

"Oh, I will sell my watch." A light Gallic shrug. "And then I will be O.K."

"But what a pity!"

Another shrug. Yes it was sad, but then—

We all shook hands warmly. Good luck! Thank you. We admired the watch. One didn't—couldn't—feel any pathos in this, he was obviously too full of adventure and youth and a sort of wry yet open-hearted joyous, light-hearted, casual, Gallic, resigned, active happiness. Off he went, and we the other way.

They walked back to Lost Lagoon through a sort of inside zoo. This on the contrary was a sort of hell. Songbirds in cages. An owl gave a pathetic mew. A hamster, like a minute chipmunk, worked a toy mill furiously in the corner, though he stopped when he thought anyone was watching him. An anteater, with elephant head and long suede nose, in which were shoe-button eyes, walking on the backs of its hands, with a raccoon coat and stuff tail like the backbone of a fish.

"I can't bear to look at that," said Mary Goodheart; but Tom made a mysterious note:

Could get anteater at home. Why go out? Perhaps while he is doing that he returns an almost blind man's watch. The man had been winding it and it had fallen out of his hands and Goodheart picked it up and returned it almost absently, though perhaps he didn't notice the time. But he was thinking of how different this would all look soon, in spring, and the pathetic love of the anteaters for each other.

Then they emerged on the right side of Lost Lagoon. Ducks against neon lights coming in downmoon to taxi, sunsetwards, in Lost Lagoon. An advertisement for Segovia. An advertisement for The Town Crier. (Tom's paper) Platinum street lamps bloomed. They walked along the edge of the lagoon, remote from the town, into the sunset behind the gold thread of the weeping willows, beyond which was the shore where they had started out for their walk. They kept trying to avoid pools left by the recently melted snow. A man came up behind them and squelched right through the pools, wearing sea-boots whose white tops were turned down, looking neither left nor right. To their left, as the day deepened, the ducks were preparing to turn in for the night. Some like sailing ships blown too near a coast in a sou-wester already had their beaks nestled in their plumage. Two little buffleheads—spirit ducks —were doing a little last minute hunting. And a harmless muskrat cruised peacefully beneath the bank and when they stooped down begged like a puppy. Sense of love between the Goodhearts. But also sense of loneliness; of Goodheart, his sense of isolation, partly occasioned by his being an Englishman, from other human beings. Their feeling of love for the ducks. The ducks are indeed their only real companions in British Columbia. There is a notice: *Do Not Molest the Ducks.* The coots, ivory-billed, squat, awkward and raucous, make a noise like twanging guitar strings (Segovia tuning his guitar), they jerk along, while the mallards sweep easily to their berths. It was touching to see the ducks here, safe and protected in the lagoon, and they wondered how many had come in from the sea where they'd been feeding this afternoon, or were the ones they'd seen earlier. The wind was dropping now at sunset and became a cool, cold, sweet, wet wind. There would be rain tonight, Mary said, sniffing the wind.

The pear-shaped lagoon now narrowed to a kind of rustic canal or neck that connected with the shipless bay beyond, bridged by little arched rustic bridges, exquisitely beautiful. There were still a few chunks of snow to the right in a gulch. A tossed bicycle, like a freak of crumpled ice, pedals, sprockets, by the edge of the lagoon. In this narrower part of the lagoon a whole fleet of ducks were sailing. A magic tin Mandarin duck in the sunset light. On the opposite bank beneath the willows, against the sunset, three children were standing like a threat. Mary was feeding peanuts to the ducks. It took Goodheart some little time to understand why the children had seemed to him like a threat, which was the word that had instantly come to mind. But then he realised they were doing something inconceivable. They had suddenly started to throw stones at the massed ducks.

There were two boys, one short and rather stout—but on the other side of the water, some 20 feet away—one thin and lanky, and a tall girl with red hair wearing blue jeans rolled up to the ankle, none looking more than 15. And they were throwing stones at the ducks, massed as for a regatta. The fat boy was skimming stones, and the tall one was throwing them very high, and as he watched one dropped on a duck's back; the poor things skimmed and flew in every direction. Bloody murder was in Goodheart's heart but he found he could only gulp and it was his wife who spoke.

"You boys!" she was saying, "How dare you throw stones at the ducks!"

"Aw."

"Stop it at once!"

"Aw, we just want to see them fly."

"How would you like it if people threw stones at you, just to see you run?"

"Aw, we've heard that one before."

Goodheart was so upset that he was tongue-tied. Anguish trees stood about the suicide lake, apprehension bushes were dotted here and there; and a fear wind rushed through him, depriving him of speech. And that all these emotions were vastly in excess of the situation, which merely demanded a few stern fatherly words—but words which he couldn't deliver—made his anguish worse than ever by frustrating him. A car's horn pealed like cathedral bells for a funeral. Then he just stood there feeling himself simply like an old buttoned up overcoat. But meantime, though more aimlessly, the boys went on throwing stones at the ducks. Finally he said:

"Don't you know it's illegal to throw stones at the ducks? Can't you read that sign?"

Flop! For answer the tall boy skied a stone that landed near a mallard and would have killed it had it not missed.

"Aw, we're not hurting them."

"Then what are you throwing stones at them for?" Goodheart heard his overcoat speaking.

"We just want to see them flyyyyy," the boys sneered.

"And anyway, what's it to do with you, you old bastard," the red haired girl asked sotto voce; the question was followed by giggles.

"If you don't stop throwing stones I'll have you run in, you, taller one," shouted Goodheart, suddenly losing his temper. He did not like being called an old bastard, for he was not old, but perhaps his beard was at fault.

"One more stone and I'll get a policeman," Mary said, shaking with fury. "I won't have anyone hurting the ducks!"

"Aw, go wonn . . ."

"And I'm well known in this town . . ." Goodheart hardly knew what he was saying, "I'm on a newspaper . . ."

"Beaver!" they shouted at him. "Beaver!"

They really stopped throwing stones at the ducks, though they pretended to go on skimming them for a while. Mr. and Mrs. Goodheart now deployed to the right slightly in order to cross the Japanese bridge which brought them abreast of the boys on the same side of the water, Goodheart looking through the trees, trying to make his overcoat appear menacing, and himself like a policeman. As the children sidled away Goodheart threw after them:

"God will punish you for this." (I think there should be an almost Laurentian analysis here, unsentimental, un-SPCA, of what such cruelty *feels* like: it was as if they were throwing stones at them, at their own love, their home, a feeling of "But they don't *understand*.")

Mary Goodheart began to laugh at her husband's portentousness, and so did Tom Goodheart, though a tear had run down his face and in fact they were very upset and hesitant which route to take (for they truly loved the ducks) in case the children should return: whether to continue this path till it crossed the bridle path that came to the stables, or walk through the miniature golf course: either way would bring them back to their apartment. They go by the bridle path and Mrs. Goodheart finds the watch.

(Mem: seagull roosting in the crotch of a tree: Tchekov's Seagull—and coincidence and tragic coincidence of this.)

Description of the watch: it seems a very good man's watch, gold, and still running. In fact it said quarter past six. The boys seemed ruled out. There was a boy now walking behind them. Psychological attitude towards watch: Goodheart had no watch (he'd lost his last one and couldn't afford another), also this is a valuable watch, a wristwatch with the clasp broken. The watch had a name on the back though it was difficult to see beneath the trees in the declining day. Goldkipfer, Goalkeeper, it looked like. But it is a man's watch and they do not connect it with the children. As they reach the street:

"Well, we can wait and see if there's an advertisement for it in tomorrow night's paper. Or tomorrow morning. Then, if nobody puts an advertisement in, you've got a watch."

It was certainly a temptation. Moreover the watch was clearly worth $100.

"Oughtn't *we* to put an advertisement in the paper?" Goodheart said.

"We can't afford to. We haven't got five dollars to pitch away on an advertisement. If anybody wants it back enough they'll advertise."

"And you mean that we should hang on to the watch? Isn't that being a bit unscrupulous? By gad, aren't you a bit of a hypocrite, Mary. Here a while ago you were accusing us Canadians to being criminals and now you're proposing to steal a watch."

"Steal it! Must you exaggerate everything?"

A minor quarrel ensues, during which Goodheart feels that he's being a bit of a hypocrite because it had been in his mind to keep the watch himself and even perhaps pawn it, which would have temporarily gotten him out of a hole.

Outside their apartment door the Vancouver Town Crier is waiting for them on the floor in the hall. And inside there is a dramatic moment when, in the better light, they see the name on the watch is Henrik Ghostkeeper.

Then, though it seems a bit absurd to do so, they leaf through the Crier looking at the Lost and Found . . . Mr. Haythornthwaite asked in the legislature what the government intended to do to prevent "use of the knout by mounted cossacks on peaceful residents of Vancouver and to protect constitutional rights to peaceable assemblage and free speech." But that was forty years ago. (Now such things were unknown: that is to say free speech was almost unknown, and of course they order twenty strokes of the lash instead of the knout.)

Under a heading What Right? Mother of Two asked:

May a Vancouver-born mother tell "Irish" just what she thinks of a so-called "uncivilized Easterner?" We think the majority of complaining, boasting, insulting people we have in Vancouver must be Easterners. How dare he call our children monsters? Perhaps "Irish" has had the misfortune to run up against one or two badly behaved children. But just what right does that give him to call our children monsters? Mother of Two.

And that was today all right.

Bill Kath and family gone. Am very sick, all alone. Please come and see me, Skinny. And that was today too, but not in the lost column, or not the right kind of Lost. But here it was: a twelve foot discharge hose with down pipe and coupling, lost, a brindle bulldog with red harness, a female Boxer pup (anyone harboring after Feb 15 will be prosecuted), a front pillar shaped piece of wardrobe 5 ft long, and a wine bedroom slipper, lost between bus terminal and Richards. And no less than three watches reported lost.

Lady's gold oblong wristwatch, gold expansion bracelet, lost in Woodward's dept. store Friday. Reward. FA 3411R.

Lady's Bulova watch inscribed "Vida" Saturday night. Reward. TA 2221.

And another watch lost in their neighborhood cinema theatre, the Bay Theatre. Apart from that the only thing of interest was that Segovia had objected to a publicity story that a guitar he was playing in Coblenz had broken at the exact moment that it's maker had died in Granada.

But the name on the watch, Ghostkeeper, caused Goodheart to recall the name Ghostkeeper carved on the wreck, and also to recall that the Englishman who'd spoken to them by the wreck had also mentioned that he'd lost his watch. A certain terror also was occasioned by the name, Ghostkeeper. Goodheart privately decides if he returned the watch it will take the curse off the name. Goodheart now decides to try and telephone. So he looks in the telephone book for the strange name, meanwhile remarking the names he encounters are anything but English, save for his own, though it is important that the real reason he is phoning is a compassionate one: he has now decided, from the small span of the strap as it is clasped, that the owner must be a child. But Ghostkeeper was an unlikely name: but then so are these other names unlikely. So was Goodheart.

Zsomber, Zingg, Zero, Pe (Ralph G.) Poffenroth, Peckinpaugh, Pennycuick, Stilborn, Soderroos, Overho, Ovens, Snowball, Shelagh, Snodgrass, Smuck, Smout (he has ceased really looking, being fascinated by these names), Smook, Smitten, Stojcic, Shish, Order of Perceptive Praetorians, Orangecrush, Goodheart, Golf, Goggin, Goranko, Gooselaw, Gathercole—but here we were:

> Ghostkeeper, Sigrid, Mrs. r 4942 Ruby. DExter 1576 R.
> Ghostkeeper, B. H. r 3655 W. 2nd. CEdar 7762.

He phones the second Ghostkeeper and this part is dramatised much as it happened, i.e., it is a female voice, who disclaims any ownership of the watch, but says that the Ghostkeepers must all be related, and that she has read in the paper that a Mrs. Ghostkeeper has "arrived from the east with her small boy". (Mem: this ties in with "Mother of Two.")

Before he phones the second Ghostkeeper they examine the watch again and Mary agrees that the owner must be a child. Suddenly it is as if Goodheart realises for the first time that perhaps the owner of the watch really was the child who had been throwing stones at the duck, or one of the children, which is a dramatic moment, and he remembers how he has said portentously God will punish you. But Mary now says no, it is far too expensive a watch to be entrusted to a young child. Then Tom thinks well, damn it, it may be a girl.

Now they look at the watch: lilliputian universe, jewelled orrery, minuscule planetarium, it now said quarter past seven. And Mary remarked how its very compact, very busy, very efficient, in a fussy kind of way: so important, miniscule order, dragging along time with it. (mem: work in ambiguous word *escapement* which is also part of a watch) It is a 21 jewel watch, comes from the U.S., not Canadian at all. Perhaps it belonged to yet another Ghostkeeper, an American, who'd come across the border . . . But the real point is, as they open it, that the reader feels that is the *thing,* the machine—

So now Goodheart rings up the first Ghostkeeper, Sigird, who turns out also a woman, but who sounds somewhat older. This conversation is dramatised, as it occurred, punctuated by Mrs. Goodheart's interpolations from the kitchen, where she is getting dinner —"Don't tell them what kind of watch it is—" "Don't tell *them,* you ninny—" "Make them tell *you*—"

But the scene should be beautifully funny and so unlikely that it has the unerring stamp of truth, viz: the husband is deaf. The woman is obviously not the widow with the small child, but a watch *is* involved here. The woman has to keep leaving the phone to relay the conversation to her husband, whose name is, to confound matters worse still, Henrik Ghostkeeper. This man says that there is yet another Ghostkeeper to whom he has given a watch when he was overseas. He had it overseas, says Mrs. Ghostkeeper, but he gives the impression that this other Ghostkeeper is about 19.

Goodheart says he feels the owner is a child, which is why he's rung up, for the child must be grieving, or even being punished. Goodheart is now reproaching himself for not having walked back to the children with the watch, he feels now that one of the children is the owner, and had he done so it would have been both more dramatic and more of a lesson, should he have said: "Is there anyone here by the name of Henrik Ghostkeeper?" "Yes, that's me." "Have you lost anything? I told you not to throw stones at the ducks." And then to have returned the watch. How salutory that would have been!

But it is relayed via the deaf Ghostkeeper that his nephew's name *is* Henrik Ghostkeeper, so Goodheart is convinced that he has his man, though his picture of him is a pretty weird one, that of an attenuated or hypertrophied unman of nineteen who had apparently been fighting overseas at the age of 12.

"Does he have a phone?"

"No, I don't think so. But there's a phone in the house."

"Can you get hold of them then."

Mrs. Ghostkeeper promises to find the nephew and have him call the Goodhearts. Tom leaves his address and phone number and Mrs. Ghostkeeper tells them that the nephew lives at 33 E. 7th St.

There now follows a slight description of the scene outside our apartment: the terricular solid house opposite, now an hotel, sense of old order changeth, and—it is snowing lightly again—the chicken croquettes covered with powdered sugar in the blooming lamplight, the antediluvian monkey tree that still kept up its liaison with the prehistoric era. This little realistic beautiful description possibly combined with a description of the scene through the Venetian blinds with the street lamps and the snow is important contrast.

The Goodhearts now decide to try and discover the phone number of 33 E. 7th. They do so, but whoever answers the phone disclaims all knowledge of the Ghostkeepers. In fact they're irritated, and suspect some sort of joke.

The Goodhearts are now slightly fed up by the whole thing so after dinner they seek relaxation at their local cinema, the Bay, where there is an English film playing called The Magnet. They greet the box office girl and manager as neighbours and good acquaintances.

But as soon as they enter the cinema Tommy Goodheart thinks he has gone to the next world, is having a dream within a dream, or suffering from some extraordinary hallucination.

For the scene before his eyes seems at first to be the very scene along the beach this afternoon, then he realises that the scene is taking place in New Brighton, his own birthplace, on the sands where he played as a boy. And the scene that is playing is that which deals with the exchange of the invisible watch!

There follows a short description of the film which is continually interrupted—for Mary Goodheart—by Tommy saying "There's the cathedral! That's Seacombe pier! That's New Brighton pier! There used to be a tower only they knocked it down. That's the old prom —called that the Ham and Egg Parade. Birkenhead Ales, my God! That's the place where I saw the Lion-faced Lady. The tunnel had not quite been completed when I left England though it was already in use," etc. Finally they stand up while the recording of God Save the King plays.

But the kid imagining that he is being chased by the cops about the magnet has given Goodheart a sense of guilt about having pretended to be a cop to the kids this afternoon in the park and he wonders if his harshness has frightened them. He has now more or less ceased to think that the wristwatch actually belongs to one of these children—unless for purposes of a hypothetical short story for his column—because of the second Ghostkeeper's story but he now is possessed by a purely humane feeling and anxiety to return the watch that he feels is valuable to its owner. And there is something pathetic about the watch ticking away in the kitchen. It is like a symbolic band or nexus relating him to humanity.

Mrs. Goodheart is tired and goes to bed when they return, but Goodheart finds his consciousness and inspiration seething to the boiling point where he thinks, "Well, now I really can write! What a marvellous story this is, right under my nose," etc. etc. So he gets pencil and paper and in a frenzy of inspiration sets down to write. First, out with all subjectivity, and tell the story just as it happened, or rather the story, just as it has not yet completely happened. But what happens to him as he tries to write is peculiar. He had been worrying himself sick over lack of material, but now he finds he had far too much. (Perhaps the earlier part of this in dialogue, excitedly and enthusiastically to Mary.)

Nor was it that exactly. Every journalist works on a basis of a plethora of material and selects from it, and he himself had long disciplined himself to turning out his 500 words a day. Moreover the short story writers he admired most, the early Flaherty, Tchekhov, Sodeborg, Jensen, Pontoppidan, the Irishman James Stern, Herman Bang, Flaubert in his tales, Maugham, Pyeskov, Kataev, even one or two of Faulkner's, James Thurber, Bunin, Saroyan, Hoffmanstal, the author of Job, God knows who, all these writers, even if they did not always succeed, aimed at economy of words. (Mem: find early poem of Conrad Aiken's about a watch and quote from it.) Even Joseph Conrad, hard though it evidently was for him, leaned over backwards to try and keep things ship shape. But here Goodheart found himself confronted with something different, something wholly unprecedented in his experience of "plethora of material." His first instinct was to cut the first part of their walk this afternoon altogether, and start at the pond in the sunset light. Lex Talionis would be, he thought, a good title for the story. Boy stones ducks. Man warns boy, tells him he'll be punished. Man finds watch. Man discovers, roundabout, that watch is property of boy—though this would be swinging the lead for it obviously wouldn't prove so in fact—man returns watch. Boy has lesson. God moves in a mysterious way, would be the moral and the result a concise heartwarming little story. But in how much more a mysterious way did God, if it was God—oh God!—seem to move in fact? (All this ties in with the kaleidoscope of life, the complexity, flying saucers, the impossibility of writing good short stories.) For where did Ghostkeeper come in? Perhaps he wouldn't be able to use the name Ghostkeeper at all, which was an uncommon name, just as he wouldn't be able to use his own name Goodheart, that was too much like Pilgrim's Progress. But without the name Ghostkeeper, where was the point of the story, even though it was the name Ghostkeeper that seemed to deprive it of all point. But what was the relation between the owner of the watch and the name on the wreck? Why should the Englishman he'd spoken to by the wreck have lost his watch too? And what was the relation between this and the watch he'd restored to the blind man by the anteater's cage? Why had the wreck seemed a bad omen, and then the tree house had to fall on the seat where the two of them, but for sheer luck, might have been sitting at that moment, which suggested a kind of "On borrowed time" theme. And what was the relation between all these watches in general and the invisible watch in the movie, and why did the movie have to be set in New Brighton which was his birthplace when he had been thinking of his birthplace this afternoon, just prior to having seen the children. And the French boy who wanted to sell *his* watch. And now he thought of a thousand other things. In fact, no sooner did poor Goodheart come to some sort of decision as to what line his story should take than it was as if a voice said to him: "But you see, you can't do it like that, that's not the meaning at all, or rather it's only one meaning—if you're going to get anywhere near the truth you'll have twenty different plots and a story no one will take." And as a matter of fact this was sadly true. For how could you write a story in which its main symbol was not even reasonably consistent, did not even have consistent ambiguity? Certainly the watch did not seem to mean the same thing consistently. It had started by being a symbol of one thing, and ended up—or rather had not yet ended up—by being a symbol of something else. And how after all could you expect the story to mean anything without at least using the name Ghostkeeper. But even as he set down the name Ghostkeeper in desperation, it was as if he seemed to see or hear yet another Ghostkeeper, sitting as it were half way up in the air like Ezekiel's wheel, smiling broadly and saying: "Wheels within wheels, Mr. Goodheart," or again, "Wheels within wheels within wheels my dear Mr. Goodheart." Yes, and controlling the escapement. (Perhaps some of this is a little previous and should take place the next day when the story has further developed.)

Finally Goodheart is so confused that he decides there's nothing to do but wait and see how the story develops in real life—for one thing the very material world seems against him, table rattling, etc. —and tired to death but still unable to sleep he goes to bed and tries to read himself into somnolence with an article in the Town Crier entitled British Columbia, Province of Mysteries. "Never," he read, "has any place had a tighter tie-up with the supernatural. From the Yukon border to Washington, from the Rockies to the coast, we found them . . . tales that would make the stoutest heart beat faster . . ." etc. etc. Tales that would make the stoutest watch run faster. There was even a little filler about watches: "Finely engraved watches were made in the shape of skulls, little books, octagons, crosses, purses, dogs, and sea-shells in olden days.

The next morning Goodheart, despite good resolutions to get up early etc. is very tired, gets up late, finds his wife cleaning house, finds watch has stopped at 10 o'clock, so he winds it up again. Nothing is wrong with the watch and it begins ticking merrily. It is a mild cloudy way, the night's snow already melted and outside the shadow of smoke, as if from a steamer's funnel on deck (actually from their own apartment chimney) was pouring somewhat menacingly over the green lawn before the chicken croquettes, streaming over the lawn and flowing up the monkey tree. Finally he goes out to buy some cigarettes and post a letter for his wife. First thing he sees is that all flags are at half mast. Then buying cigarettes he sees the headlines at the news stand: The King is Dead. He feels shocked, and after a while something like crying. He does not however buy the paper, since he's waiting for it to be delivered at the apartment. Death of King makes him very melancholy. Then he remembers that last night in the Bay Theatre was a historic occasion, the last time God Save the King was sung. He wanders along the promenade: he glances at the octopus and the piteous horrible wolf eel: people are still rehearsing on the pier, the ghostly ballet behind the bon-amied windows. Somebody swimming. People still playing tennis despite the cold. But all the time he seems to be hearing the ghostly voice saying, "Do you remember yesterday, when you said, For God's sake let us sit upon the ground and tell—" Strange stories of the death of kings. Wheels within wheels, Mr. Goodheart. Deciding against having another look at the octopus in the aquarium he goes back to the apartment where the Town Crier has arrived with the news of the death of the King.

Mary is very sympathetic about the death of the King. In the paper however it says that the King has died about 10 o'clock. This reminds Goodheart of something else, though he can't remember what it is. (Of course it is that the wristwatch has stopped at ten o'clock, which he remembers later), but all it now suggests is Segovia—perhaps this in dialogue—the story about Segovia in yesterday's paper which he has forgotten and he hunts all through yesterday's paper looking for the bit about Segovia which he feels he should put in his story but can't find it, meantime feeling he's going completely cuckoo. Then they look at tonight's paper again, and feel gloomy with its report of people—the King's neighbours and friends—already in mourning clothes. "Queen Mother Elizabeth and Princess Margaret remained in seclusion during the day. At dusk, as rain began to fall, lights burned in only one room of the house." Then he looks out of the window and sees a newsboy passing with the headline: *"Long Live Queen Elizabeth."*

This suggested to Goodheart that writer or not, he was now an Elizabethan and he thought that this remark: "Writer or not, nothing could prevent Gooselaw Goggins from being an Elizabethan," would make a good end to the story, so he made a note to that effect, feeling more cuckoo than ever. Then suddenly he remembered the watch again and looked in the Lost section of Wednesday's paper.

There was no report of flying saucers in today's paper, though there was a guarded editorial warning against guided missiles, something about "braced for disaster," and "well balanced people," and "the situation calls for a little pulling up of reason's socks." And "Almost every age has seen things in the sky it could not explain."

In the Lost and Found, the same black and white cat, part Persian, was missing; the same wine bedroom slipper remained lost between the bus terminal and Richards Street, the same front pillar shaped piece of wardrobe 5 feet long was missing, nor had the one 12 ft 2 inch discharge hose lost off Harrington Motors tank truck between Boston Bar and Vancouver yet been recovered. The other watches were still missing, and so was the wallet or watch reported missing in the local theatre, the Bay, where he'd seen the film about New Brighton and the invisible watch. But here it was:

> Man's Gold Bulova wrist watch
> vicinity Riding Academy, Stanley
> Park, Fairmost 1869. Reward.

Goodheart now phones this number, and the exchange is dramatised as it happened. The phone is answered by a girl, who laughs excitedly, "Mummy, I think they've found the watch," and then by another woman.

Their conversation is important, you must help me, Margie, with it, but I can't see quite how to dramatise it at the moment. Goodheart does not want to speak to the woman, thinks that he should talk to the watch's owner. Her description of the watch with Henrik Ghostkeeper engraved on it is perfectly correct however: on the other hand Mrs. Ghostkeeper insists that the owner is a minor, "I'm his mother and have to handle all this for him," etc. Goodheart is now convinced that he has found the owner of the watch at last and moreover now feels sure for some reason, though it is a million to one chance, and though it contradicts what the other Ghostkeeper said, that the boy actually is the boy, one of the boys, who had been throwing stones at the ducks but feeling somewhat exhausted by this time he turns the telephone over to Mary.

"Tell her to bring the boy with him," he says, "so he can see who we are."

"Why?"

"So that he can see we're the people who told him not to throw stones at the ducks."

It is decided she will come about seven, and try to bring the boy. For some reason the King's death has made Goodheart feel ten times more isolated and lonely than ever. At the same time the solemn stately occasion makes him feel very formal, even prefectorial, and he dresses very carefully, putting on his old school tie. What is worrying him now is how to make plain to the boy the lesson about the ducks. On the other hand this has to be done subtly without letting the mother know, for ethically speaking it would be unsporting to give away the boy in front of his mother. In any case the death of the King seems to have called forth an added obligation to behave in every way like a very chivalrous Englishman indeed. But at the same time Goodheart is furiously making up further endings for his story. One of these was somewhat sinister: They would refuse the reward. "No, no. You can buy us a drink some time." "I will. I'll be seeing you," said Mrs. Ghostkeeper, and as she and her child departed a tree fell on them.

This scene of Goodheart dressing carefully for this interview should be done realistically and is important and should be exciting for the very good reason that although this is simply a short story, Goodheart so far as I can see is in the kind of *philosophical* situation (although on one plane it is absurd) of the highest dramatic order. That this situation must be in some sense a universal one (even though it is not generally recognised) is what I count on to provide the excitement. What we need too—or rather therefore—is not merely imagination, but hard boiled logical thinking. If this logical thinking is as good as the reasoning in one of your detective stories, Margie, it should more than suffice. In any case Goodheart is now standing *within the possibilities* of his own story and of his own life—something like Sigbjorn in relation to the Volcano, though this is both more complex and of course less serious. The point seems to be that all these possibilities, of his story (as of his own life) wish in some way to fulfil themselves, but what makes it terrifying is that the mind or intelligence that controls these things, or perhaps does not control them, is outside Goodheart and not within. If this intelligence (that which *we* mean when we say "they're on the job") the *name* Henrik Ghostkeeper is the symbol. In himself (or themselves) of course Ghostkeeper is many things at once, and many persons, including a child, and so is incomprehensible to human thought. Perhaps what happens is something like this. The minute an artist begins to try and shape his material—the more especially if that material is his own life—some sort of magic lever is thrown into gear, setting some celestial machinery in motion producing events or coincidences that show him that this shaping of his is absurd, that nothing is static or can be pinned down, that everything is evolving or developing into other meanings, or cancellations of meanings quite beyond his comprehension. There is something mechanical about this process, symbolized by the watch: on the other hand the human mind or will or consciousness or whatever, of which the owner knows nothing, at all yet which has a will of its own, becomes automatically at such moments in touch as it were with the control tower of this machinery. (This brings me to Ortega—"A man's life is like a work of fiction, that he makes up as he goes along: he becomes an engineer for the sake of giving it form etc.") I don't think any of the above should appear in the story—or do I?—of course and indeed now I've written it I scarcely know what it means. But that I am on the right track I am certain —at least to the extent that the *lies,* literal falsehoods in this story, such as the name Ghostkeeper on the wreck, the falling tree house, seem valid, as produced by my unconscious. They merely parallel other coincidences we haven't space for such as Dylan Thomas etc. In any case the average short story is probably a very bad image of life, and an absurdity, for the reason that no matter how much action there is in it, it is static, a piece of death, fixed, a sort of butterfly on a pin; there are of course some flaws in this argument —it is a pity I have no philosophical training for I unquestionably have some of the major equipment of a philosopher of sorts. But the attempt should be—or should be here—at least to give the illusion of things—appearances, possibilities, ideas, even resolutions—in a state of perpetual metamorphosis. Life is indeed a sort of delirium perhaps that should be contemplated however by a sober "healthy" mind. By sober and healthy I mean of necessity limited. The mind is not equipped to look at the truth. Perhaps people get inklings of that truth on the lowest plane when they drink too much or go crazy and become delirious but it can't be stomached, certainly not from that sort of upside-down and reversed position. Not that the truth is "bad" or "good": it simply *is,* is incomprehensible, and though one is part of it, there is too much of it to grasp at once, or it is ungraspable, being perpetually Protean. Hence a final need probably for an acceptance of one's limitations, and of the absurd in oneself. So finally even this story is absurd which is an important part of the point if any, since that it should have none whatsoever seems part of the point too.

In any case Goodheart dresses carefully, rehearsing: on plane (a) what he is going to say to Mrs. and Master Ghostkeeper, (b) the possible endings for his story. Activity (b) begins to make him feel as if he is going cuckoo again, nor is this feeling mitigated when half way through shaving his eye falls on a phrase in an article by Karl Jasper on Nietzsche in an American magazine: "He himself corrected his ideas in new ideas," he reads, "without explicitly saying so. In altered states he forgot conclusions formerly arrived at." This seems to have some bearing on the situation though Goodheart can't make out quite what it is. "For Nietzsche leads us into realms of philosophy which are anterior to clear logical thought, but which strive toward it." H'm. "Not long before his madness he declared that for a number of years he wished only to be quiet and forgotten, for the sake of something that is striving to ripen." "Shortly before the end he wrote: 'I have never gone beyond attempts and ventures, preludes and promises of all sorts.'" I'll say I haven't, thinks Goodheart. "There remains to be sure a residue of insoluble absurdities—" I'll say there is, thinks Goodheart, tying his tie.

Finally he is ready for Mrs. and Master Ghostkeeper's arrival and this part should be dramatized with considerable feeling of tension and suspence, though quietly and realistically, as it were New

Yorker style. On the other hand I think by this time one should be afraid of the onset of the Ghostkeepers, almost as if on one plane Ghostkeeper is a symbol of death. At the same time the numerous channels of the story now narrow for the moment into one main one (or at least not more than 3 or 4!) Mr. and Mrs. Goodheart now emerge as if integrated, kindly, wise characters very much in love with each other, their attitude toward the boy largely parental in character. Their ethics will not allow them—should the boy prove to be the one that was throwing stones at the ducks—to give him away in front of his mother. However, can Goodheart take the boy aside? Would the boy laugh at him? *Would he see the point?* Or spoil the whole thing. At the same time perhaps Goodheart wonders if the mother is going to prove to be a pretty girl and perhaps he is wishing in advance to impress her. (Absolutely disregarding the novelist's touch, and the usual laws of selection the story is preparing to end therefore in a manner not remotely suggested by its beginning or indeed having very much to do with it.) At the same time fact is so confounded with fiction in Goodheart's mind that he is sometimes not sure that he is experiencing any valid emotion and has the sense—even while we draw him and Mary realistically —that he is now a character in a story of which perhaps another or that other Henrik Ghostkeeper is the author, though perhaps Henrik Ghostkeeper hasn't yet made up his mind either what to do with him. Goodheart feels as though in short—in Aiken's words— "the whole buzzing cosmic telephone exchange" were going on in his head. Every now and then he walks nervously to the door to see if their visitors are arriving and the Goodhearts have a slight dissension about whether to take the reward or not. Finally Tom clairvoyantly opens the door just as Mrs. Ghostkeeper is coming down the corridor. She is of course alone, and not pretty. What happened in fact is now dramatised briefly in neutral entertaining fashion. They do not disclaim the reward perhaps but accept half of it. "We can make a lot of money that way," Goodheart could say. Nor does he say "You can buy us a drink sometime," and Mrs. Ghostkeeper replies sinisterly, "I'll be seeing you." Of course the child *is* the child who'd been throwing stones at the ducks, this must be firmly established (and of course he could have, and has, written his name on the wrecked boat), and all during the conversation Goodheart is trying to work in his little prefectorial spiel, while remaining chivalrous.

"Just tell him we were the people who spoke to him about the ducks," he tries to say several times.

"Just tell him that we—"

"Just say we saw him with the ducks—"

But he never manages any real message at all for the boy and a feeling of frustration becomes so strong he is confused and the incident ends in complete absurdity. And Goodheart looks out of the window after she leaves. Secretly he is wondering whether a tree is going to fall on her after all.

Then, feeling completely frustrated and irritated that the boy will *never know,* but on the whole a sense of pleasure and satisfaction that they had managed to do good, he sits down to write his story (in which the boy does find out) sipping away at a glass of milk. Already he has decided that the shorter version is the one he must write. Lex Talionis. But in this he has to miss out the name Ghost-keeper altogether which even if he could use it, would perhaps involve a libel suit, etc. And naturally his own name in real life he couldn't use anyhow. Finally he decides to give his protagonist no name at all. First he is "I" then he changes it to "he". The man and his wife. The name on the watch—the boy—must, he decides be a perfectly neutral name like Smithers or Miller—but then he wouldn't be able to find them in the phone book. There is no mention of the falling tree house, the other coincidences of the watches, the invisible watch, or the death of the King, or the feeling that the protagonist is now an Elizabethan. Everything was selection, concision, the story writer's touch. The protagonist himself was not a journalist nor any sort of writer in any kind of crisis about writing. In fact you would never realise what he was. Well, at least this story was touching, Goodheart thinks, compassionate, simple, on the side of "goodness." And having the advantage of a lowly and unpretentious theme it could scarcely offend the Almighty Spirit. The only trouble was it wasn't "true", that is to say that though it seemed true that the stoning of the ducks had brought upon the child the immediate retribution of the losing of the watch, so much other material that seemed mysteriously relevant had to be tailored away for the sake of art (or cash) that the result was the same: it was a touching little conte perhaps, but by trimming the whole down to what seemed its bare essentials, what was left did not seem even a synecdoche of the events of the last two days, as their seemingly almost insane series affected him.

But as he thought these things it was as if he seemed to hear, as if from on high, a certain divine assent, nodding, as if to say: "Yes, yes, that is very nice, very touching, Mr. Goodheart, it is just as you say," he seemed to hear yet another voice, as from half way up in the air, saying "No, no, Mr. Goodheart, that is very lousy, what did I tell you? What about the King? What about Canada? What about the blind man? What about Segovia? What about the invisible watch? And the young Frenchman? What about the wheels within wheels, Mr. Goodheart, and not merely the wheels within wheels, but the wheels within wheels within wheels, Mr. Goodheart, that are even now still turning and evolving newer, yet more wonderful and more meaningless meanings—"

And yet within himself he knew there was a meaning and that it was not meaningless.

Goodheart laid his pencil aside. He had finished his story but his mind was still sorely troubled. That Ghostkeeper! And "I Walk in the Park." But who else walks in the park? Who else, up there, was writing? Suddenly before his eyes the tree house crashed down on the bench again. And tell strange stories—Who else was writing, up there, about Kings dying, Elizabethans, invisible watches, flying saucers, blind men, mandarin ducks . . . Henrik Ghostkeeper! If only one could be sure he were playing a game!

What did we know? And into his mind again came a vision of the ghostly ballet, seen through the half cleaned windows, on the pier at the entrance to the park. If one could only be sure!

But suddenly his fear was transformed into love, love for his wife, and that meaningless, menacing fear was transformed into a spring wood bearing with it the scent of peach blossoms and wild cherry blossoms.

Pray for them!

Enter One in Sumptuous Armour

It was the last day of the Christmas holidays. There were white horses out to sea, and the smoke of an outward-bound steamer lay along the horizon. But the evening sky looked desolate. The Welsh mountains across the Dee made me sad. It was freezing cold, there had been snow in the bunkers, yet I came home slowly, dragging my feet. My golf clubs seemed to weigh me down. It was dark when I reached home.

I put my clubs in the cloakroom and went straight through into the kitchen for tea. The firelight set Chinese dragons dancing on the wall. Our two old servants, Nelly and Minnie, sat beside me at the kitchen table. We were still talking there when the headlights of our car roamed down the drive; the brilliance filled the room, blinding us. Thus I did not know my father had brought a stranger home with him until later. Then the stranger, who had a club foot apparently, limped out to our car under the light from the front porch. Our chauffeur, Featherstonhaugh, held the door of the Minerva open. The car drove away with them beneath the wet swaying nameless trees. I could not guess who the man was since I was never at home long enough to get to know even any of the neighbors.

"Who was the man with the club foot, Dad?" I asked when I'd greeted him, but my father put off answering the question until after dinner. I thought he was a little annoyed I hadn't declared myself earlier. Nellie had cleared the things away; we were alone by the fire.

"Mr. Snow," he explained then. "He called on me at the office and I brought him home. He seems to think you would be a good boy to look after his son at school."

I laughed. "Good? Why?"

228

"I didn't know you were in, you rascal, or I would have introduced you." My father was lighting a cigar. He wore his velvet coat, from which something sweet and wholesome emanated, not exactly an odor so much as a quality, as of new golf balls, that seemed to belong to him in this mood, putting me at my ease.

"Is Snow junior a new bomb?" I asked.

"What's a new bomb?"

"A new boy."

"That's what I'm driving at, he's going to the Rowans this term."

I took a turn around the room. I drew the curtain aside a little. The night was black. The light fell out, down the bank of the desolate soaking tennis court. The rings on the iron netless poles were jingling restlessly. The north wind howled among the rhododendrons. Beyond the abyss of the fields a train was struggling along the little single-track railway, its wet lights sliding past, and it seemed to be taking me away from home already. I let the curtain fall back.

"It's ghastly being a new bomb," I said. "But this term I may be a subprefect—"

"Ah, I'm very glad to hear that."

"Well, I'm not sure. I only think so."

"Wouldn't you be in a position of—ah—authority then, to do something for him?" my father asked me after a pause.

"Not really I shouldn't, Dad." I came over and sat on the edge of the table. "It might be a disadvantage to him, sort of. The other fellows would accuse him of sucking up to me and stage a nip-on."

"What's a nip-on?"

"A rag. They'd rag him. Bully him."

"I thought they didn't rag any more these days," my father said, flicking cigar ash off his elbow. "Why, they don't even have fagging at your school."

"That's true, Dad," I said, "but that hasn't got much to do with it."

I looked at my father. His grey, gentle eyes looked back at me rather anxiously. I knew he had no ulterior business motive in wanting me to help young Snow. I felt that he was sorry for Mr. Snow but the real thing was that he sincerely wished me to show him some sense of responsibility.

"The point is," he was saying, "Mr. Snow has had to withdraw his son from two prep schools because of this very—ah—"

"Nip-oning?"

"Nip-oning you speak of. For the last few years his son's had a private tutor and now he's got through his entrance exams. He's taking the 10.05 from Lime Street tomorrow." My father cleared his throat. "I've assured Mr. Snow you'll keep an eye on the boy during the journey. And of course you'll do your best in every way for him at school."

"Isn't that a bit of a tall order?" I slid down from the table. "What if he gets—" I wandered toward the window and pulling aside the curtains looked out into the wet night again. "Worms?" I let the curtain fall. "Or something. I suppose I'd get the blame for it."

"Can't you do just one little thing for me?" My father sounded slightly ashamed of me.

A little later, shouting "All right, Pater, I'll do my best" over my shoulder, I ran upstairs to help Nelly finish my packing.

After, I came down to say goodbye to my golf clubs: iron, niblick, putter, mashie, brassie. For all these weapons I would tomorrow substitute a hockey stick, field hockey being the accepted game of the spring term. I had been oiling it to prevent stinging and there it lay, flat on some brown paper in the corner. There was something about the wool smell of the cloakroom which already suggested the journey in the morning.

I slouched into the lounge, where my mother and father were reading in their usual places by the fire. For something to do I looked up 'golf' in the dictionary. It said the word meant a game played with a small hard ball and a club headed stick and was perhaps derived from the French word gouffre, meaning gulf. Near it 'good' was given as meaning virtuous, honest, just, suitable, solvent, that which possesses desirable qualities. Hockey it didn't give at all. I found myself at a window once more, peering out. Over the Dee in Flintshire the furnaces glowed red. Gulf—that was like the night. Out there, beyond Hilbre, Lycidas had drowned.

"So you're leaving us again," my mother sighed. "All the boys grow up and leave us. Do you think you'll bring us any cups this term?"

"I don't know," I said, from the window.

"Come on over here and talk to us," said my mother.

"Yes: come over here and let's have a look at you."

Still holding the dictionary, I went over to the fire, kissing my mother's forehead on the way.

"You never seem happy to be home these days. Are you glad to be going to school?"

"Yes and no," I said. "I might be a sub this term."

"Will you get in the hockey—it *is* hockey this term isn't it?"

"I'll get in the house team, I think, Mum," I interrupted her. "If not in the school team. It depends rather on whether Greer's left and Harold—"

"Well, Dick's growing into a fine handsome boy," my father said appraisingly, "isn't he, Mother? He's a good boy too, after all."

"Dick was a fine whale too," I said. I was taking the dictionary back to the bookcase. "Father means I'm virtuous honest just suitable solvent and possess desirable qualities." Closing the dictionary I jammed it back next to The Surgeon's Log. Then I returned to the fire. "Eh, Dad?"

"I'm certain you're not solvent," my father said, and silver half-crowns shone from his eyes.

I stood with my back to the fireplace looking down on my parents. It was difficult to explain the fear I had of discrediting them, of hurting them. And how was I to tell them that this responsibility of Snow was already touching me with a sense of foreboding? I saw the man with the club foot again, limping toward the car, our chauffeur, his greatcoat storm-tossed, holding open the door, as if—

"I forgot to tell you that Mr. Snow is a friend of Mr. Stoker's," my father said suddenly.

I laughed. "Old Stuttererhoof's Dad? What's that got to do with it?" So Harold *was* returning this term after all. That meant getting into the first eleven was doubly uncertain. My heart sank. "Is Mr. Snow lining up the whole school on his brat's behalf?" I asked.

"Why do you call Harold by that awful name," my mother asked.

"Oh, he used to stutter," I said. "He still does, a bit."

"You mustn't pick up any bad habits," my mother said. "Now Percy had a friend, one of the Ross boys, and he twitched."

"You'll probably all be going down in the train together," my father said.

"Like this." My mother was twitching for me. "And of course when Percy came back from staying with him, he twitched too. Just like this."

"That is, Harold Stoker and Mr. Snow's boy—Row, Ralph, I don't just recall the name," my father said, "and yourself."

After a sort of twitching competition with my mother I went up to bed, hoping I had not been too abrupt on my last night. Alas, I could see the complications beginning tomorrow. I threw open the window. Bitter weather! Over in Wales the furnaces still glowed.

As for Harold, I thought, getting into bed shivering, old Stutterhoof, he was the best of fellows, whose unsuitability for any role of protector was flawless, however. I presumed he would have to sneak out into the corridor away from Snow to smoke. First eleven or not I was glad Harold was returning. I lay awake a long time, unhappy to be going, unhappy because I didn't want enough not to go, unhappy that I had not told my mother how much I loved her, unhappy about Snow. How would he be feeling tonight, poor chap, on the eve of being tossed out once more into the gulf—

II

Featherstonhaugh brought the Minerva round to the front door early while I was saying goodbye to the servants. The collar of his blue greatcoat with brass buttons was turned up. After a while he left the porch and stood under the shelter of the arch of the front door. I greeted him and he muttered some piracy—a kind of code between us. The servants and myself, and my brothers when they were home, were all vaguely in league against my parents, albeit in the friendliest way.

"Goodbye Nelly," I was saying. "Goodbye Minnie."

"Be good now," they said. "Bring home lots of cups, there's a good boy." I said goodbye to the gardener. "Run away laughing," he said and stamped back to the kitchen garden.

My mother stood waving to me from the front door; the servants waved from the side of the house.

I sat in the back of the car with my father watching Featherstonhaugh's shoulders. When my father wasn't there I sat with him in the front where we talked a freebooting language of our own. "Chew glass and spit blood, eh? eh?" he would say. Or he would tell me about the war "when I was on the Gall-eye Pole-eye Peninsula."

But now he looked stern and forbidding as the day itself.

It was just about freezing still, bitter cold and wet. We sloshed through a crossroads and up a hill. Moors smelling of wet gorse stretched away to our right. A lone fingerpost said: Public Footpath to Thingwall. There was a sea of mud round the farm yards. We splashed through little villages named Frankby and Greasby.

I noticed the pubs longingly. In Frankby there was the Farmer's Arms—Caerwyle Ales and Stout: now, in Greasby, the Coach and

Horses. I was sorry to be leaving the pubs behind though I had never entered one.

Crossed signposts read: Irby 1 mile; Chester 22; Neston and Parkgate 6.

"All on one side, like Parkgate," my father said, which was the only thing he ever said about Parkgate.

Old walls with 'stick no bills' chalked on them fell behind. A board stood in a field: Come to Blackpool.

Fine motorcycles whizzed by or splashed past us: a Zenith Gradua, a Rudge-Multi, with their involved gearshifts: two Sunbeams with laminated spring forks. I watched for the blue Indian, an American make, which we usually encountered at nine fifteen in Upton, just before reaching the Ring o' Bells. I had never got rid of the childhood impression that its rider was somehow identified with the machine, that together it was a real Indian who lived somewhere in a hollow.

Then, occasionally, a thing would approach us, seeming at first less like a motorcycle than a terrestrial visitor; a pre-war Bat or Roc, of enormous length with open belt drive, and racing handlebars over which its rider crouched, flat on the tank. With unearthly explosions they voyaged into the gloom: discarded experiments, as I see them now, of the Industrial Revolution, obsolescent monuments to foundered genius—

As we left Upton the blue Indian slanted by, a little late to-day, almost half-past nine. Featherstonhaugh turned his head a fraction so that I could see the slight smile on his lips, a signal. His impassive mien reassembled itself quickly. Drawing near the Birkenhead dockside the pubs came thick and fast, with sea-sounding names here: the Dolphin, the Blue Peter, the Right Whale. Funnels appeared over sheds; the crosstress of a windjammer. Smells of cordage wafted to our nostrils. An advertisement for the Hippodrome said: Little Tich, 6:30, 8:30. While the Argyle announced Harry Champion, Brown's Bioscope. It was melancholy to be bidding adieu to these familiar placards which were like friends.

At Birkenhead Park we left the car. I said goodbye to Featherstonbaugh, giving him one of the half-crowns that had already taken shape from my father's eyes that morning. Out of the corner of his mouth he said: "Chew glass and spit blood." We took the Mersey Underground Railway. My father was getting off at James Street: we said goodbye, under the sea, without ceremony. I went on to Central.

The advertisements were now for the Liverpool theatres. At Olympia, Jack and the Beanstalk was still playing. A German film called the Nibelungs was at the Futurist.

Going to school was an insanely complicated business. To be brief: at Lime Street Harold saw me first and he shouted and waved his hat.

"Oi," he said.

"Oi."

We never saw each other during the holidays for he lived on Merseyside, and I on Deeside: now we were going to school and I wondered if he had been told about Snow. He had; but before we had time to discuss a plan of campaign the man with the club foot rose up beside us. Behind him I saw my brother grinning. He had come from the office to see me off and to point me out to Mr. Snow. He had been to our school before the war and wore the old boy's tie.

"Hullo troops," Percy greeted us. "How's Faugh?" he said to me, "Still chewing glass?"

"This is my son, Raoul."

We were introduced to a timid, featureless youth, hanging his head, whose presence was so entirely negative we hadn't noticed he was there. He shook hands with us coldly. My brother took me aside. "What do you think of little Foul?" he said.

"Not Foul—Raoul."

"What are you going to do with him? Throw him overboard?" He said this so disarmingly it could not be considered cruel. "Maybe he'll push you overboard."

"He looks as though he might jump."

"I've heard all about Raoul—or Roll, as the pater calls him—every day for the last week at the office," said my brother. "It's a sort of plot, but it's a long story and your train's going."

I watched Stutthererhoof conferring with Mr. Snow and his son. The boy was obviously frightened though at the same time he seemed as if inwardly quaking with anger at this flaunting of his dependence. A tear ran down one cheek on which there was a large smut. He wore narrow blue trousers under his new brown overcoat and carried yellow wash leather gloves. A wisp of hair stuck out beneath his new bowler. And he wore our house team tie, to which he was not entitled.

I stood under the titanic dome of the grimed stations with my brother until the train was actually moving. There were deafening blasts, satanic convulsions of escaping steam; sirens wailed from the river. An obstacle race of porters with barrows of luggage swept round us. Conversation was difficult. My brother shook my hand vigorously till the last moment and I grasped Mr. Snow's hand too as we moved away.

All around us in the fog lay that extraordinary terrain of the Industrial Revolution and the first street cars, where Wilfred Owen was at school and Nathaniel Hawthorne was Consul, where Karl Marx wrote Das Kapital and Herman Melville made up his mind to be annihilated.

III

We had lost the Mersey but at Runcorn it appeared below us, yellow and clayey. Precariously swinging above it the huge gondola of the aerial bridge slid by into the murk.

Stuttererhoof and I were nervous. Once we giggled shamefacedly. But we sat in almost complete silence till we reached Crewe where we bought, and offered, our charge a pork pie.

This article of diet has so impressed itself upon travellers that a hat is named for it. The crust, upon being bitten, secretes a queer fluid. It does not contain pork. Snow refused.

"Did you have a g-good hols?" asked Harold, munching, as we moved out of Crewe.

Snow looked palely at us. "What are hols?"

"Oh, you know, holidays," I said with my mouth full.

"I didn't have any holidays," Snow said gravely.

"Oh, s-sorry."

We must have sat in silence for another five miles.

"Did you d-do a panto?" asked Harold at last.

"The man means pantomime," I said.

"Yes," said Snow. "We went to Jack and the Beanstalk."

Snow was not doing so badly: at least he had not called us 'sir.' Nevertheless there was another long silence. After a while I read the Wodehouse story in the Strand Magazine; Snow too had picked up a Strand. But out of the corner of my eye I could see that he was not concentrating. Suddenly I laughed loudly at some drollery and Snow started: I felt he thought I was laughing at him. Laying aside my magazine, I looked at him.

"Well, now," I said, "I expect your mater and pater are sorry

—" at this point I caught Harold's eye and stopped. I should say I caught both his eyes because he was winking each of them alternately, in rapid succession. And his mouth was forming the words: 'He hasn't got any mater.' Then Harold kicked me and I saw that the tears were streaming down Snow's face.

"Do you remem-member when I sat in Horses' study and w-winked both eyes like this?" asked Harold, and he went on winking one eye after the other as if from an inner compulsion. I thought of my own mother then, and her warning about 'bad habits' and smiled at Snow in a way intended to be kindly.

"Well, old fellow," I said to him, "It's sort of hard going to school after the Christmas hols, I know—pantos and all that—"

"I only saw one," Snow said in anguish.

"—and of course parties, but—"

Harold kicked me again, mouthing and winking. "He obviously doesn't go to parties, you blight—"

"Do you like hockey?" I interrupted myself, and Snow shook, then nodded his head, his lips compressed.

"Have you got your hockey-knocker?"

The tears only ran the faster down Snow's face.

Harold and I went out into the swaying corridor for a smoke. I offered him an expensive "Grays' from an expensive case. To-day I smoke the cheapest cigarettes I can find, keeping them loose in my pocket, but when I was fifteen and a half it was different. We looked out at England. We were going right down through the Midland plateau. The railway, with considerable cunning we decided, was avoiding towns like Wolverhampton and Birmingham. The fog had broken up on the fields. Snow lay in drifts. I don't remember if there were any cattle. But the fields rushed backward with a homeward drag on the heart. And there was a new note of loneliness in the crying out of the wheels against the iron. I think we realized that we were getting older, and that each time we left for school now it was as though we went a little further away from home. We whistled through Tamworth.

"What kind of a term do you think we'll have?" Harold asked.

"Pretty foul."

"H-hope we'll get some good hockey."

Neither of us mentioned the possibility that Greer might not have left. Cold vapour and multiodoured hot whiffs of smoke came through the open window against which we flattened ourselves to let people squeeze past—sleepwalkers. We counted sixty-six trucks of asphaltic slag from Llay Main in Wales; *Llay-Main*: *Llay main*: that was what they seemed to be saying and there was an indefinable plangency about these words as each truck clicked by.

"I'm Welsh," said Harold. "When I was a new bomb I couldn't speak much English. But I didn't stutter in Welsh."

"I don't notice it now," I said. "But I thought all Welshman said 'look you whateffer.' "

"Not after they've been to school in Eng-Eng,England."

"Well, that was before my time," I said. We snuffed the nostalgic schoolward smell of the train in silence for a while. Then I laughed. "Chew glass and spit blood—that's our chauffeur's prescription. I suppose in the end the disaster Snow—" it was the first time he had been mentioned directly "—will be all right, eh?"

Harold excused himself at this point. When he returned he said with avidity, "The d-disaster's not on the train."

"What!" I said. "Well, we'll pull the communication cord."

"D-doubt if we have f-five quid to pay the f-fine," said Harold, "if we're wrong."

"Let's look again."

We were hurling through England now. Before we reached the end of the train three stations were behind us. It was as though at each one the engine drew a breath and whizzed on screaming faster than ever. Careening through Nuneaton we found Snow in a forward deserted dining car. He had drawn a dirty table cloth over his head and he was weeping and kicking the opposite seat.

"Better let the kid cry it out," said Harold. "He's best left to himself for a time."

Over to the right were the great industrial towns of the Midlands we had eluded and through the windows the sky was red with the glare of furnaces. We were still looking for our compartment when the train pulled up at Rugby.

Dropping off to the platform from the nearest door, the first thing we saw was Raoul disappearing into the crowd. We could not find him: when we got back on the train he wasn't there either.

We found our compartment and Snow came in. The train was moving. "I had to be sick," Snow explained, "and I couldn't do that on the train standing in the station."

"So you were sick on the platform," said Harold. "S-stout fellow."

"No. I couldn't find anywhere on the platform so I had to come back on the train again."

"You made it?"

"No."

"Do you feel better now?"

"No."

"Perhaps you're hungry," said Harold. "Have some s-sards."

"What are sards?"

"Sardine sandwiches. Pretty sordid, I admit. But it staves off the gnawing for a w-while."

"No, thank you."

After a long silence I asked Snow what he'd like to do when he left school.

"Insurance," he said, finally.

"What kind of insurance?"

"No kind of insurance," Snow said. "Just insurance."

Harold and I looked at each other. For a mile or more we contained ourselves. Then we burst out laughing. It sounded hysterical, so we tried to stop. Failing, we tried to include Snow who was watching us gravely, tittering. The result was that we all felt better though I do not believe another word was spoken till we reached London.

Here we began to go slowly. The fog had come out to meet us. The greyness was stabbed with vermilion, with weird wandering lights. You could always tell when you were approaching Euston because the lines fanned out and to one side was a high sloping stone wall with sharp cruel spikes on it. I always thought these spikes were to catch people flung violently from the obscure windows of the houses above. But today it was too dark to see the spikes though I knew they were there and that we were getting into London.

It was about two in the afternoon. Soon we were all packed in a taxi going to Liverpool Street. Harold and I looked after Snow's luggage and our own. From Liverpool Street we were to take the train to Cambridge. Plays were advertised on the sides of the great numbered buses that loomed out of the fog. *Outward Bound* was at the Royalty: *R.U.R.* at the St. Martins, with Leslie Banks. At the Little, Aubrey Smith, Tallulah Bankhead and Nigel Bruce were in *The Creaking Chair*.

"What does *R.U.R.* mean?" asked Snow.

"Look," said Harold, pointing to another bus, "R-rossums Universal Robots."

"What's a robot?"

"I don't know," we had to admit, and at that moment were

wrenched round into Liverpool Street Station Yard. Horse drays were being allowed through a traffic jam. Mighty horses bedecked with medals were pulling up the cobbled slope from the station. They bowed, puffing out their breaths, which mingled with the fog. First there was the pandemonium of the drays and the magnificent, pungent smells of the skidding animals, then, after we had left the taxi, in the station itself a queer vacancy, a sense of gigantic, sounding emptiness. Here was a complexity of closed ticket offices: abandoned weighing machines: meaningless cardboard clocks: a lost child.

We discovered our train at the wrong platform and its smell was bitterer than that of the one we had left. While Harold was seeing about the luggage our ticket office opened. Handing Snow his ticket I felt a sharp pang of sympathy for him. For not only was there in the name of this station, Liverpool Street, a certain derision, a hopelessness, but to make matters worse, on every hand advertisements invited us to go home again, to spend our holidays at Merseyside, at Deeside, to come to New Brighton, or Blackpool, where, in spite of midwinter, the Great Wheel awaited us.

Snow was crying as Harold returned and to cheer him up we offered to buy him something at the bookstall. He accepted a Sketch, and while he stood, pretending to glance at it, and to have stopped weeping, looking the other periodicals over I experienced an even sharper pang of sympathy for him, sure he must feel utterly remote from all it portrayed. Anyone could laugh at Wodehouse in the Strand. But Nash's, Country Life, the Tatler, Snow's Sketch— I flicked them through wondering whom these papers were intended for and if anyone read them. Nothing was ever said in them about Liverpool. There were no picture of Lancashire. Whose opinions did they express and why? Whose were these horses they talked about? Could it be that that was somebody's idea of what our relatives looked like? The comic American magazines hanging in the corner, Life and Judge, on whose cover wooden cuties jigged with abandon, did not open on a more tramontane world, in which we surely did not exist.

I bought the evening paper and we boarded the train for the last lap to Cambridge. There were a few other Rowanites, a few greetings, and a few glances at Snow. Giant, pimply undergraduates returning to the University regarded us with scorn. But we had a compartment to ourselves fortunately. The train moved off. We passed the Star Brush Company. There was an apron of light outside the Finsbury Park Empire. We crashed through Barnet and in no time at all were beyond Welwyn Garden City and Hatfield where the Zeppelin had been brought down in the last war, and Lord Lytton, the author of Eugene Aram, had lived once, and there were the mounds of the seven kings.

"It says in the Standard that Sherlock Holmes could have made the journey from London to Cambridge in 1897 in less time than it takes us now," I said.

"G-good for him," said Harold sleepily.

There was no fog now. Neither was there any obverse hope that if the engine failed on a hill we might run backwards to Liverpool. The hedges slipping behind returned only to London where they were brought up short. I could see stars printed on the night like ukulele music but knew the names of none. Soon, out of the dark, the half-verified landmarks of Cambridge began to clutch at my vitals. An advertisement for a forbidden, familiar cinema said: Victoria, Emil Jannings in the Last Laugh.

Snow began to look sick again. He was searching in his waist-coat pockets. At last he said:

"I've lost my ticket."

Harold woke up and guffawed. "Walk straight through the b-bar-rier as if you meant it and they won't bother you. We'll show you how it's done."

It was not till we were hauling out suitcases down from the racks that we remembered Snow's tie. This we changed hastily for him.

At Cambridge we all walked straight through the wicket without being challenged, as Harold had said. The first thing we did then was to send telegrams to our families and we sent one for Snow too. To my family I sent the code word my brothers had used before me. *Atwowah*, which meant, 'All travelling went off without a hitch.'

IV

Our subprefects' study in Chaucer's house at the Rowans was smaller than the bosun's cabin of a British tramp steamer.

Through one barred window it looked out on the side of the roofed swimming baths fronting which was a small quadrangle. To the left of this was the science building, to the right, the master's common room. Sitting in the corner of our window Harold and I could see beyond to the main quadrangle with Shirley's and Campion's houses on the left. The chapel was on the right but the great hall blocked our view of it. The library ran the length of the far side of the main quadrangle. Most of the buildings visible contained classrooms; gargoyles leaned out from their walls; flying buttresses propped them up.

On our free morning from this window we watched the ebb and flow, and flood, of school affairs obliquely. Each hour, regularly as a geyser erupting, humanity poured out of the high classrooms, spilling over into the quadrangle and walks. Then all was still once more.

This free morning we had thus far had the opportunity of watching Snow being 'nipped-on' by his colleagues of the lowest form, of which he set at the bottom, from three points of the compass. At nine he had been catapulted eastward by them out of the science building. At ten he had been the centre of an unseemly hubbub progressing westward between the hall and the master's common room. At eleven, bludgeoned by atlases from behind, he had come bounding south out of the black gap below the library. It was now a few minutes to twelve: the bell had given its discreet hiccup before announcing the end of morning school. A few fellows were already speeding toward the tuckshop or the playing fields. Suddenly the bell was tolling merrily. The geyser began to erupt and spill over. Hounded north across the flank of the master's common as if by fiends appeared Snow. He cowered among the fiends without retaliation save once when he hacked one of his tormentors on the shin viciously. They disappeared and I got down from the window sill.

"I want to hear the end of Snake's Hips," I said, putting on the gramophone and setting the needle towards the centre of the Memphis Five record. I didn't know how to express it, but it had to me the beauty of algebra.

"Let's take a walk around the pitch," said Harold.

"All right, get your stick and we'll knock about."

We found our sticks and a ball under the table. "What about this Snow menace anyhow, Harold?" I asked him, switching off the gramophone.

"When we stopped it for a time we only m-made it worse for him in the end," said Harold. "Come on."

Passing the ball between us we ran around the house by the fives court. Then we cut up behind the pavilion to the cricket pitch. There was the pitch with the track circling it and the pavilion behind us. Away to the left was the desolate white cricket screen and the Head's house. In the distance were the playing fields which a few chaps had already reached. The netted goals were like queer isolated places of meditation.

It was a lowering February day, dark with the darkness which presages snow. It was cruel weather and far from spring, but the grass was green. We practised tackling for a while without gusto.

"I wish it was last term," Harold said, shivering. "I prefer rugger."

"Yes, I'd rather football too," I said, flicking the ball to him. "I expect you're thinking the same thing as I am."

"You mean if we shall beat Campion's?"

I hit the ball past Stuttererhoof. We began to run after it.

"No," I said, my teeth chattering, "I was thinking we might not get in the house team at all. Unless someone drops on Greer from a great height. Or teaches you or me to play somewhere else. Even then," I added, coming up with the ball, "only one of us might get in."

We began to dribble up and down furiously to keep warm. Greer had proved still at school and the situation was involved for both of us. For Harold and I still played best in the same place—outside left. Though neither of us had our second colors we alternated in the school second eleven. Sometimes one or the other of us actually played in the first eleven. However that was only when Greer—outside left for the school—was absent. But Greer, a short tempered fellow, was our house-captain too. He liked to play outside left for the house. Chaucer's forward line was very strong; the three insides were second colors and the outside right was also a first color. Neither Harold nor I shone as halves or backs and those places were well filled anyhow. It looked to me as though Chaucer's might win the house cup but without our assistance. The snag was that Chaucer's could not win against Campion's, probably our opponents in the final, without a good goalkeeper. For Rocyn-Blenkinsop was Campion's terrific centre-forward and at seventeen Rock not only represented his county in the holidays but was accepted as one of its hardest hitters. And we had no goalkeeper at all. Stuttererhoof's thoughts must have been running on similar lines for he said suddenly:

"C-can you play goal?"

"No. I'll die before I play goal," I said, missing the ball neatly.

"You'll die if you do," Harold said. "But I tell you that's what that f-fellow Greer is plotting to do with one of us."

"He can't expect both of us to play goal."

But I was wrong. That was precisely what Greer did expect us to do, and in a house game that very afternoon. Playing on opposing sides Harold and I let through five goals each. Harold could not see the balls coming. While I saw them, I was unable to stop them with my pads. And we both kept forgetting it was not a foul for a goalkeeper to clear with his feet. After Rocky we were probably the hardest hitters in the school yet it availed us nothing. We were penalized for sticks. Worst of all, the position struck us as somehow humiliating. Our hearts were not in it. Goalkeepers at field hockey can be made but they must be born first and the same might be said about an outside left.

"I absolutely refuse to stand shivering all afternoon in a b-blasted goal," Harold told Greer. "Why the hades don't you play there yourself?"

"Too cold, nothing in it," I answered for Greer.

We could foresee ourselves being hoofed out of the house team for insubordination, even if we were selected in some unaccustomed place.

"Let's give up hockey altogether and p-play fives," said Harold as we strolled back toward the baths, grimed, bruised and angry.

On a remote pitch a late game of juniors was straggling to its close. It was the lowest pitch of all and we paused to watch because we noticed Snow playing right half. As we came up, he was feebly tackling a forward who just shoved the ball to one side of him and ran round the other. The forward movement carried on past Snow's full backs into the circle. But Snow had not fallen back to cover them. In fact his own forwards had fallen back further than Snow, who was pretending to tie his bootlace. He was obviously puffed and fed up. The opposing side scored and he was rebuked by the pitch captain. Snow signalled to us wanly.

We stood watching a few minutes longer. Snow was now simply wandering aimlessly about the field by himself. Then, suddenly, the forwards of both sides overran the ball which fell, camouflaged in mud, before him. There was Snow—only one back between himself and the circle. Given a modicum of subtlety it would have been easy for him to score. We wondered what he was going to do.

Snow charged forward. With a snort of complete contempt he kicked the ball right out of the field altogether.

Stuttererhoof and I strolled back toward the showers thoughtfully. Snow, playing half-back, had committed a flagrant and spiteful breach of the rules; he had also been sent off the field in disgrace. It could not be said that our ward was getting on too well or that we had done much to help. We were perhaps more concerned than we admitted, not liking to think of all the grief Snow's behavior might entail.

That night it was my duty in Snow's dormitory and as I went in they were slugging him with knotted towels. I stopped them, giving drill to two offenders, who promptly asked for a thrashing instead. I obliged them readily, letting the others off with a caution.

"What have you fellows got against Snow," I asked, handing my second victim back his hairbrush, "besides this afternoon?" Where everything else had failed, I thought complete simplicity might do the trick. Snow had turned to the wall as if asleep. The offenders giggled. "Shut up cackling," I said. "I want to know because everyone's here. There's nothing being said behind anyone's back. Why do you pick on Snow? Weren't you a new boy yourself once, you, Brough? Eh? Eh?"

"Yes," said Brough muffledly, from beneath the blankets, "and I got it hotter than any of the fellows ever give it to Snow."

There were giggles too from non-offenders.

"That doesn't answer my question," I said sternly, "Or if it does, I'm ashamed of you."

There was a silence. Then Snow spoke.

"I'm not complaining," he said, and he giggled also. I felt that he was sure he had said something wonderfully astute. Everybody laughed; I silenced them. "You don't hear any complaints from me," Snow added, and laughed again. It was clear he thought he had taken their side against me.

"No," I said to him, "You don't complain. That's just the trouble. How often do I have to tell you people would respect you more if you did?"

This time I thought Snow's laughter sounded almost maniacal.

"Well, why don't you hit these swine back?" I demanded.

"He does, he kicks," a voice said.

When I rapped on a cubicle for silence there were more giggles, frankly at myself, I decided. But no, someone had got under Snow's bed. Half relieved, I hauled the culprit out.

"Now," I said, "you fellows. Stop plaguing Snow. One day he'll have the tables turned on all you damn kids. Then it will be his turn to laugh."

I switched the ceiling lights out on them, thoroughly confused by what I had said and disgusted with everybody, including myself.

This turning-the-tables notion must have been suggested by the book I was reading them: *Vice Versa,* by F. Anstey, a favorite with the dormitory. Tilting the lamp down I began where I had left off on my last duty.

The story dealt with an elderly merchant named Bultitude who by some legerdemain swaps identities with his son. So far as I remember it was mostly very funny. There was a good scene in which the merchant, who is going to school instead of his son, and in a queer way *is* his son, offers the headmaster a cigar. Later, the father meets his son's sweetheart—the one poignant note.

I forgot what part I was reading to them that night though I do recall the whole thing struck Snow as insupportably amusing. The laughter was generally unroarious: it was still perhaps half rebellious but Snow's howled above the loudest. It was more of a screech than a howl, I thought, and finally, as I feared, it brought the housemaster down and I had to stop reading.

When he had gone I paced up and down the dormitory once or twice before speaking.

"Did you absolutely have to yell as loudly as all that?" I demanded. "The next thing the Balf will crack down on our reading altogether."

"I'm sorry," whispered several voices. I paced the room again, stopping by Snow's bed. He was still laughing, it seemed to me, in half choked, muffled convulsions. I pulled the sheet from his mouth.

"Cut that out," I said.

But Snow was crying. He was crying with awful anguish.

"Oi," I said to him. "Cut that." I sat down on his bed. His weeping did not subside. "Remember what I told you," I said out of the corner of my mouth. "Chew glass and spit blood. Then you'll be all right, you'll find."

And at that moment I had a strange, a triumphant, a transcendental idea.

V

It was the day of the final housematch: a blue, gusty March afternoon. The daffodils lay flat in the woods. The slow stream which flowed beside Trumpington Street was choppy. But the river Cam raced under the little bridges on the fens by windswept deserted boathouses.

Words carried a long distance, sounding like voices over water. Sometimes, borne down a gust, they seemed to overshoot you. Three miles high an engine was beating fiercely in the blue. It would let down a great sheaf of sound, as from a gigantic derrick, then abruptly withdraw it.

The crack of hockey sticks on the ball was clean and loud. It is a fine thing to watch a hockey game in England on a March day. There is a beauty about the speed and light of a match being played against a background of the flexible limbs of big trees, when the towers of Cambridge are falling against the scudding clouds, that is powerful in memory. The scene is very clear to my mind now. It is even finer perhaps to play in such a game, but Harold and I were watching; and we were watching because we had been dropped from the houseteam for insubordination.

As the whistle blew for half time the score stood at one all; Campion's had been pressing. Harold and I walked round the cricket pitch, occasionally flicking a ball at each other.

Other chaps similarly engaged detached themselves from the spectators. They would run a little way, dribbling the ball between them, then merge with the crowd elsewhere. We saw a group of masters talking; the Balf glanced once in our direction, smiling and digging in the earth with his heel.

After a while we saw a man on the track trying to catch our attention. He limped toward us; it was Snow senior.

"Hullo, hullo," he greeted us. "Why aren't you boys out in that field?"

"We—oh," I said. "That's a long story."

"It's a fine day for the game, isn't it?" asked Mr. Snow, looking about him.

"It certainly is, sir," we agreed.

"I don't know quite how to express myself," Mr. Snow said then, "but I feel I must thank you boys. I notice things and I'm not deceived. I've heard from several sources today—yes, even from your housemaster—that Chaucer's has you to thank for Raoul being where he is."

I made a fake pass at the ball. "That's not quite true," I said.

"No," Harold said, "He's one of the best natural goalkeepers I ever saw. Why, in five years he might be an, an international."

"I never thought," Mr. Snow said "—you see, Raoul didn't seem to have much aptitude for sport. Some boys are like that of course. I was, myself. But then he isn't exactly the studious type either, as far as that goes."

We said nothing; I looked up. High above us a lone shoregoing seagull was staggering homeward towards the port of Kings Lynn. We were trying not to laugh. It was a relief when he went on, fumbling in his pockets and smiling at us.

"Perhaps," he said, "perhaps you would accept a very little token of—now I told you I was a boy myself once, though you might not think it!" He had brought something out of his pocket. "You won't be insulted?"

"No, no," we said, politely curious. "Definitely not. Thanks awfully, sir," we added, as he handed each of us two glittering half-crowns. He limped away.

"Gawblimey."

"Gawblimey."

Harold and I strolled vaguely in the same direction. The game had not yet been resumed. On the field both sides were flinging away their lemons. Snow stood in the centre of a group talking in the goal mouth. He had not moved from his net during half-time. We saw him wave at his father who was heading for the covey of masters, looking delighted. Someone skimmed a peel down wind and it flew a long way.

"For three hours work a day," I said, scooping the ball over a blue pool in which, miles deep, white clouds were galloping, "six days a week, for less than six weeks, we produced Snow. Now if we only worked for ourselves for one hour, even two days—"

"I say Dick, whatever gave you idea about the d-disaster?"

The whistle blew.

"Oh, I dunno," I said, scooping the ball over another pool. "He always seemed to be kicking something."

We lowered our voices as we were coming up behind Snow's goal. The game had begun, though the play at the moment was being carried into Campion's half.

"O-one all," Harold said. "It's going to be close."

"All square."

We brought out our half-crowns, chuckling because Snow was just in front of us but didn't see us and didn't know what we were talking about.

"Well, they're good half-crowns," I said, biting one. "They shine. They have the King's head on them."

We put them back in our pockets. The game was approaching us, swift as the shadows careering along the turf. In the goal, Snow suddenly tautened like a spider, on the periphery of whose web another spider has just appeared. Rocyn-Blenkinsop had the ball, just beyond the circle, towards which he was edging it.

It was an extraordinary moment. All the hopes and fears of spectators and players alike seemed poised on that instant of wild expectancy between the motion of the inevitable trajection, and the thing itself. You could hear the wind blowing.

Then Rocky hit. Swift as cannon shot the ball whizzed toward us. We ducked instinctively. But the ball had rebounded from Snow's pads. Following up, Rocky shot again. He shot again and again, four times into Snow's pads, and each time he shot we winced. When Snow lumbered out to clear with a well directed kick there were terrific cheers. Though he had kicked with his right foot the ball went singing off to our outside left, to Greer.

Greer fumbled, somewhat to our satisfaction, and soon the game was brought back into our circle. Roycn-Blenkinsop now tried to flick the ball past Snow: Snow cleared to Campion's inside right; the inside shot; Snow cleared to their inside left; he shot and Snow saved again, the ball skimming off his pads behind the goal line where we caught it ourselves. There was a corner. Rocyn-Blenkinsop stopped the ball; he blazed away at the goal and Snow saved. The ball rebounded to Rocky again; Rocky shot again: Snow saved: Rocky shot: Snow saved. Snow was as if renitent, and his thick pads and clothing gave his movements the grotesque quality of machinery. Snow cleared once more, this time with his stick: one of their halves returned the ball and Snow cleared it with a final kick, eight saves in all, and the spectators, all the spectators, were cheering all the time.

I looked at Stuttererhoof. It was still anybody's game. Our own position was ironic. Yet there was something about that day, won by Snow surely, but a sort of entity too, formed by the trees, the towers falling against the clouds, the emerald turf, the peculiar but splendid encounter with his father, the closely fought housematch, which told us we would be lucky indeed if we ever again enjoyed such triumph. Raising our eyes into the sun we broke into a sound-less gigantic laughter that engulfed the whole sky.

The ball was in midfield now and Snow, resting on his stick, took off his gloves and wiped his brow.

"Oi," we said.

He turned round, looking a bit sheepish.

"Oi."

"Do you like this job?" we asked him.

He seemed a little self-conscious of his padding, his absurd, mediaeval appearance. But he considered our question a moment seriously.

"Yes," said Snow, "and no."

Kristbjorg's Story:
In the Black Hills

The German lived in the Black Hills and he drank himself to death. Apparently he wished to obliterate something. This was in 1906. At that time there were three saloons in Deadwood: The Green Front, the Topic, and Lent Morris'. The Green Point was a fancy bar and dance hall and it had a stuffed buffalo in a glass case I remember. The Topic was not so fancy, and Lent Morris' was a bare bar. Calamity Jane used to go to the Topic, a big, mannish woman. I've seen Buffalo Bill there too, but they called him something else. The German used to go to this bare bar.

In those days the bars were open twenty-four hours a day and the bartenders worked in three shifts like miners.

The German didn't seem an average person who came from a rat hole. He was about thirty-five or forty maybe, had a fair moustache, blue eyes—German physique. He would drink a bottle of whiskey in five minutes, then he'd plunk. Sometimes he'd get half through the second bottle before keeling over, and when he did this beside you, if you didn't know him and weren't expecting it, it was a shock.

But it was no shock to Lent Morris. He wouldn't leave him in front of the bar though; they'd drag him away and prop him up against the wall; or he would lay flat. After a few hours he'd come to and frisk himself, and if he had any money he'd start priming himself once more, and then keel over plunk.

He'd keep this up till he was broke, then he'd just go off.

Nobody knew his name, or where he came from. When he went home nobody knew what home he went to. When he wasn't working in the hills his only home was the bar, perhaps in an occasional flophouse. He never said a word to nobody, just drank. If you asked him how he was he'd grunt resentfully, "Ah," perhaps, that was all.

250

He looked very solemn-like and he wouldn't take up the cudgels on no circumstances.

Yet he didn't bother you. He never bummed any money or drinks off you. He kept himself clean and he wasn't the sort of drunk that comes into a bar with ten dollars and then after an hour is bumming drinks off everybody. The German was no bum.

Wages were very low, twenty-five cents an hour—still, in South Dakota people didn't go hungry. If you proposed to go to Butte or Aladdin on foot someone would be sure to offer you their horse. "But I'm not coming back." "Never mind, leave it there. I'll collect it sometime." God help the man who lied however.

The German was not a bum, he was a bundle stiff. Bindle stiff is a more polite way of saying it. He wasn't a hobo; a hobo carries nothing, and never works. This German carried a bundle, and he worked up in the Black Hills where there were lead mines.

In the Black Hills was a town named Lead. Perhaps it was there he worked—he was a big husky man—till he had a stake to come down to Lent's and drink.

Or maybe, at times, the German did have some kind of a home in Deadwood besides the bar. That would have been in the jungle. Every town in the Black Hills had a jungle in those days. There was a town named Cyanide, with a poison mill where they crunched the mercury, and even that had a jungle. Nemo, that had a jungle. They were some place off to the side, like the city dump, or a lot where worn out railroad box-cars were put. The hoboes and bindle stiffs lived in these boxcars and you'd be surprised to see how they fixed them up. Some of them had cut holes in the sides, and picked up panes of glass from the dump and made windows. They even had geraniums blooming in the windows. And some of them were clean and homelike as you could imagine. There were women there too. Mostly the bindle stiffs lived there in winter. But if the German had a home like this it would only been in winter.

Had he seemed hungry he would have been fed. Or in need of a bed he would have been given a bunk, be it never so lousy. Maybe people sometimes felt sorry for him when they dragged him to the wall, out of the way of the drinkers perhaps, I don't know. Perhaps not.

This particular day the German came in it was summer and we were all drinking in Lent Morris'. He come in and pretty soon he plunked as usual and we dragged him over and propped him up against the wall. Some of us went off to the Green Front, and when we got back three or four hours later the German was still laying against the wall.

"Hey," I said to Lent, "Ain't it time he waked up and primed himself again?"

"Naw," said Lent. "To hell with him."

"But he usually don't sleep more than a couple of hours."

"Hell with him. Let him lie."

"What's the matter with him," I said, "It's time he woke up and had another priming."

So I walked over to him. He was lying with his cheek sort of cupped in his hand. I gave him a shake and he fell over. And where his hand had been his face was snow white, and the rest of his face was purple.

"Hey," I said to Lent. "He's stiff."

"Naw," he's just drunk. Let him alone."

"Drunk nothing," I said. "He's stiff."

And he was stiff too. Rijer Mortes had already set in. The German had drunk himself to death, right in front of our eyes.

I knelt down and put my hand inside his coat and felt for his heart, but I couldn't feel nothing. So we called a doctor who lived across the street.

"Why hell," he said, "the guy's been dead two or three hours."

Well, that was just one plunk too many.

But nobody knew who he was or what to do with him. He had no papers on him. Nobody knew where his folks were. Nobody knew anything about him except he was German. And he'd spent his last dime.

So we laid him on an old door Lent had that had fallen off in his basement and we put him down in the cellar on this door across two sawhorses.

Then, that afternoon, we took up a collection. It wasn't much of a collection, pretty small: we got thirty-five dollars.

We knew a carpenter who said he'd make us a box that would do good enough for twenty-five dollars, and another guy who had a sort of truck and some horses who said he'd cart him up to the boothill for ten dollars.

A boothill is the back part of a cemetery, and they call it a boothill because that's where they bury the guys who die with their boots on, guys who get hung, or shot. Every town had a boothill in those days. Cyanide, Nemo, they all had a boothill.

So the next day, or maybe it was two days later, we took him up to the boothill in Deadwood and planted him. We couldn't put up no tombstone or even a marker, but unless somebody's moved him I guess he's lying there still.

And maybe after all it was a glorious death. In those days a man could get away somewhere.

PART FIVE

Lunar Caustic

Malcolm Lowry and the Outer Circle of Hell

The themes of *Lunar Caustic*, like unreliable demons, pursued Malcolm Lowry for most of his writing life. He first undertook the story in 1934, during his particularly black discovery of New York in his youth. The city, he once wrote a friend, "favours brief and furious outbursts, but not the long haul. Moreover for all its drama and existential fury, or perhaps because of it, it's a city where it can be remarkable hard—or so it seems to me—to get on the right side of one's despair . . ."

Lowry's encounter with New York was almost entirely in terms of loss, of departures and the beginning of long voyages. He was already, at the age of twenty-seven, a veteran seafarer (he had shipped around the world as a bosun's boy on a tramp steamer before taking an English tripos at Cambridge). Behind were a first novel, *Ultramarine*, and a broken marriage. He carried little else with him besides the horrendously developed sense of the "drunken madly revolving world" that was to receive such intense expression in *Under the Volcano*.

On his arrival from France, when asked by a New York customs officer if he had anything to declare, he replied, "I don't know. Let's see." They opened his large trunk. It contained one football boot and a copy of *Moby-Dick*. Existing on a small income from his well-to-do cottonbroker father, for the next year he lived in a near-slum, communicated with almost no one, drank and wrote. He always insisted that his stay in Bellevue Hospital during that time was voluntary, a "deliberate pilgrimage" to gather material. Towards the end of this period he completed the first draft of what was eventually to be *Lunar Caustic*.

He took the manuscript with him on his subsequent journey to Hollywood and continued to work on the story sporadically, first in

Cuernavaca, later in British Columbia and finally in England, for the next twenty-two years.

Lowry would have placed the present version in the category of work-in-progress, although two complete manuscripts and a partially finished third draft, plus a mass of notes, existed at the time of his sudden death by accidental suffocation in the tiny Sussex village of Ripe in 1957. He was a brooding, relentless, almost pathologically dissatisfied reviser of his own writing. At one point in the mid-1930s, an early draft, under the title *The Last Address*, was accepted by Whit Burnett for *Story Magazine*, but Lowry called it back. He permitted a French translation of the first version (it appeared in *L'Esprit* in 1956) only because, he explained, he was afraid of losing the manuscripts, something that had happened to him more than once. The author, although admitting the French version "has an air of completion," declared that he would have to put in at least six more months of solid work on it before he could offer it as finished.

In England during his last years, Lowry had decided to do another draft of *Lunar Caustic*, this time as a novella, to get the feel of it before undertaking it as a novel. At the time of his death he had reassembled and mixed the two drafts in the working method he always used. He often had five, ten or even twenty versions of a sentence, paragraph or chapter going at once. From these, he selected the best, blending, annealing and reworking again and again to obtain the highly charged, multi-leveled style that characterizes his best writing.

Lunar Caustic was to have been a major segment in *The Voyage That Never Ends*, a sequence of seven novels that Lowry planned round the central work, *Under the Volcano*. He saw the projected cycle as a modern *Divine Comedy*, with the ultimate goal Hell and redemption. *Lunar Caustic*, he once said, was only Purgatory. Yet he conceived of its characters as "the caryatids of human anguish" that hold up the world from below, and for the protagonist, William Plantagenet, the sound of the hospital door closing behind him "with a dithering crack" is the true sound of a damnation as immense and terrible as the City itself.

—*Conrad Knickerbocker*

Lunar Caustic

I

The editors, Lowry's second wife and Earle Birney, an old friend and neighbor of the author and professor of English at the University of British Columbia, describe the present version as being primarily a job of splicing, in an approximation of Lowry's method and intent. "We have not added a line," Mrs. Lowry has said in a letter to me. "Malcolm, of course, would then have rewritten, but who could do it as he would have?"
—C.K.

A man leaves a dockside tavern in the early morning, the smell of the sea in his nostrils, and a whisky bottle in his pocket, gliding over the cobbles lightly as a ship leaving harbour.

Soon he is running into a storm and tacking from side to side, frantically trying to get back. Now he will go into any harbour at all.

He goes into another saloon.

From this he emerges, cunningly repaired; but he is in difficulties once more. This time it is serious; he is nearly run over by a street car, he bangs his head on a wall, once he falls over an ashcan where he has thrown a bottle. Passers-by stare at him curiously, some with anger, others with amusement, or even a strange avidity.

This time he seeks refuge up an alley, and leans against the wall in an attitude of dejection, as if trying to remember something.

Again the pilgrimage starts but his course is so erratic it seems he must be looking for, rather than trying to remember something. Or perhaps, like the poor cat who had lost an eye in a battle, he is just looking for his sight?

The heat rises up from the pavements, a mighty force, New York groans and roars above, around, below him: white birds flash in the quivering air, a bridge strides over the river. Signs nod past him: The Best for Less, Romeo and Juliet, the greatest love story in the world, No Cover at Any Time, When pain threatens, strikes—

He enters another tavern, where presently he is talking of people he had never known, of places he had never been. Through the open door he is aware of the hospital, towering up above the river. Near him arrogant bearded derelicts cringe over spittoons, and of these men he seems afraid. Sweat floods his face. From the depths of the tavern comes a sound of moaning, and a sound of ticking.

Outside, again the pilgrimage starts, he wanders from saloon to saloon as though searching for something, but always keeping the hospital in sight, as if the saloons were only points on his circumference. In a street along the waterfront, where a bell is clanging, he halts; a terrible old woman, whose black veil only partly conceals her ravaged face, is trying to post a letter, trying repeatedly and failing, but posting it finally, with shaking hands that are not like hands at all.

A strange notion strikes him: the letter is for him. He takes a drink from his bottle.

In the Elevated a heavenly wind is blowing and there is a view of the river, but he is walking as though stepping over obstacles, or like Ahab stumbling from side to side on the careening bridge, 'feeling that he encompassed in his stare oceans from which might be revealed that phantom destroyer of himself.'

Down in the street the heat is terrific. Tabloid headlines: Thousands collapse in Heat Wave. Hundreds Dead. Roosevelt Raps Warmongers. Civil War in Spain.

Once he stops in a church, his lips moving in something like a prayer. Inside it is cool: around the walls are pictured the stages of the cross. Nobody seems to be looking. He likes drinking in churches particularly.

But afterwards he comes to a place not like a church at all.

This is the hospital: all day he has hovered around it; now it looms up closer than ever. This is his objective. Tilting the bottle to his mouth he takes a long, final draught: drops run down his neck, mingling with the sweat.

'I want to hear the song of the Negroes,' he roars. 'Veut-on que je disparaisse, que je plonge, à la recherche de l'anneau . . . I am sent to save my father, to find my son, to heal the eternal horror of three, to resolve the immedicable horror of opposites!'

With the dithering crack of a ship going on the rocks the door shuts behind him.

II

Looking down from the high buildings on 4th or 5th Avenue and 30th Street in New York you would never have thought there was grass growing down to the East River. But between the Observation Ward of the Psychiatric Hospital and the water, in a little lot to the left of the powerhouse—a building distinguishable even from midtown because its derricks are out of alignment and yearn over towards the hospital—you might have seen this grass as it grew there.

At the edge of the grass was a broken coal barge and beyond that, a little harbour bounded by two wharves. On the wharf to the right was the powerhouse and in front of it a shed used by the doctors as a garage, near which a green hospital ambulance was often parked.

The wharf to the left, though complicated by an extraordinary arrangement of wind-chutes, foghorns and ventilators, whose purpose was undiscoverable, had nevertheless a friendlier, more simple quality of holiday, of the seaside. Here white and blue motor boats were moored, with such names as 'Empty Pockets II', 'Dunwoiken', 'Lovebird', boats which seemed as they nudged and nibbled ceaselessly at the suicidal blackness of the stream to tell tender tales of girls in summer.

The only boat that tied up to the wharf by the powerhouse was the ferry, Tekanas. This, so someone said, went to the Ice Palace at Rockaway.

But between the two wharves and fast against the poverty grass before the hospital lay the coal barge, sunken, abandoned, open, hull cracked, bollards adrift, tiller smashed, its hold still choked with coal dust, silt, and earth through which emerald shoots had sprouted.

In the evenings, the patients would stare out over the river at the Jack Frost Sugar Works, and if there was a ship unloading there it seemed to them she might have some special news for them, bringing deliverance. But none ever came. . . .

Sometimes, when there was a mist, river and sky merged in a white calm through which little masts and tilted, squat towers seemed to be slowly flying. A smudged gasworks crouched like something that could spring, behind the leaning, vaporous geometry of cranes and angled church steeples; and the factory chimneys waved endless handkerchiefs of smoke.

Farewell, farewell, life!

Every so often, when a ship passed, there would be a curious mass movement towards the barred windows, a surging whose source was in the breasts of the mad seamen and firemen there, but to which all were tributary: even those whose heads had been bowed for days rose at this stirring, their bodies shaking as though roused suddenly from nightmare or from the dead, while their lips would burst with a sound, partly a cheer and partly a wailing shriek, like some cry of the imprisoned spirit of New York itself, that spirit haunting the abyss between Europe and America and brooding like futurity over the Western Ocean. The eyes of all would watch the ship with a strange, hungry supplication.

But more often when a ship went by or backed out from the docks opposite and swung around to steam towards the open sea, there was a dead silence in the ward and a strange foreboding as though all hope were sailing with the tide.

III

The man who now gave the name of Bill Plantagenet, but who had first announced himself as the s.s. Lawhill, awoke certain at least that he was on a ship. If not, where did those isolated clangings come from, those sounds of iron on iron? He recognized the crunch of water pouring over the scuttle, the heavy tramp of feet on the deck above, the steady Frère Jacques: Frère Jacques of the engines. He was on a ship, taking him back to England, which he never should have left in the first place. Now he was conscious of his racked, trembling, malodorous body. Daylight sent probes of agony against his eyelids. Opening them, he saw three Negro sailors vigorously washing down the deck. He shut his eyes again. Impossible, he thought.

And if he were on a ship, and supposedly therefore in the fo'c'sle, the alleyway at the end of which his bunk was must be taking up the fo'c'sle's entire length. He considered this madness—then the thrumming became so loud in his ears he found himself wondering if he were not lying in the propeller shaft.

As day grew, the noise became more ghastly: what sounded like a railway seemed to be running just over the ceiling. Another night came. The noise grew worse and, stranger yet, the crew kept multiplying. More and more men, bruised, wounded, and always drunk, were hurled down the alley by petty officers to lie face downward, screaming, or suddenly asleep on their hard bunks.

He was awake. What had he done last night? Played the piano? Was it last night? Nothing at all, perhaps, yet remorse tore at his vitals. He needed a drink desperately. He did not know whether his eyes were closed or open. Horrid shapes plunged out of the blankness, gibbering, rubbing their bristles against his face, but he couldn't move. Something had got under his bed too, a bear that kept trying to get up. Voices, a prosopopoeia of voices, murmured in his ears, ebbed away, murmured again, cackled, shrieked, cajoled; voices pleading with him to stop drinking, to die and be damned. Thronged, dreadful shadows came close, were snatched away. A cataract of water was pouring through the wall, filling the room. A red hand gesticulated, prodded him: over a ravaged mountain side a swift stream was carrying with it legless bodies yelling out of great eye-sockets, in which were broken teeth. Music mounted to a screech, subsided. On a tumbled bloodstained bed in a house whose face was blasted away a large scorpion was gravely raping a one-armed Negress. His wife appeared, tears streaming down her face, pitying, only to be instantly transformed into Richard III, who sprang forward to smother him.

After a time he was aware of two people looking at him kindly, a small old man and a little boy. The boy looked about ten years old with a handsome, intelligent face and fair hair brushed forward. The man thought vaguely of a portrait of Rimbaud at twelve or thereabouts.

'I'm Garry,' said the boy. 'My father makes moulds on terra-cotta . . . One day one of the pipes collapsed and the terra-cotta burst and collapsed. It was fallen through and reached the shore. It was condemned.'

'My name is Kalowsky,' said the old man. 'But you shouldn't be here. It is a terrible place.' Sweat laced the old man's forehead.

'But you'll get better soon, you're better already,' Garry continued. 'I'll tell you stories, then you'll get better. Do you know it's a funny thing, it's like a miracle, but wherever I am if I'm up in the air, or under the sea, or in the mountains, anywhere—I can tell a story. No matter where you put me, even in prison. I can be sitting, not sitting. Eating, not eating. I can put the whole thing into that story, that's what makes it a story.'

'His father's in prison,' Mr. Kalowsky whispered, 'but this is worse than a prison. I even heard the guard say: "Crooks ain't the only bad people, they're worse than crooks in here." ' He sighed. 'I have high blood pressure and this never was no place for me whether I am sane or insane. I might be dead by now, so you see—'. He patted him on the shoulder, smiling, 'but you will get better soon,' he added.

The man tried to reply but no words came.

'You understand me,' Garry said, taking his hand. 'I know, I can tell.'

Bill Plantagenet now knew himself to be in a kind of hospital, and with this realization everything became coherent and fell into place. The sound of water pouring over the scuttle was the terrific shock of the flushing toilets; the banging of iron and the dispersed noises, the rattling of keys, explained themselves; the frantic ringing of bells was for doctors or nurses; and all the shouting, shuffling, creaking and ordering was no more than the complex routine of the institution.

The thrumming came from the powerhouse next door, the sirens from the East River. And that noise at this moment, that roaring like the terrified lions he remembered, crated forward in a hurricane on a ship in the Bay of Bengal, was only an iron bedstead being moved.

The sailors washing down the deck were, it proved, sailors indeed, who swept the alleyway out of habit. But no one had been sweeping for a long time now; it was evening.

A Negro came tap-dancing down the ward, mouthing, and the man turned to the wall, to shut his thoughts away from this vision. 'That's Mr. Battle,' said Garry. 'He's crazy but you can't help liking him.'

Battle seemed to be dancing, singing, whispering and talking all at once—

> 'Joe started a poolroom in 1910
> When the monkey and the baboon came slowly
>   tipping in.
> The monkey could shoot rotation but the baboon
>   was no fool.

The monkey axed the baboon, shoot a game of
   pool?
That ole monkey—'

'Get back to your room, Battle!' an attendant shouted, and Battle vanished.

What time was it, Plantagenet wondered? What day was it? . . .

Mr. Kalowsky looked small and melancholy in bed. 'We can only wait and see,' he said, pursing his lips in and out. 'So many things can happen in a lifetime . . . I am eighty-two years, and my father lose his money—that's one thing. I hike from Berlin to Paris, that's another.

'I was one little Jew and my father became rich in Memel, Lithuania. From there he moved to Konigsberg and from there to Berlin. In Berlin I served my time as a silversmith. Then I roamed around.

'I hiked from Berlin to Paris. A rich woman paid my fare the first time but the second time the Germans went to war—1870. Anyone who couldn't speak fluently French was a Prussian. So I walked over the Jura mountains . . .'

The lights went out.

Battle, luminous in white pyjamas, was tap-dancing in the dark, his white teeth gleaming as he soft-shoed, whispering:

'That old monkey put the ace in the corner and deuce
   at the side
Say, Hightop, give the ace a ride!
The monkey broke the ball, made the 8, 9, 10,
Put deep bottom on a cue ball and kicked the fifteen
   in! . . .'

IV

Sweltering, delirious night telescoped into foetid day: day into night: he realized it was twilight though he had thought it dawn. Someone sat on his bed with a hand on his pulse, and forcing his eyes he saw a wavering white form which divided into three, became two and finally came into focus as a man in a white gown.

The man—a doctor?—dropped Plantagenet's wrist. 'You've certainly got the shakes,' he said.

'Shakes, yes.' The quivering of his body was such that, after his initial surprise, it impeded his speech. 'Well, what's wrong with me?' He tried to rise on his elbow which, jumping, did not hold him; he sank or fell back with a groan.

'Alcohol . . . And perhaps other things. Judging from your re-marks in the last few days I'd say it's about as bad as you suspect.'

'What did I say?'

The doctor smiled slightly. 'You said, "Hullo, father, return to the presexual revives the necessity for nutrition." Sounds as though you once read a little book.'

'Oh Christ! Oh God! Oh Jesus!'

'You made some fine giveaways.' The doctor shook his head. 'But let's be concrete. Who is Ruth? And the six Cantabs?'

'Bill Plantagenet and his Seven Hot Cantabs,' he corrected and continued with nervous rapidity, 'We went a treat in Cambridge, at the May Balls, or at the Footlights Club. We were all right with our first records, too, we took that seriously. But when we got over here we just broke up.' He grasped the doctor's arm. 'I couldn't seem to hold the boys together at all. Damn it, I don't know just what didn't happen. Of course there were complications about unions, income taxes, a price on our heads—'

'You're British, of course?'

'God knows where they all are now. The bull fiddle's fighting in Spain, and the saxophone section—and it's all my damn irrespon-sible bloody fault too.' He put his head down, burying it under the pillow. 'In a way I lost my contract, I lost my band, I lost Ruth.' He sat up, shaking, looking at the doctor furtively, yet with a certain rebelliousness. 'I've been playing in dives. But it's my hands, my hands, look—' he held them out, shaking. 'They're not big enough for a real pianist, I can't stretch over an octave on a piano. On a guitar I fake all the time.'

The doctor shook his head. 'You didn't leave Ruth because your hands couldn't stretch an octave,' he said. 'And where is Ruth? I assume she's your wife.'

'I don't know. I don't care. Hell with her! She only brought me back as a sort of souvenir from Europe. Perhaps it was America I was in love with. You know, you people get sentimental over England from time to time with your guff about sweetest Shake-speare. Well, this was the other way round. Only it was Eddie Lang and Joe Venuti and the death of Bix . . . What about a drink? And I wanted to see where Melville lived. You'll never know how dis-appointed I was not to find any whalers in New Bedford.'

The doctor rose and stood looking down at him. 'I'll send you a paraldehyde and splash. Perhaps it was your heart you couldn't make stretch an octave.'

'Please don't go!' He tried to sit up, grasping the doctor's arm. 'I've got to tell you—'

'Try it here for a few days, you'd better,' the doctor said not unkindly. He disengaged his arm, and wiped his forehead, sighing. 'It won't do you any harm. Where did you get those muscles?'

'Muscles,' said Plantagenet, his teeth chattering. 'Yes. I suppose so. That's weight-lifting. And I once took a freighter to the Orient, came back full of lions, one day I'd like to tell you about the lions. After that I read Meville instead. Four years ago I held the Cambridge record for the two-arm press; matter of fact, the only weight I can't lift—'

He managed to stagger to his feet, feeling the hospital tilt under him like a ship . . . Still trembling violently he walked to the high barred windows that gave on the East River. Heat haze hung over the waterfront. He looked down, his knees knocking together, at the wet grass below, and the broken coal barge. Amid ships where the hull had split, a mass of wet iron balanced. He glanced away— the tangled object had become a sailor sprawled broken on the deck in brown, shining oil-skins.

From the steel scaffolding that shored up the powerhouse, a pulley dropped a loop of rope; he saw a man hanging by the neck from this; it was the drummer of his band—but the vision faded instantly.

Staring out at the river his agony was like a great lidless eye.

Darkness was falling; through the clearing haze the stars came out. Over the broken horizon the Scorpion was crawling. There was the red, dying sun, Antares. To the south-east, the Retreat of the Howling Dog appeared. The stars taking their places were wounds opening in his being, multiple duplications of that agony, of that eye. The constellations might have been monstrosities in the delirium of God. Disaster seemed smeared over the whole universe. It was as if he were living in the pre-existence of some unimaginable catastrophe, and he steadied himself a moment against the sill, feeling the doomed earth itself stagger in its heaving spastic flight towards the Hercules Butterfly.

'I'se bin here just up to almos' exactly let me see, men, seventeen days and a half exac.' Battle was tap-dancing behind him.

'Dat guy talks wif his feet.'

'Yes sah,' said Battle, whirling around, 'I do that thing, man!'

'He comes from Louisiana; he knocked that old engineer's tooth out,' said Garry beside him.

5

'Now I catch Jersey Blues,' Battle said. 'I'se got fifteen customers.' He skipped off.

—He was conscious that time was passing, that he was getting 'better'. The periodic, shuddering metamorphoses his mind projected upon almost every object, bad as they were, were no longer so atrociously vivid. Moreover he had at first forgotten for long periods that he was able to get out when he wished. Now he forgot more rarely. He was only a drunk, he thought. Though he had pretended for a while that he was not, that he was mad with the full dignity of madness. The man who thought himself a ship. And time was passing; only his sense of it had become subject to a curious prorogation. He didn't know whether it was the fifth or the sixth day that found him still staring out of the window at twilight, with Garry and Mr. Kalowsky by his side like old faithful friends. The powerhouse no longer was a foreign place. The wharves, the motor boats, the poverty grass, he had received into his mind now, together with the old coal barge, to which Garry often turned.

'It was condemned,' he would say. 'One day it collapsed and fell apart.'

Garry looked at Bill wildly, grasping his arm. 'The houses of Pompeii were fallen!' His voice dropped to a whisper. 'And you'd see a house suddenly fall in, collapse; and the melted rock and the hot mud poured down; people ran down to the boat. But it was collapsed.' Looking up he added breathlessly, 'Gold rings and boxes of money and strange tables and they dug down the side of the great mountain.'

'Yes suh, man,' Battle danced. 'He's de ole man of the mountain. He track along wit a horse and ban'. Put a jiggle in his tail as you pass him by—' he danced away singing. 'De biggest turtle I ever see, he twice de size of you and me.'

Kalowsky stood quietly watching, pursing his lips continually in and out like a dying fish. What was that film Plantagenet had seen once, where the shark went on swallowing the live fish, even after it was dead?

Garry clutched Bill's arm again. 'Listen. What do you think will be left of this building in a few years? I'll tell you. They'd still find the brick buildings but there wouldn't be any beds, only a rusty frame, and the radiator, you would touch it and it would fall to pieces. All that would be left of the piano would be the keys; all the rest would rot. And the floor.' Garry paused, considering. 'And one of us sat on it and the whole thing fell down, collapsed. We went out the door where the fire escape was and it fell off, seven storeys off, it fell down.'

But what had really begun to make things a bit more tolerable for him was this very comradeship of his two friends. Sometimes he even tricked himself into imagining that a kind of purpose united them. Part of the truth was that, like new boys in a hostile school, like sailors on their first long voyage on a miserable ship, like soldiers in a prison camp, they were drawn together in a doleful world where their daydreams mingled, and finding expression, jostled irresponsibly, yet with an underlying irreducible logic, around the subject of homecoming. Yet with them 'home' was never mentioned, save very obliquely by Garry. Plantagenet sometimes suspected the true nature of that miraculous day they looked to when their troubles would all be ended, but he couldn't give it away. Meanwhile it masqueraded before them in the hues of various dawns—never mind what was going to happen in its practical noontide.

As a matter of fact, with one part of his mind, he was seriously convinced that Mr. Kalowsky and Garry were at least as sane as he: he felt too that he would be able to convince the doctor, when he saw him again, that an injustice had been committed, which never would otherwise have come to light.

But trying to explain their whole situation to himself his mind seemed to flicker senselessly between extremities of insincerities. For with another part of his mind he felt the encroachment of a chilling fear, eclipsing all other feelings, that the thing they wanted was coming for him alone, before he was ready for it; it was a fear worse than the fear that when money was low one would have to stop drinking; it was compounded of harrowed longing and hatred, of fathomless compunctions, and of a paradoxical remorse, as it were in advance, for his failure to attempt finally something he was not now going to have time for, to face the world honestly; it was the shadow of a city of dreadful night without splendour that fell on his soul; and how darkly it fell whenever a ship passed!

V

Pneumatic Tube Station 382; Electro-cardiograph dept. 257; Operating Rooms 217; Physiotherapy 320; Neuro. Path. Laboratory 204; Dial O for Psychiatric numbers . . .

Occupational Therapy Dept. 338 . . .

The room was filled by an almost continual unebbing surf of noise. Unable to stand it at first, Plantagenet had ended by so loudly hammering the soft metal into a fluted ashtray that it seemed he wished to drown out this bane of noise for ever.

But there were quieter occupations. Beside him, Garry was painting a wooden duck green, and Battle was plaiting with straw a cymbal-shaped hat, and singing 'Ole Man Mose Is Dead', though this therapy always brought on his fits, and back in the ward again it was certain he would try to get up the chimney.

'Well, how are you, Battle?' An attendant glanced at the group, paused long enough to jingle his huge keys, then passed on. Bill heard voices from up the ward muttering, 'Is this a hospital or a prison?' 'It's a prison.' 'Well, I have to come down here once a week, mister . . . Anything more, I draw on interest.' 'That guy asleep over there, see? He had two guns in his pocket, two twenty-twos and a suitcase plenty full of bullets. Held up that store, you know.'

'It fell apart, collapsed!'

'Well, I don't know exac'ly wen dey gonna let me out,' Battle murmured vacantly. 'I axed de doctah but he don' say yet, but I guess it gonna be soon.'

'After you've taken yo' temp'rature.'

'De ole lollipop, yes sah, man!' said Battle. 'When dey come an' give you de lollipop den you go an' play de piano, sho.' He shuffled round a corner.

'Come on. I'll teach you semaphore,' Garry said. In a moment Battle was signalling in imitation.

'Move yo' lef' ha' to E. To make M, move to F,' Battle repeated after Garry, then immediately he started to shadow-box again, though Garry went on signalling. A little man with a beard passing by said to himself loudly, 'That's semaphore. All Boy Scouts use it.'

Battle snorted and returned to semaphore, to the delight of Garry, shouting, 'Ayeh! Beah! Gee!' while Garry shifted his pink-palmed paws for him. Two other Negroes appeared now as the semaphoring was being transformed into a grotesque dance. 'Doo, tee, da, do,' they shouted, pouncing around the beds. 'Tee, da, do, aw-aw, do pup depup, da woo!'

Battle was hitting Garry playfully. 'See dat lef' jab! Is yo' scared of me?'

Plantagenet suddenly caught sight, through the bars, of four operations being performed simultaneously in the wing opposite in high sunlit rooms of glass, so that it seemed as though the front of that part of the hospital had suddenly become open, revealing, as in the cabin plans of the 'Cunard' or in charts of the human anatomy itself, the activities behind the wraith of iron or brick or shin: and it was strange to watch these white-masked figures working behind the glass that now glittered like a mirage. At the same time the whole scene that lay before them suddenly, like the looming swift white hand of a traffic policeman, reeled towards him; he felt he had only to stretch out his fingers to touch the doctor working on the right side of the table sewing up the incision, or the nurse plastering and binding the patient or placing the blanket over the body; and it seemed to him that all these dressings and redressings in these hours of north light were at the same time being placed, torn away and replaced, on a laceration of his own mind.

Or—was he dead? Ah ha, watch the surgeon slit the foot of the dead man! What next, Nostradamus? Will blood appear? Or has it clotted, in some vital organ? Bleed, dead man, bleed, set the poor surgeon's mind at rest, so that he won't have to get drunk and go through the jumps and the blind staggers; the horror of the rats, the wheeling bushmills, and the Orange Bitters; bleed, so that he won't find himself reflecting in summer that even Nature herself is shot through with jitteriness, the neurotic squirrel and the sparrows nibbling the dung where the octoroons, the creole and the quadroon have galloped past in black dust; bleed, so that he will not have to think how much more beautiful women are when you are dying, and they sway down the streets under the fainting trees, their bosoms tossing like blossoms in the warm gusts; bleed, so that he will not have to hear the louse of conscience, nor the groaning of imaginary men, nor see, on the window blind all night the bad ghosts—

'But Mr. Battle, you're taking the hat all to pieces. You're doing it all wrong,' a schoolteacherly voice was saying.

'Ah'm doin' it all wrong, am I Ma'm? To ma' way of thinkin' Ah'm doin' it O.K. Is dis treatment 29 or what?' And a moment later, as the gaily coloured hat was being torn to pieces, 'Ah'll give yuh treatment 63!'

Later, when the nine high candles in their circular base were lighted above the old men who were considered too jittery or too obscene to eat with the others in the regular room, and they were bent over their stew in a grey, trembling despair, some seeming not to know they were eating at all, the food perhaps tasteless to them as they cuffed it slowly and sleepily with their harmless spoons, others not even attempting to eat but wearing a fixed smile, as though the thought even of misery afforded them some perverse comfort, Plantagenet, watching them, gradually thought he understood the meaning of death, not as a sudden dispatch of violence, but as a function of life. He stood up, as if to strike off an enemy, then let his hands drop limply to his sides.

There was a huge clanking of keys, the bathroom door was being unlocked, and Battle, blundering around just then, shouted 'Toilet! Toilet! Ah don' feel like sittin' down. Ah just feel like shittin' on de flo'.' 'Time for a butt,' a voice murmured and the shuffling sounded quicker.

The door of the bathroom clanged shut and the keys went clinking down the corridor.

When they got back to the main ward Battle was trying to climb up the chimney. The attendants pulled him down and he fell flat on his face, refusing to move.

Garry and Bill stood near. Mr. Kalowsky was watching them, his spoon poised, his gaze passing mechanically, like a slowed fan, from them to Battle and to the attendants and back again.

After a while the heroic Battle stirred and, sitting up, rubbed his head and remarked with consummate sanity, looking full at the nurse:

'No matter what a woman play, whether she know or whether she don' know, she beat you at it.'

VI

One of the hottest days of all was the day of the puppet show. The three friends made their beds early.

'I don't say this to many people,' Garry was saying to Mr. Kalowsky as he smoothed down the grimed sheets, 'but I wish you were my father.'

Keys clashed like cymbals, the bathroom door banged open, the daily routine was beginning. Presently the rooms were filled with the dreadful noise of shuffling feet. Heads bowed, the patients scraped their cord soles along the floor, save when they were called to the lavatory or for a smoke. For a minute or two after that they held themselves erect as if they had forgotten the horror of their lives, but soon one head bowed down again, then another, while their senses, that had almost thrilled to life again in that momentary,

trembling order, became numbed, unaware of their foreheads gleaming with sweat or their dirty feet and bodies. Occasionally when
some one sat down on his bed, an attendant shouted.

'Get up there! Keep moving!'

Then he would take his place once more in the procession which
Garry, Plantagenet and Mr. Kalowsky had long since joined.

'I am just the Wandering Jew,' Mr. Kalowsky said with a wry
smile. 'It was in 1870,' he added, 'and the Germans went to war.'
They were passing the tall barred window which gave on the east
side of the hospital, round which the sunlight seemed to be racing
like a small vicious boy, he thought, bursting with health and din,
tormenting them. 'That evening it was sunset and the French peasants came from work. I had a cane in my hand with a big piece
of iron in the end of it, and a Frenchman approached me with a
scythe and asked me: "Quelle patrie avez-vous?" . . . and he understood me that I had said . . . "Yes," I said, "I take your challenge" . . . and he said—no, . . . I said,' the old man turned to
Bill suddenly. 'Will you tell the doctor that? I would like to go to
a sanitorium. Perhaps they will give us some work to do. But we
are behind bars now.'

The window, raging with the sunlight, came round again. Then
Plantagenet noticed that it was really only he who hated the sun:
both Garry and Mr. Kalowsky could spare a smile for it.

'And this man with the stekel grasped my hand and said, 'Bien
garçon, you are a brave boy." And he took me to a café and ordered
dinner with a glass of wine. I walked a little further and I met a
rich miller. Well, I met him and I went to him and I said, "Voulez-
vous me donner un verre de l'eau?" And he said, "Venez avec moi."
That means come with me,' Mr. Kalowsky explained politely. 'And
he bought a big bottle of wine and it was the month of January,
1870 and it was so hot I sent my overcoat to Berlin.'

'Why, that was before my father was born,' said Plantagenet.

'Yes, it was the south of France, you see,' Mr. Kalowsky said.
'When I finished the glass of wine that's the time I got my high
blood pressure.'

And as the old man talked on and on, the confused story of his
wandering seemed to be following the weary pattern of their walk,
though it always came back to the melancholy refrain: 'But now
we are behind bars.'

And Plantagenet thought that their tramping might have been an
extension of that wandering; it was as if an obscure yet cogent

necessity had arisen out of their meeting, like some meeting at the day and place of Judgment, for them to make an account as best they could, to cover again the steps of their life to this encounter at what was, perhaps, the end.

'Whatever made you hurt that little girl?' he asked Garry carelessly, after a long silence, during which the steady shuffling of feet had become intolerable. He had forgotten when it was he had learned that Garry had cut the child's throat with a broken bottle. 'I don't believe it!' he added, immediately regretting his question. They were standing aside for Battle who, pursued by a laughing nurse, was running through the corridors, tearing a bright-coloured basket to pieces, shouting, 'Ah'll give you treatment 63—'

'Gee, it was only a little scratch,' Garry said, with enormous emphasis, as they approached the beds once more. 'Besides, she chalked on the pavement that I and my mother and father were bad people who should be in hell.' He began to cry.

'Don't remind him of it,' whispered Mr. Kalowsky. 'He must go to court soon to see the judge. But perhaps you'll be seeing the doctor before that. You shouldn't be here, Garry,' he said aloud. 'You'll only get worser here—whatever do they want to put you here for?'

The nurse had given up the chase but Battle banked towards them. 'Once I run right through de state of Ohio wit'out takin' my bref,' he announced, holding his breath; then he had gone.

'—when you should be reading the works of Dickens?' Mr. Kalowsky added to Garry with a polite nod to Bill, as if he had implied, 'the great Englishman.'

'I know them all,' Garry said, quickly forgetting his tears. 'And I know Elengland too,' he addressed Bill. 'After you've seen the doctor, I'll tell you, you'll take us to Elengland. Mr. Kalowsky and I and maybe my brother; I can see it all plainly. There are some farms there. I know I might see artists on the hillside or cows and sheep grazing in green pastures. I can see them there, the artists, painting pictures of flowers and the different birds and the mountains and the lakes and trees. Or,' he dropped his voice, 'you might go to one part where an artist is painting pictures of ruins.'

In the ward a game of ping-pong had been instituted between Battle and the nurse, but Battle was already firmly taking down the net, the ball a red bubble in his mouth: 'Dis ain't no bean parlour, nor yet no tennis parlour,' he complained and a moment later, when they had reached the tall window, he overtook them, dancing and singing: 'I was goin' down Main. I met a police. He ask ma name. Battle, Ah said. And around ma arm was a bracelet chain—'

They had come round to the ward facing the East River again. 'Do you see that old coal barge?' asked Garry. 'I can tell you about her. Yes sir, I can tell them . . . In 1914 she was loaded with fine coal, but the rope snapped, she drifted with the current, and most of the coal is all at the bottom now. The rest is buried here and the barge is smashed, broken.'

'Now Garry, tell us a humoristic story,' said Mr. Kalowsky with a kindly look at both of them.

'Sure,' said Garry, and their step became a little brisker. 'Over in India in the jungles there was a mother and a baby elephant. The natives wanted to trap the baby elephant and bring him back alive. The mother elephant and the baby were out one day in the jungles and the baby was chasing a butterfly and fell in the pit and the white men tied her up—'

VII

Then it was time for the puppet show. The patients took their places slowly, plucking the cotton thread out of each other's gowns, made of towelling.

'Stop pulling things off me! What you think you're doing?'

'Going to hit me?'

'I ain't going to hit you.'

'Quiet, boys, please! Quiet now.'

'I hit you two time. I hit you one there and one there.'

'Jesus Christ up in the sky, look up dar, Ah can see him: Abraham Lincoln down under de flo'—but whar George Washington? dat's what I want to know—Let no one take ma seat while Ah'm gone,' Battle danced out of the room and returned swiftly with a tabloid newspaper.

Plantagenet looked over his shoulder and read:

TWO SNAKES WRITHE IN COURT
WOMEN QUAKE AS REPTILES SPIT VENOM AT TRIAL

Buzzing their hollow rattles so loud that women in the far corners of the crowded courtroom shivered at the frightening sounds, two diamond-backed rattlesnakes, glittering in their new skins, today were placed on the council table in Superior Judge Fricke's court,

where Robert S. James, Birmingham barber, crouched ghost-faced
and jittery at his trial for the murder of his golden-haired bride—

He noted the date line with a flash of terror. That long!

Garry read with difficulty: 'Vice Queen back from cell to reign
in Atlantic City.'

'Jesus, those old snakes,' said somebody. 'Have you ever had
those old snakes?'

'The wheels. They're worse. Who'll cure a man of the wheels?'

'What's the matter with your head that you read all these lies?'
said Mr. Kalowsky. 'And all this dirt.'

'Suppose I tried to tell the doctor I thought you'd been framed,
Mr. Kalowsky.' Plantagenet said, almost to himself. 'You're as sane
as most people I know. Trouble is: am I? And would he listen
to me?'

'Two snakes—in court—at trial.' Garry was spelling out. 'Gee
whiz!'

'Jesus, I know a guy on the News, and when I get out of here
I'm going up there and tell him what I think of this goddam place.
Now Jesus, listen to this, will you? I was sitting on the wharf drinking whisky when this cop came up and said, "What are you doing?"
I said, "Why, man, I'm just drinking this pint of whisky and now
I think I'll finish it." Well, he watched me finish it and the next
thing I knew I was being taken here. Why, I was in complete control of myself. I had eighteen toothpicks, I knew exactly—see—
and I told this cop so, and I used one of them, for Christ sake . . .
That makes nineteen toothpicks I've got waiting for me downstairs
and I'll get them when I go, goddam if I won't. And they say I'm
crazy!'

There was a roar in the building, shaking the doors. 'See dat
plane comin' down?' said Battle. 'That's no plane, that's an automobile.' 'An automobile can't fly.' 'Yes sir, that's an automobile can
fly. Let no one jump off after women now!' Battle yelled, leaping
to his feet.

'Hullo,' said a voice in Plantagenet's ear. 'How's Mr. Remorse
today?'

'Oh, hullo, Doctor,' he said, half rising. 'Not bad. Fine. I've
quite a lot to tell you, if you have time one day.'

'I see by your chart you've been coming along all right.' The
doctor sat down beside him heavily. 'I meant to see you before this,'

he said, 'but I've never been so busy . . . and the heat . . . What's on your mind?'

'Oh—never mind now. I'll come to your office, if I may?' The doctor nodded, absently. 'Well,' Plantagenet added nervously, 'what about this puppet show?'

'Mmm. My idea, mostly. It represents a definitely socializing influence, giving the patients an opportunity to get together and control their usual tendencies for emotional outbursts.' He glanced around, frowning thoughtfully. 'Then too, the patients have a common experience which they can share later, and talk about. It is sometimes moderately successful.'

At one end of the wardroom table a wooden rectangular construction had appeared, with an oblong slit for the stage, covered by green and yellow curtains, against which leaned the puppeteer, a sane man from 'outside', arms akimbo, face ochre from a dark lantern. 'There's been some mixup with your music,' he said. 'Music next week. You remember,' he added with a little laugh, 'Caspar bought himself a balloon, and we shall see what adventures he will have.'

"Yes sah!'

'All right, here we go.' The puppeteer drew down the blind on the window nearest to him, creating an illusion of coolness, though the room was by no means dark.

'Yes sah boss,' said Battle, scratching himself. 'Ready for sho'.'

The curtains disclosed that Caspar was Punch, and that Punch was an American who had just fallen from a balloon into the African jungle.

'I t'ink I come for de opera season,' Punch said, then as if instantly realizing he was supposed to be dying, 'Watah! I'm dying, dying, dying.'

An airman in red, gold and green, he looked up at the sky and the eyes of Battle followed.

'Jesus Chris' up dere but you won't see him. An' Abraham Lincoln down under the flo'. But whar's George Washington, dat's what Ah wants to know—'

Judy was an Ethiopian with a brass ring in her nose who approached with a whisky bottle in a convulsion of mincing jerks. 'Watah,' gasped Punch, and Judy gave him the whisky bottle. 'How you feel now? You feel better now?' 'Where am I?' 'This is Kayonka country, Africa.' 'You can't fool me.' 'It just so happens I'se de

sister of de chief ob de tribe and here comes my brother now.'
'You're the chief of police?' Punch greeted the chieftain. 'Well, I was
in New York myself.' 'Do you know Billy Minsky's?' 'Yes sir, and
let me tell you I wish I was there now for the giant is eating all
our tribe up.' 'The Giants in New York?' 'No, no baseball here.'
'I'm a college guardian myself . . .'

Mr. Kalowsky was getting restless. Leaning over to Plantagenet
he said, 'What do they want to give us this nonsense for? They
should give us humoristic stories.'

Garry was also restless. 'I'll tell you a better story than this,'
he said. 'Say, will you tell him I can tell better stories than this?'
he whispered, half looking at the doctor, who did not appear to
have heard.

On the stage the chief was saying, 'Meet my sister, Sakoluki,'
while Punch-Caspar shook hands with the ring in her nose, to the
enormous delight of Battle.

Suddenly, from the back of the stage, there was a roaring like
the seaplane that had been circling the harbour, and something
began slowly to rise there, over the horizon. It was the hand of the
giant. Just as Punch and Judy were snatching a kiss it grabbed the
chief, slowly sinking from sight again with him.

'Look, the giant got him,' Garry said.

'We should have humoristic stories,' complained Mr. Kalowsky,
'not this nonsense. We should have Charlie Chaplin two times a
week—he would be only too pleased to come.'

'Take dat ring out of yo' nose,' advised Battle.

'The giant's blind,' said Garry.

'Sometimes the most creative suggestions come from patients,'
the doctor said to Plantagenet in an undertone. 'We often get many
leads for analysis from these things.'

'Where's the giant gone?' asked Punch.

'Behind me,' said Battle, 'getting dat ole shoe shine.'

Mr. Kalowsky clicked his tongue.

The hand of the blind giant rose again. Judy was captured.

As the hand plunged about reaching for Punch with a weird
accelerated motion which cast glowering shadows on the wall, it
struck Plantagenet that the drama was being diverted from its
course by some sinister disposition of the puppeteer's; he sensed, or
thought he did, the doctor's increasing discomfort, as of a god, he
thought, who discovers all over again that man is not long to be

trusted with the strings of his destiny. Was it only his imagination, or was the puppeteer trying to deliberately frighten them? If so, the attempt was not proving much of a success; both Garry and Mr. Kalowsky were contemptuous, and of the others only Battle was encouraging. The rest were indifferent.

Plantagenet suspected he was the only one who was frightened; nor was he frightened now so much by the hand, nor the shadows, which partook of the familiarity of his delirium, as by that fact. He had the curious feeling that he had made a sort of descent into the maelstrom, a maelstrom terrifying for the last reason one might have expected: that there was about it sometimes just this loathsome, patient calm.

My God, he thought suddenly, why am I here, in this doleful place? And without quite knowing how this had come about, he felt that he had voyaged downward to the foul core of his world; here was the true meaning underneath all the loud inflamed words, the squealing headlines, the arrogant years. But here too, equally, he thought, looking at the doctor, was perhaps the cure, the wisdom and vision, more patient still . . . And goodness was here too—he glanced at his two friends—yes, by what miracle did it come about that compassion and love were here too?

And he wondered if the doctor ever asked himself what point there was in adjusting poor lunatics to a mischievous world over which merely more subtle lunatics exerted almost supreme hegemony, where neurotic behaviour was the rule, and there was nothing but hypocrisy to answer the flames of evil, which might be the flames of Judgment, which were already scorching nearer and nearer . . . He saw that the doctor, sweat trickling down his face, leaning forward anxiously, was almost exhausted.

With this realization, his mind wandered. He began, as often before, to imagine himself abandoned. The doctor, his last hope, on his final frontier, would have no time for him, or his friends. He saw the plunging hand only as his fate, the hieroglyphic of 'they', which was seeking him out, to take him away: now he became Caspar, dodging absurdly from one side of the stage to the other; now he envisaged himself in the familiar role of one driven friendless through hostile country into ever darker corners, more remote hiding places.

The show was at an end and he did not know whether Punch had escaped or not.

'More next week,' the puppeteer said, laughing.

'If he'd got hold of him he'd been mashed potatoes by now,' Battle said, getting up, 'been skinmeat.'

'It's a lot of nonsense!' said Mr. Kalowsky. 'We should have humoristic stories.'

The blinds ran up, letting in the glare; the stage was put away, the giant, Punch, Judy, the chief and the balloon laid in boxes neatly, the magic lantern telescoped into a canvas case. The doctor went off rapidly with the puppeteer, without a glance behind.

Soon, as if the patients had been merely resting on their pilgrimage, the obsequious procession round the wards was resumed. Faces that had been intent for a time, however negatively, upon the antics of Caspar, collapsed in grey misery. At first there was a little speculation about the show: then not a nod. The shuffling began all over again. An attendant, jangling his keys, shouted, 'Get up, keep moving there!' while Garry, Bill, Mr. Kalowsky and even Battle walked in silence too, finally, their heads bowed like the others in that marathon of the dead. The audience had broken up, each man to his inner Africa.

VIII

Pneumatic Tube Station 382; Electro-cardiograph dept. 257. Operating Rooms 217; Physiotherapy 320; Neuro Path. Laboratory 204; Dial O for Psychiatric numbers . . .

Sometimes it was only when he read the writing on the wall that he remembered where he was, and now, entering the wardroom annex, he remembered. Yet gone for a few minutes late that hot thundery afternoon was the atmosphere of a City Hospital. There was about the curtained scene a ghastly cosiness, a deceptive gaiety. As he sat down to the piano and swung into 'Sweet and Low', he was harrowed to think how obliquely perfect an expression his rendition was of the tortured memories it might have evoked had he been playing it straight. But he was not playing it straight, no one could have recognized the tune, and yet he was absurdly disappointed by the indifference of his audience. They might have been watching the puppet show again. He began to play a little louder, smiling at Garry, who was leaning over his shoulder, and at Mr. Kalowsky, who was sitting near in a wicker chair, nodding encouragement, as he chorded into 'These Foolish Things'. His hands trembled still, but their trembling was stayed now by the vise of his determination. As he felt at the moment he might have had no more than a medicable case of the jitters, the kind of morning-after during which he suffered agonies between bromides over the spectacle he had made of himself last night; quite overlooking the anonymity, the inconspicuous precision, even the courtliness of his behaviour: for who had seen him, in the deserted corridor, wander mistakenly into the ladies' room, who had remarked that vomit placed with inimitable, circumspect painstakingness under the fire extinguisher? And then the upright journey down in the lift, the humming hotel lobby reeling under the palmettos where not an eye turned his way, and the miles on miles upon miles swimming home with the instinct of a salmon . . . No, were his past just such a feeble sum of prankishness, were his past not as the nations—and which of them dared stop drinking, dared face the knees of the years knocking together?—did there not exist in it, quite apart from what details he accurately, remorsefully recalled of the criminal folly of his life, or the irreparable damage he had done, such a long weary heritage of unsalvageable aftermath, he might have been able to persuade himself, by his physical symptoms, that he had such a hangover, with its attendant harmless delusions, that it really 'relieved' him to imagine what his brothers would say to the game of whist Battle was conducting with two glistening Negro sailors in the centre of the annex, could it have been transferred to the drawing-room he had in mind.

'Oh Lord,' Battle caracoled, 'look at Miss Diamond there—gwine to make plenty money, bo.'

'You tellin' me.'

'Jesus it's de King ob Man,' Battle slapped down the King of Hearts, 'I break de table with dat.'

'Kill 'em!'

'Too young and he lays on de Jack like dat.'

'T'ank you, boss, we cleaned him up.'

'Goodbye, I'se de ace ob whist!' Battle was half singing now, but not to Bill's music. Something in the rhythm of his blood, it seemed, did not like Bill's music; not because it was alien music, it was precisely because it sounded too cognate that he would not conform to it.

Glancing sideways at Battle, Plantagenet felt the Negro was jealous of his music, that he resented it, as that poor defective behind him with the long blond hair and a hanging jaw resented it, though from an envy of a different quality. Altering his tune to 'Milneburg Joys', he looked carelessly about him, at the patients lolling against the piano opposite Garry, out of some surviving domestic habit doubtless, since they weren't listening, at the poor defective, at the two nurses interminably, ethenically discussing an autopsy, at the closed door of the doctor's office.

'When we get out of here,' Garry whispered in Bill's ear, 'some Saturday morning I'm going to buy some rope and put it in the crabbing nets, and then get some fish heads and I'll tie them in the net, and I'll put the net on a wagon, and my lunch, and get my brother and me and we'll go down—and you'll come with us of course, and Mr. Kalowsky—and we'll all go down to the dock and stay all day, and then on the way back we'll sell a couple of dozen and maybe get a dollar and then go back and cook the rest and then after we eat them and go to the show we have some sort of candy and then do the very same thing the next day.' Out of the corner of his eye Plantagenet could see Battle and the Negroes watching him with disdain as his fingers picked out the pattern of Garry's innocent day.

'I was standin' in de window one day,' Battle announced, 'when de captain and de mate dey had a few words, when dat great Titanic struck,' he slapped down a card.

But his song gradually assembled itself into something with a strange encompassing rhythm to which the feet and hands of the other Negro card-players responded as with a soft beating of Haitian tambours:

> 'When dat great Titanic hit dat cold iceberg
> Say back up Shine and take another blow,
> I got a concrete bottom and a barfroom flo' . . .'

'Yeh man,' whispered the other card-players, 'yeh man,' they drummed with their feet and hands while Battle flung down each card he played violently.

> 'So up jump Shine from de deck below
> Says, Cap'n don' you know
> Water comin' in your barfroom do'?
> Say Shine, go back and pack a few mo'sacks
> 'Cause I got fifty-four pumps to keep dis water back . . .'

Plantagenet began to strike some chords having little in common with each other save that they were minor.

'I can tell you a better song than that,' Garry whispered uneasily. 'Go on playing and I'll tell you.' He played 'In a Mist'. 'I saw a ship a-sailing, a-sailing on the sea, and oh, it was a lady with pretty things for thee, there were comforts in the cabin and apples in the hall, there were four-and-twenty white mice stood between the decks—'

> 'Say yes sir, Cap, I know dat too
> But dis one time yo' work won' do;
> So Shine went down, he began to think,
> Ah t'ink dis big boat won' sink.'

'Dis big boat won' sink,' repeated some of the others thoughtfully, cards poised.

Battle raised his card aloft and turning his eyes ceilingward as if in benediction declared:

'Shine look up and said dese people take me fo' a fool.' Battle smacked down his card, shuffling his feet under the table.

'But Ah'm gwine to jump overboard and gwine to Liverpool.'

The word detached itself from the card game like a missile directed straight at Plantagenet, who abruptly changed to 'Singing the Blues'. He played Frankie Trumbauer's old version fast.

> 'So Shine jumps overboard and begins to swim
> So all de people on de boat were lookin' after him!'

The card-players swayed in their seats.

'Listen!' said Garry, 'I can tell you a better sea poem. Listen! We were shattered in a cabin; not a soul dared to stir; the storm was on the deep while the angry sea roared; and the thunder sounded like the trumpet and the lightning cut away his mast. Well, the captain staggered down the stairs and the little daughter gripped his icy hands and the father said, "Tis well, little daughter, for we are done." Next day we anchored in the harbour, safe.'

> 'Why dat de Cap'n's daughter standing' on de deck
> With her drawers up around her neck
> Say, come back here and save po' me
> Ah'll give you a lot of dat what you want, you see,
> But go back whore and get yo'self ready
> You ain't no good standin' shiverin' like a cold box
>   jelly . . .'

'Like a cold box jell—'

'Listen! I'll tell you a better story about an iceberg. Better than that.' Garry's eyes were fixed on Bill's face. He leaned closer. 'It was late in September when a large whaling boat headed north going to catch whales in the cold sea—' Plantagenet was becoming so nervous he kept putting his hand to his mouth thinking he had a cigarette in it; once he even leaned out for an imaginary cigarette consuming itself in an imaginary tray, but 'Singing the Blues' rattled on like some combustion engine he had set in motion. '—and in the bay one of the men spotted this black whale—' 'Are you sure it wasn't a white whale,' he asked. He fumbled a break, recovered and went on. 'It was a black whale all right, whales are black, not white.'

He was playing with furious quiet now, 'Fierce Raged the Tempest O'er the Deep'.

> 'And dere was de Cap'n standin' on de deck
> He say come back here and save po' me
> I'll make you richer dan any shine should be . . .
> But Shine had his head in a gap
> And his tail in a swing
> Dis is one time dese ol' people
> Can't tell Shine a thing . . .'

'—well, so they stuck the harpoon inside the whale and the whale went along and smashed into the iceberg and it was killed and they hauled him up and tied it alongside and they salted it and packed it in the barrels until there was only bones.'

> 'And the iceberg,'
> 'That was all broken, smashed.'

'Say dis ole sun going' down and dis ole water gettin' cool Ah got to shake a wicked tail to get to Liverpool—'

'Say, look here, all you people! God don! Ah gonna hippertize him! Ah gonna hippertize you!' Battle shouted. He got up, scattering the cards on the floor.

'Go on playing, go on playing, please!' Garry said, and he softly played the 'Death of Ase' for him in ragtime, with his right hand in the base.

'Listen, wherever I am I can tell a story. No matter where you put me, even in prison. Will you tell the doctor I can tell them?'

Battle and the other Negroes gathered round the piano, elbowing aside the patients lolling there. Glancing at Battle for approval, Plantagenet struck four jagged chords, one for the death of Ase, one for the doom of the Titanic, one for the Pequod, one for the whale, white or black it didn't matter which, Battle eyed him stonily. Plantagenet struck up 'Clarinet Marmalade'. He was playing wonderfully well, he thought.

'Say listen,' Battle demanded, 'lets have some truckin'—don't you know any truckin'.'

'Very nice,' said Mr. Kalowsky encouragingly. 'Now give us some humoristic music.'

Suddenly the detective got up. "You don't know nothing, you souse,' he said, pushing him. 'Lemme at that piano.'

'Yeah, yuh give us truckin',' said Battle.

Plantagenet vacated his seat for the defective, who immediately began to play.

'Huh hum! Doom doom!' boomed the negroes, cheering and stomping: the lolling patients took up a cawing: 'Tee da, do; aw-aw, de pupdebup, da; wooh!'

Battle started to signal in time to the music. 'Move yo' han' to E. Wen yo' do make M yo' do move to F.'

The little man with a beard, passing, said to himself loudly, 'That's semaphore, all Boy Scouts use it.'

Plantagenet was holding his trembling hands out before him, fascinated, though none save Garry and Mr. Kalowsky appeared to be paying any attention, when he saw the doctor beckoning from the open door of his office.

> 'All you good peoples come on down to me.
> So de debbil turned over in hell
> And began to laugh and grin
> Say, yo' took a mighty long time comin', Shine,
> But yo' welcome in!'

IX

'Come in,' said Doctor Claggart gravely, letting him pass through the door first. The doctor, in a white robe, seemed to people the room with phantoms. An electric fan was droning with multitudinous monotony. 'Now,' said Doctor Claggart, still behind him, 'it seems that you can't stay here as a public charge, since you're a foreigner.'

'I—what,' said Plantagenet, looking round him, bewildered. He couldn't find the doctor among the phantoms, for the curtains, blowing in at that moment, made one whiteness with his robe. A chill had entered. Though still bemused by the incident at the piano, and sweating with heat, he felt it touch his spine.

'And I don't suppose you want to pay five dollars a day to stay here.'

Next door a typewriter rattled and stopped. He found the doctor, seated opposite him, at his desk.

'I've arranged for you to stay the night, but you'll have to leave in the morning.'

A drop of sweat fell from Plantagenet's forehead to his toe. After a moment he said: 'Things are going too fast for me. I don't want to go just yet. I knew I could of course, though.'

'Yes. It's far too soon of course. Pity. I'd like to help you, if I could—you're an interesting case.'

'There are so many things I wanted to talk to you about—'

'You might begin by telling me your real name. First you said Lawhill, and that's the name we booked you by. Then you said Plantagenet. Plantagenet!'

The man in the dirty robe stared back at the doctor mutely, his eyes blank.

'Can't remember? Or don't want to? First you thought you were a ship, and then a jazz band, or you played in a band, is this so? . . . Well, feel any craving for liquor?'

'I want food more . . . I missed my supper last night because your snaggle-toothed horny-faced so-and-so of a Head Nurse— excuse me—'

'I've—we've heard all about that.'

'Do you think it is excusable?'

'What do you think?'

'There are always two sides, nicht wahr, Herr Doktor, to a show like this? My side is this. At four p.m. sixteen or so of those whom you call nuts in my, sorry, in your ward, were taken up to play baseball on the roof—now don't you think I don't appreciate that, just as I appreciate hydrotherapy et al, the old man screaming for mercy under the needle shower reminded me of stories of George III— then there was the view of the men screening sand outside, and the rubber tree that really seemed to be enjoying the atmosphere in the locker room!—and on the roof there was a big hot wind and a particularly nice view of the river sparking like, shall we say, glass—'

'A glass of what?'

'—well, we played anyhow, and as some people refused to go out I never went to bat—even if I'd known how to play your American game, which I do not—but I certainly enjoyed it as much as those fielders who just played imaginary twirly-whirly-trill picking the grey threads out of their gowns. Be that as it may, the idea is, these gowns were the garments we had to sleep in, though at the time I hadn't realized it.'

'Don't forget it's the City Hospital.'

'Well yes . . . But it being difficult also to play in our stringless canvas shoes, most of us went barefoot and what with the heat and all we became damned dirty. I was also very jittery, but not too jittery to notice, after the excitement was over and we were being sweatily herded back, how each patient dropped back into his own world again, how senses that had thrilled to the game quickly became numbed to stupor. It isn't difficult to see, therefore, why these should conform to the routine of the hospital, should do what they were told—since they waited to be told everything—even if that happened to be not to dare to take a shower before supper at all, or even, like the disciples, to wash their feet.'

'Is that what they were told?'

'A couple of more or less sane fellows, that old paranoic Swede and the other fellow who thinks he's falling apart since a Sanitube froze on him last winter—the same fellow whose name you forgot —and that's another thing I want to talk to you about—managed to throw some water on themselves in a perfectly good bathroom upstairs adjacent to the roof entrance while we were waiting for the elevator; but they were pulled out by attendants before they had finished. They dried themselves on their gowns, in which they had to sleep, like those in which we all had to sleep, are still sleeping for that matter, this is the same gown now—I wore it then and you will no doubt bury us all in them. Well, the others, including myself, just stood there sweating in the all-time high, that same all-time high that felled one hundred and eighty-six people out in the sane world, in this city.'

'The "so-called" sane world, I suppose you think? Here. Have a cigarette.'

He took the cigarette with shaking hand, feeling the doctor's eyes on him. 'Thank you,' he said slowly. 'You're not a bad chap, you know, but—' He inhaled deeply and the room, the whiteness, spun around him with a jagged dazzle; he closed his eyes a second: where was he? what was he saying? 'Oh, yes. When we got back to our floor the others, who hadn't been playing, were eating their supper. Four or five of our crowd, including Garry and, believe it or not, Battle—who, having been a ship's fireman still remembers days of comparative cleanliness—made for the bathroom, but they were pulled back by Mrs. Horncle or whoever, that paranoid Head Nurse whom I have never, never seen smile at anyone save only you, dear Doctor.'

'She does her best.'

"She reminds me of an old nanny of mine, the first one I ever had, she ended up in an asylum too, she used to beat me with bramble sticks when I was five years old—'

'Those are a couple of fine give-aways you've just made.'

'—and I asked the male nurse, a sympathetic egg, who gets his carfare from giving blood for transfusions, poor devil, if I could have a wash. He nodded but said to step on it though . . . Then, as I was preparing to step—'

'Wait a moment now, you said the others were pulled back and accepted the thing, they took it, in other words, but you wouldn't. That's one of the things I'd like to get at, Lawhill—'

'Don't call me—the Lawhill was a windjammer that survived more disasters than any ship afloat.'

'Oh? That's interesting.' He made a note. 'It may have been inconvenient but you could have conformed, as the others did—'

'—Nurse who said: "Come back here. If you're going to wash you must go without your supper." I said, "Right. To hell with supper then," and—'

'In effect that's what you've said all your life.'

'I ran round to the bathroom and threw some water on my face, but there was nothing to dry on. So I went to my bed, took the sheet off and was drying myself on that when Mrs. H. suddenly rose up before me breathing fire.'

'And what did Mrs. H., as you call her, say to you then?'

'She said: "Your conduct is going straight to the office. You're going to pay for this. You're just a conceited Englishman, a back-alley drunk who thinks himself superior et cetera, et cetera." She said an inspection had to be made later, and "Don't you know everything has to look neat in the hospital? You're going to suffer for this." I said the sheet was no worse than it was before, they're all filthy anyway.'

'Yes,' said Dr. Claggart. 'All of them are, I'm afraid. It's the City Hospital.' The buzzer on his desk rang and he rose and went off whitely.

Plantagenet walked over to the window behind Claggart's desk. The glass tower, he thought. Pulling the curtains aside he looked out at the hospital, at the empty high windows in the wing opposite, through which the other morning he had seen those four operations being performed simultaneously in north light. Then he looked beyond the buildings to the town, where the taverns were.

The doctor returned, glancing at his watch. 'Sorry,' he said, 'what were you saying?'

'I don't remember. I expect I was talking about hangovers, horrors . . .' He looked out over the huge nervous city above which the last blimp of the day was trailing an advertisement for Goodyear Tyres while far above that in still merciless but declining sunlight one word was unrolling itself from the wake of an invisible plane: Fury. He was afraid. He was afraid to leave the doctor and go back to the ward. He was afraid—'The horrors,' he said abruptly. 'Well— do you see New York? That's where they are. They're out there waiting, the horrors of war—all of them—already—and all that delirium, like primitives, like Christ's descent into hell. And the tactile conscience, the lonely soul falling featherless into the abyss! I daresay you don't know what I'm talking about.'

'Oh?'

'But I suspect that you yourself are underpaid and shockingly overworked. I know the nurses are, even perhaps Mrs. H. Twelve-hour shifts, sixty-five hours a week, for seventeen dollars, or fifteen, or less, and no days off and always in fear of being fired. All that lady with the lamp stuff . . . And the internes, uninsured, unsalaried, sweating and selling blood. Yet you—you're as resigned as your wretched patients, and you not only stand for it, but persistently your technique is to try and adjust them back to the system—perish the word but let it stand—just as you might imagine wounded soldiers being patched up to be sent back to fight again by surgeons who had been smashed up themselves. Yes, smashed, as Garry would say.'

'It's only inevitable of course that you should speak like this. But I must say most of the patients—anyhow in this ward—are used to a much worse life outside.'

'But good Christ, Doctor, in this place the people, the patients, are resigned, resigned! Can't you see the horror, the horror of man's uncomplaining acceptance of his own degeneration? Because many who are supposed to be mad here, as opposed to the ones who are drunks, are simply people who perhaps once saw, however confusedly, the necessity for change in themselves, for rebirth, that's the word.'

'If you're talking about yourself, all this is very helpful. If not, I don't think you have a grasp of the facts.'

'Look here, Doctor, take Battle for instance. Battle, who could take four watches in succession down below and who knocked the second engineer's teeth out for hazing him, well, he's a case in point. You have an officious word for undirected energy: hyperaction or something. But do you realize that now you've got him resigned—and now he's happy here because he's completely irresponsible—his hyperaction is nothing but hyperaction. Watch him play all four hands at whist and you'll see what I mean. All that magnificent power going to waste. Of course now he wouldn't hurt a fly, he's grown to like degeneration.

'Then there's that poor old man, Kalowsky. He's not mad. I've been here long enough to know. In fact tragedy is now the only companion of my soul. Then there's Garry!'

'You seem very fond of the word tragedy. And degeneration. And death. Try another one.'

' "Abominable prurigo d'idiotisme, tel est l'esprit de la population!" '

'Tut tut.'

"My God, Doctor, that child, in this place! Putting the sick and the halt, the blind and the dumb, the insane and the diseased, the quick and the dead, all into one dirty room is bad enough without giving them only one towel, which isn't even a towel but only a sheet—yes, just a winding sheet—for all to dry themselves with on the rare occasion when we're allowed to be wet—I say nothing of the fact that at least half of them think they have syphilis, and probably have—yes, and one drinking cup between the lot of us, that's enough to give old Wasserman the needle, isn't it?'

'You see, Lawhill, it's a City Hospital, and—'

'Ever pulled a crab off yourself, Doctor? Hold them up to the light and see how they wave their little legs. They can send a shock right down the hair. Clever little bastards. Still they're not serious. Not so serious as they are in Suez. Or in Singapore.'

'When were you in Singapore?'

'Crabs! With a university education. You know what you polish the fire-nozzle with? That's what they use to get rid of them. Metal polish. Then there isn't any skin left to feed on . . .'

'When were you in—'

'Suez? They've got what it takes. And in Singapore. No, Kowloon. Jesus! We shot every bastard on the way whether they were innocent or not . . . They shot him through the rectum but the bullet blew his brains out . . . What am I talking about . . .' The white jagged dazzle whirled, spun to a glittering point and disappeared in the enfolding blackness.

'Steady there. Take it easy now. Keep your head down.'

'It's all right, I'm not going to faint.' He sat up and the doctor returned to his seat. 'And is there any earthly reason,' he heard himself saying suddenly, in a loud voice, 'or point in making people walk around all day from six in the morning till God knows when at night? And not even letting them lie down? I did faint the other day in your torture chamber.'

'You may tell the attendant I said you could lie down.'

'I'm leaving tomorrow. And anyway, the other poor bastards have to walk around; all right, I'll walk too.'

'It does some people some good, we think.'

'Very likely. Particularly the alcoholics. But the noise, the noise?'

'That's just part of your nervous state, Lawhill, or Plantagenet. Your peripheral nervous system—'

'I know you mean well, Doctor. But there's one thing I must tell you. A man in my ward, the Sanitube fellow, he's been here months, during which he imagines you've been working on his case, or at least knew his case. He looked to you for the solution of it. You've been the only star above his life, for months and months his only possible hope. The other day, after all this while, you came up to him, patted him kindly on the back and said: "What's your name? What's your trouble?" '

Doctor Claggart gave him a startled glance and shook his head slowly. 'That's—that's too bad. I must look into that.' He made a note and looked up again. 'Do you feel you can come out with any of your problems now?' he asked gently.

'For Christ sake don't look at me so hard . . . I'm sorry.'

'I'm sorry too. I wish we could go about this a better way, and there is a better one, but you know how crowded we are, and now there's not time.' Doctor Claggart sighed deeply, moving in his chair. 'But you know, Lawhill, there are few here I can talk to as boldly as I do to you. You've had some education, from somewhere.'

'Must you always look at me as though you've got a scalpel in your hand, probing my thoughts?'

'Go on . . .'

'. . . Sorry. I'm only a passenger on the ship. With these people, with Garry and Mr. Kalowsky, it's deadly serious. They're the crew. Kalowsky's been abused, kicked around, persecuted. He doesn't have proper reading glasses. He should be in a sanitorium, not here, with his high blood pressure. He's just a poor old chap, he's not crazy.'

'His brother thought differently,' said Doctor Claggart. 'His brother brought him here because he was always threatening people's lives and turning on the gas.'

He was silent. It was coldly shocking to hear his friend spoken of in such terms. 'I think he was framed,' he said, finally. 'I think his brother only wanted to get rid of him because he's an expense and a trouble. I don't believe he ever threatened to kill anybody! He's sick, damn it! He can't live much longer, and certainly not here. Couldn't you allow him to die in peace, in clean sheets?'

'He is going to a sanitorium as soon as it can be arranged. You may tell him, if you wish. We're not altogether inhuman.'

'Well, thank God. And thank you, Doctor.' Then, after a silence that lasted too long, 'And Garry? There's hope for him too?'

'That depends on what you call hope.' The doctor opened his eyes wide. 'Everyone's fond of him, sure. But you know what he's done, and you've probably heard about his father. Garry's a borderline case, surely you know that. He can't grow up. Do you realize the boy's almost fifteen? Actually, you only encourage him to stay in that dream world of his by encouraging his stories. If you were staying on, we'd have to separate you.'

He thought he was going to weep; in his mind was still the pain of the incident at the piano, which was something like the pain of insulted creation, only now he felt it on Garry's behalf. 'Christ!' he said, and he was almost unable to speak. It was impossible to meet the doctor's sane, friendly eyes. Ash fell from his cigarette to the floor. 'Christ,'' he repeated softly. 'He likes to tell me those stories, and some of them have a queer quality. Have you thought of the way they're all about disaster? It's a kind of prophecy, perhaps. Perhaps? I know. I've seen it all a thousand times in dreams, and when it comes it will be boring. Garry sees disaster encompassing not only himself but the hospital, this land, the whole world . . . I don't know, it's funny how people want to create, and do, in spite of everything—order and chaos both.' The doctor seemed about to interrupt, tapping his pencil on his desk. The typewriter rattled on. 'Listen, these stories take the form of illiterate fables, or children's stories.'

'But don't you see that all this is precisely what we want him to get away from? His problem is to get away from that dream world.'

'Did you see him in a dream world when he was playing baseball? He's a sensitive child and he's being killed in here. What he wants to do is get out and go fishing in the sun. Christ! I feel about it as though I were his father . . . It also seems to me that I should have to come all the way from England to a madhouse to find two people I really care about.'

'Not at all; living under abnormal conditions, absolutely natural.'

'Now look, I've got some of his stories here that I took down. If you'll only listen.'

'All the stories that you took down have already been read. Everything the patients write is read.'

'—You don't know the agony of spirit that informs them. And even if you did you're about as qualified to speak on the subject of creation as I am on polychromatophilia or megoblasts.'

'You're wasting your time and mine.'

'Listen. If you'd read them, the first thing you'd notice would be the curious symbolism and if you had ever read any French poetry —or any poetry at all for that matter—you would see some similarity in the process of selectivity to, say, that of Rimbaud, taking an obvious example . . . Forests, soleils, rivers, savanes. Don't you see it's the same kind of thing? Mélant aux fleurs des yeux de panthères—etc. And all his stories are about things collapsing, falling apart. Don't you see buried in all that wreckage his craving for freedom?'

'His? Or yours?'

'It extends to the world—do I have to shriek to you?—that sense of decay, the necessity of blasting away the past, the feeling of vertige; of industriels, princes, senats; perissez! . . . Puissance, justice, historie! à bas. Ah passez républiques de ce monde! Des empereurs, des regiments, des—I miss my cue—des peuples, assez! . . . Of course, in Rimbaud's poem the expression is in nature, with

Garry it is degenerate, there I go again, unnourished. But the necessity for expression is there just the same.'

'Are you talking about Garry or about yourself?'

'I am talking about Garry. For God's sake, such a boy has no hope, no tradition, no books, no education, and is probably incapable of being fructified by such ubiquitous and generally accessible works as the Pentateuch, the Revelation of St. John and the Song of Songs. Don't you see that what he is doing is to express primitively—'

'Yes indeed.'

'—and in symbols, what a maturer artist expresses with greater complexity and literacy, but still in symbols, however close he may think he is to reality, the conflicts of his own life. Garry chooses Tarzan, the comic strip, as his design-governing posture, since that is all he knows. If Garry were only given a chance to read, to learn, to live.'

'Have you ever wanted to be a writer?'

'No. But if you are concerned with Garry's adjustment to the society which you accept, I think the first thing you ought to realize is that this dream world is one from which he could, with proper training, make that acceptance of the other world you think so highly of, whether he ever gets out of form two or not, or even knows the difference between an isosceles triangle and pi times the radius squared, or throws bottles, or merely takes to drinking from them, like myself. I—oh hell!'

'2342, Dr. Claggart please; 2342 Dr. Claggart please; 2342 Dr. Claggart please—'

'Pardon me a moment. Hullo . . . Speaking. Yes . . . Yes . . . Say, call me back, will you? Okay. Goodbye . . . So, Lawhill?'

'It is my intention to give up not only drinking, but the world altogether.' Plantagenet gazed out of the window. 'I think what I would like to do is to buy a horse and trap, and drive through Ireland peddling sticks, sifting slowly with a jingle through the white dust of the evening. Or I would like to walk in the rain for ever and ever, just getting wetter and wetter . . .'

'Ah, these simple hearts! Excuse me a moment. Good evening, Nurse.'

'That defective with the long blond hair, you know,' the nurse giggled. 'He's got me almost believing my thighs are the girders of a new skyscraper going up in the town.'

'Have hope, Maggie, it may be a conquest. Did you want something?'

'Nothing special. I didn't know you were busy.' At the door she paused, giggling. 'Give me a ward of private cells any time. They're always the most refined.'

'Plantagenet, do you mind if I see what you wrote down when the nurse was here?'

'I wasn't writing down your therapeutic conversation if that's what you mean.'

'You better give it to me. I cannot allow you to make notes on us.'

'There you are. It's very simple.'

>Maison de Pendu. For Billy Budd.
>a house where a man has housed himself.
>a house where a man has hanged himself.

'So you think that's without significance.'

'At least as a poem. It just ran through my head, I didn't write it. And I've forgotten who did.'

Doctor Claggart glanced at his wristwatch and took some papers out of his drawer. 'You said to me on being admitted here, didn't you—wait a minute till I find it—you said "Drinking is not the problem." And—' he ruffled the papers—' " return to the presexual revives the necessity for nutrition." '

'Did I say that? I must have been drunk. But drinking is not my problem.'

'So you've said. What is it then?'

'Ah, but remember, "the road of excess leads to the Palace of Wisdom." '

The doctor almost laughed. 'Place of Wisdom, eh? I'll have to remember that. Well, here you are.'

'But my God, it's horror! . . . And it's all there waiting for me: the ghosts on the window blind, the scarlet snowshoe, the whispering of lost opportunities, and all the fury, the anguish, the remorse, the voices, voices, voices; the doll that turns to Ruth, the brownstone—brimstone—fronts transformed into judges, the interminable helpful but—alas—non-existent conversations, clinching one's case and pointing a solution, a way out into the morning light and freedom, offering an outpost between yourself and death; though only death is there in the morning and the morning is midnight and yourself forgotten, only the gulf is there . . . The horror not woman, not man, not beast, glimpsed through the bell-sounding darkness of Death Avenue, and posting a letter with hands that were not hands—' He broke off. What was in that terrible letter? What was the address on the envelope? Who was it for? Was it for him?

'—see any similarity between the nightmare world you've been escaping into,' the doctor was saying, 'and the dream world Garry lives in?'

'I—well, I—'

'I suggest that your companionship with Garry is a form of vicarious drunkenness.'

'Well, good God, isn't any alcoholic's cure a form of vicarious drunkenness?' He jerked his head sharply, startled to find the doctor was standing behind him.

'How is it that you remember these things and yet forget—or pretend to forget—your own identity? Why have you never told us anything concrete about yourself? Why did you believe, or pretend to believe, you were a ship? . . . And if you don't forget, why the bogus brainstorm? If it is bogus.'

'Why—I tell you this pained forgetfulness—somebody said it was like rain, and he remembered much of it—is the converse of trying to remember what happened the night after one has been really drunk.'

'So, there have been occasions?'

'Well, Doctor, you remember everything up to a point of that conversation about Chagall or Horoshige or the loxodromic curve or the marines; then everything is blank and the future drones disaster and there is only remorse left for the past, which is a romantic passion . . . But you see I remember well the last few days before I came here and I was then drinking heavily, I remember every movement, every slow lurch, every place where I welched ten cents, every evil face, each bright one. Notices on walls, names of taverns, conversations about baseball, or heaven. Every man I met, whether paralytic or not, stands out in my mind with the clarity of a Durer. It is only of before that time that the memory is an abyss, like an imagined look backward before birth.'

'Are you sure you never wanted to be a writer?'

'I had rather be a bacon scrubber, a watcher of manholes, wanderer under trains in stations to see that nobody is using the toilet.'

'But "return to the presexual revives the necessity for nutrition," Lawhill?'

'What do you want me to say? To say that I remember saying it? To say that this is the end of my night journey across the sea? . . .'

The doctor was standing in front of him now, looking at his watch. 'I'm truly sorry,' he said kindly, 'that we don't have more time.' He held out his hand, smiling. 'It surely was a funny way to see America.'

X

The wind!

It seemed to be blowing cleanly from the four corners of the earth. Then it stopped. Were those falling leaves, or drops of rain? A veined leaf going, then dead drifting blossoms like buds. He was standing outside Claggart's office in the now deserted annex, from the windows of which the curtains had been drawn back, revealing the bars. He was staring curiously at the people asleep in the park outside, but that these people, content still in an eighteenth-century day, should be as yet unaware, even as the sun was setting, of the approaching storm while he could peer out at them through the bars of a madhouse, of a prison from which he was subtly free, and could see the inevitable deluge approaching, gave him an odd sense of omniscience, of fateful, prophetic power. He took two steps in the direction of the ward, then, changing his mind, two steps back again towards the window. He could not bring himself to return to Mr. Kalowsky and Garry.

The scene below him was so extraordinarily clear it was as though each object in it were part of his consciousness. Strange, he hadn't noticed before that this park was here at all. How lovely it was! The feeling of storm communicated itself to him; he drew a deep breath—outside there was life, with all its infinite poignancy. A little children's fountain had sent up a rainbow, an outspread peacock's fan of water, whose coolness could almost be felt, and for a moment connecting this with rain falling somewhere already, something like a hope flickered in him, though of nothing in particular, perhaps just of hope itself. But of course it was the fountain, not the rain, that made the rainbow: his hope was a false hope, an artificial one. By the time the rain really came, bringing relief to the drought, the sun would be set, just as it might happen that by the time madness came to a man, the mind would not know it was a relief.

There was a rumble of thunder; the sleepers, who had been lying down there as the dead might lie, resting for a while in some green niche of Paradise, he thought, or in a no-man's-land between two worlds of light and dark, began to stir, stretching themselves. The leaves and buds were dropping faster now, falling straight like rain, and now, in the gathering darkness, they were like ghosts of leaves or buds, or truly rain. There was an urgent note, suddenly in the cries of children: a pigeon whirred up in a silver panic, making a short parabola: one leaf was spinning, another spiralled downwards, squirrels scattered. Again he took two steps towards the ward, again he returned to the window. As he watched those yellow buds like rain, or little flowers, he was filled again with his old persistent sorrow, and sorrow now for his two friends. The cries of children, the falling leaves, the lovers who were now running for shelter, laughing, their arms round one another—what part had all these in their stricken lives? Even the riven trees, yearning into the gloom, lit now by the heliotrope of lightning, still felt their roots in the true earth, their crests in the sky, at least they could speak to each other according to the special reality of their existence, they sensed where they were going, or what they had become; when their leaves fell they were aware also that that was what must be, it was right. Now their branches nodded, the nameless trees were nodding to each other; he could hear the rustling of leaves, or of water falling on leaves. The deepest sleepers were awake, drawing their coats around them.

But one ragged man sat motionless under a tree watching, as though he knew the storm as the trees knew it; Plantagenet wondered if he had ever been such a one, to whom a lost moment of tempest was a lost moment with God. Far above him a young girl with a white collar was leaning under a blue sunblind which suddenly bellied like a sail. Far below, the leaves were blowing towards the solitary man, an army viewed from a mountain top, advancing over the plain.

Perhaps this solitary man, perhaps this young girl, were the very ones who would yet lead his friends out of their bondage? Perhaps, but he would never know.

Then the evening storm broke in earnest. Aloft, a thousand striped sunblinds were set dancing; through the drunkard's rigadoon of the raindrops, through the black park, white mariners were luminously gliding.

He moved over to another window where he could see the river below: it was sparkling like ginger ale; now it seethed with a million sequins. A lull came. The rain lifted, though a few large drops still fell: under the lowering sky the river was very swift. Looking down at it a delicious sense of freedom possessed him, a sense of being already outside, free to run with the wind if he wished, free to run as far away from the hospital as he liked. Yet the bars were still there, and they resembled the bars of his mind, set by the cause of his presence at all in this place. He had not escaped them yet, nor would he escape them merely by leaving. His thoughts flowed past with the rain-swollen river, but his thoughts did not escape either, they contracted always to the point from which he was watching, the hospital itself. And he understood obscurely that what he'd said to the doctor about Garry was true: the boy had become a part of himself, as had Mr. Kalowsky, a part of the shadowy meaning of his destiny. He pressed his face against the bars . . . à fuir, là-bas!

Where were all the good honest ships tonight, he wondered, bound for all over the world? Lately it had seemed to him they passed more rarely. Only nightmare ships were left in this stream. All at once, watching the strange traffic upon it, he fancied that the East River was as delirious, as haunted as the minds that brooded over it, it was a mad river of grotesque mastless steamers, of flat barges slipping along silent as water snakes, a river of railroad boats the shape of army tanks with their askew funnels appearing to have been built on to outriggers, or they were strange half-ships, preposterously high out of the water with naked propellers thrashing like tuna fish, with single masts out of alignment. This world of the river was one where everything was uncompleted while functioning in degeneration, from which as from Garry's barge, the image of their own shattered or unformed souls was cast back at them. Yes, it was as if all complementary factors had been withdrawn from this world! Its half-darkness quivered with the anguish of separation from the real light; just as in his nightmare, the tortoise crawled in agony looking for its shell, and nails hammered held nothing together, or one-winged birds dropped exhausted across a maniacal, sunless moon . . .

He started as though someone had touched him on the shoulder. Nobody. But Doctor Claggart, his hand on the polished knob of the open door of his office, was watching him from a distance with eyes which said plainly: 'Get back to the ward.' He had gone.

The piano was still open; Plantagenet shut it carefully. Then he started reluctantly. Electric numbers twinkled on a board before him: '7', '11', '7', '11'. The deserted corridor, where he so often walked with Garry and Mr. Kalowsky, seemed queerly beautiful to him this evening under the dust. The last stormy light cast its curdling brightness in the reflected steel prison bars at the foot of the far bed. As he lingeringly approached the room facing the wharves there was another savage scribble of lightning across the windows, from which some of the patients were moving away. Others were laughing nervously, though Garry and Mr. Kalowsky were in their usual places, waiting for him. He joined them without a word. No attendants seemed to be about. There was a perplexing silence.

'Did you tell the doctor I was sane?' asked Mr. Kalowsky at length, cheerfully.

He nodded. 'We're all going to be O.K.'

The old man looked at him sharply.

'That's keen,' Garry said. 'Do you think I can get out soon? But I don't care. All I want is to tell stories. I've got a story for you now.' His eyes strayed to the familiar old barge lying below them. 'Well, I went down to the beach and I met two of my friends. We went on this rotten old barge full of mud and sand and a lot of junk. We were playing follow the leader and I got dizzy. I climbed out. I looked all right, I was small. When I got home my mother threw me in the tub and I got some clean clothes on. Yes sir. A few years later the barge fell apart.

'It was all collapsed,' he added, as thunder rocked the hospital. The rain started to souse down again from the eaves.

'You will only get worser here, what are you here for? What's the matter with your head, Garry,' Mr. Kalowsky said sternly but kindly, as thunder shook the building again. 'Put something in your stomach, otherwise you won't last it. Look at you! Look at this hospital full of lunatics half starved with hunger, they go crazy— look at them—and they all come clopping to the hospital. He pointed to a poor trembling old man running by with a grey shawl over his shoulders and Plantagenet remembered how whenever you spoke to him he drew it over his head with fright. 'Your stomach's going on the revolution. Wake up, you brains! Brains of the world unite! My experience in the hospital is that the workers are against us more than the capitalists. I don't believe in God. I talk too much

Bob Ingersoll wisdom and that's why Police Megoff wants to lock me up. Jesus Christ! If the workers will wake up and buy brains I won't need to go to the hospital! Give the patients nicer to eat! Listen, once they pulled three teeth out of me, out of my mouth. That's the capitalist system. I should have knocked the three teeth out of him.' Mr. Kalowsky added, 'these young fellows who say I am in my second childhood should go home and clean their diapers. Whether I go or not—'

There was another lull in this twilight storm and in the silence the rain could be heard hissing in the river. Some of the patients who had been frightened were returning to the room. The moon had risen over a ragged tantivy of clouds; an oil barge was passing, her tiny contiguous funnels pillowed by tanks; following her was a dredger, to which a float many fathoms to starboard was attached in a remote, umbilical way. After her, at some distance, a Fall River sidewheeler was steaming close inshore. Fall River! How delighted Ruth had been that day long ago because they had a cabin on the top deck of the *Providence*! It was his first day in New York, summer then too, and they had paced the deck arm in arm. In the evening they had wandered around the ancient, lacquered ship, like a vast London hotel with its guilt stairways. From the muffled corridor they saw the firemen shovelling, down below. They had listened together to that pulse of the ship he could hear now. What had they not learned about the world and each other in that cabin so high up in the ship? They had not learned that with all the beauty of the evening, the softness of the night, the tenderness of the blue morning, that every beat of the engine which took them nearer to New York, nearer to Herman Melville, was also taking them nearer to their own white whale, their own destruction.

The thunder started again. The sidewheeler was much closer now, her paddles lashing the spasmodically stormlit water into a creamy foam. All at once, as if an anguished desire to teach her, to touch her before she was gone, had spontaneously seized them, three gesticulating Negro sailors rushed to the bars: climbing up within the steel meshes they started a roaring which was instantly taken up by almost everyone in the ward. Was the ship the *Providence* herself? He couldn't be sure. But he stood, transfixed with anguish, watching her go. The roaring had become an uncontrollable yell by now, the Negroes were beating on the bars, shaking the windows. He remembered his freighter with the cargo of animals: there had been not only lions but elephants, tigers, jaguars, all bound for a zoo. The panthers died, in the Indian Ocean at night the lions roared, the elephants trumpeted and vomited so that none save the carpenter dared go forward: when they smashed into the hurricane the jaguars moaned in terror like frightened children. No forest had ever plunged so deeply in the long bending winds as that ship, while 'Let us out, let us be free,' was the meaning of that wailing during these bitter hours. He had thought, 'Let us be free to suffer like animals.' And that cry was perhaps more human than the one he now heard. The lightning had become so nearly continuous that the heavens seemed to be full of flaming trees and icebergs. The moon had gone. A forked tree of light shot up diagonally. Somewhere there was the long hiss of shattering glass. An iceberg hurled northward through the clouds and as it poised in its onrush, tilted he saw his dream of New York crystallized there for an instant, glittering, illuminated by a celestial brilliance, only to be reclaimed by dark, by the pandemonium of an avalanche of falling coal which, mingling with the cries of the insane speeding the *Providence* on her way, coalesced in his brain with what it conjured of the whole mechanic calamity of the rocking city, with the screaming of suicides, of girls tortured in hotels for transients, of people burning to death in vice dens, through all of which a thousand ambulances were screeching like trumpets.

Then the ship had gone, the excitement subsided. The patients drifted away from the window, keys clanked, the attendants were arriving to lay the table for the supper of the poor old men who were considered too disgusting to eat with the others.

'We can only wait and see. So many things can happen in a lifetime,' said Mr. Kalowsky calmly, as they turned from the window.

Garry caught Plantagenet by the sleeve of his soiled dressinggown. 'You haven't said one word,' he said.

'There was too much noise.'

'They want to smash our friendship, isn't that it?' Garry said. 'Isn't that what the doctor told you? It is condemned.'

He shook his head. 'Of course not, Garry. We're all O.K.'

'You can't fool me; they don't want me to tell you anything more. No more stories, nothing. They aren't going to put me in another ward. All right, let them try. They won't break us. The world won't let anything good be.' After a moment he said absently, 'Look at Mr. Battle.'

Battle was now semaphoring by the window at the night. 'Ayeh, Beah, Gee,' he was saying. 'To make X yuh do AX den yuh make

D with an H and that's H, no sah!' Only the vast heliograph of the lightning responded distantly.

Plantagenet drifted back to the window, from which Battle had departed. It was clearing up; there were fluctuant sable pools on the wharves. Concertinas of orange and green lights quivered in their depths. Scattered wild steam rose from the gratings by the powerhouse. He could see the moon reeling through the sky taking refuge from time to time in clouds, as does a man in saloons, but she was never quite hidden from sight. Soon her insane light fell on the wet grass where the hospital lights were now reflected. The grass was very green and the sparrows hopped among little white skulls of clover lying among its narrow blades. Mr. Kalowsky nudged him, he turned.

The nine high electric candles in their hollow circular base were lit above the poor old men who were having their dinner.

A seaplane was gliding whitely past, and now it was turning, to Plantagenet suddenly it had the fins and flukes and blunt luminous head of a whale; now it roared straight at the window, straight at him.

A bell was ringing shockingly somewhere, keys were rattling, and there was the slop-slop-slop of feet in the corridor. Battle was signalling again; without purpose or need or hope he signalled at the night, at the approaching seaplane: 'A, B, C, D—'

'—to make H you do make AX and den you make D with A and that's H—no sah!'

Something extraordinary was happening to him, he tried to struggle with the words, with whatever it was that was going on, to struggle with this maniacal force which was—which was changing him, for that was it, he was changing—

'I was dizzy,' Mr. Kalowsky said, 'I lay down, 'tis not the gutter, 'tis more like a trench here where I took a schnooze.'

Garry joined them at the window.

'It only looks like spring,' Garry was saying slowly, 'and it's summer. It takes such a long time to grow. It looks as though it's only spring, when the grass is just sprouting up, it's so small, and the clover's growing slow, the dandelions are not out quite, but they will be, yes sir, and look, there's a path running through the little grass hill. It only looks like spring, that's all.'

There was a furious crash of thunder and simultaneously Plantagenet felt the impact of the plane, the whale, upon his mind. While metamorphosis nudged metamorphosis, a kind of order, still preserved within his consciousness, and enclosing this catastrophe, exploded itself into the age of Kalowsky again, and into the youth of Garry, who both now seemed to be spiralling away from him until they were lost, just as the seaplane was actually tilting away, swaying up to the smashed sky. But while that part of him only a moment before in possession of the whole, the ship, was turning over with disunion of hull and masts uprooted falling across her decks, another faction of his soul, relative to the ship but aware of these fantasies and simultanities as it were from above, knew him to be screaming against the renewed thunder and saw the attendants closing in on him, yet saw him too, as the plane seethed away northwards like the disembodied shape of the very act of darkness itself, passing beyond the asylum walls melting like wax, and following in its wake, sailing on beyond the cold coast of the houses and the factory chimneys waving farewell—farewell—

XI

Once more a man paused outside the City Hospital. Once more, with a dithering crack, the hospital door had shut behind him.

Outside, he felt no sense of release, only inquietude. He kept gazing back with a sort of longing at the building that had been his home. It was really rather beautiful, he felt, turning at a corner store.

Here he bought a packet of stamps with little reproductions of tigers on them from the Straits Settlements, and elephants from India: A Negro climbed a tree of a Senegalese variety, there was a duck-billed platypus from Australia, another more terrible sort of tiger, from Obangui-Tchaeri-Tchad.

He had thought of sending these up to Garry but instead he pocketed them himself with a queer cancelled feeling. It was too hard to return to the hospital. Then such a feeling of absolute tragedy possessed him at leaving his friends behind that he conquered his fear, and retraced his steps, buying a dollar's worth of oranges on the way. At the hospital again he found a nurse and had the oranges and the stamps sent up to the observation ward for Mr. Kalowsky and Garry.

Approaching midtown he began to hear strange noises, the faces of the patients were swarming about him, once he jumped nervously, imagining that Ruth was just behind. The face of Mr. Battle, grinning, swooped up at him. Once he thought he saw his parents curtsying down the street with pained, terrified looks. He ran after them for half a block but they turned mysteriously into two small Indians. A member of his band disappeared into a music shop. He crossed the street. Now every stern face he encountered was that of an Immigration inspector, dogging him. After some hesitation, he threw away the bottle of whisky he had.

This had been simply, without any irony, returned to him by the janitor as his property. 'You won't be using that any more, pal,' the janitor had said. 'Thanks,' he had replied, 'I'll throw it away myself.'

So now he threw it away, into the ashcan. Then he went back and got it.

He was keeping an eye out for Melville's house, this must be the site, though all he could find was a shop, Zimmerman, carpenter, with next door a humble Spanish restaurant, d'Alarcon, proprietor. Strange, he said. He entered a church he knew, gazing about him. In the painting above, Christ was being offered a drink; he stood a while in meditation. The thought even of vinegar sent the blood coursing through his veins. There was only one other person there, a woman in black, kneeling. Here was his opportunity. When so much suffering existed, what else could a man do? With a guilty, flurried, yet triumphant motion he took a long draught of whisky. Replacing the bottle under his coat tails he hurried out.

He was elated now, feeling the fire of the whisky. Nevertheless he shunned the lovers walking by in the wind. Later he followed two more lovers, sure the girl with the silver fox fur was Ruth. Suddenly they vanished.

Signs along the street mocked at him: Business as usual during alterations: Broken Blossoms: Dead End: No cover at any time. World's loveliest girls. Larger, more modern. He waved them aside.

In the subway, the roar of the train seemed to be trying to communicate with him. First it said 'womb', then 'tomb'. Then it said both in succession, very rapidly, over and over again.

Above ground, under the El, he paused in the dappled sunlight swept by enormous shadows. Here he took another drink. This was like a forest; out of the forest had grown the church, from the church, the ship. So he had learned: but soon they would scrap the El, soon there would be nothing at all: no ship, no church, no forest, no shadows, no learning. It would all be collapsed, as Garry would have said.

Stepping out of the sunlight he turned unconsciously towards the waterfront. At the corners of streets loomed up the deathly white of hamburger stands: Whale steaks 5¢. There was a smell of ropes here, seafaring, and strange merchandise, a smell he knew well, but which hurt, like the smell of women's furs in the rain.

His footsteps took him to the sailors' tavern he knew, a bad spot. He odered a whisky and sat down in a corner. Here was no one: no lunatics to jeer at him, no sane people to encourage or exhort him, not even a piano this time, only the world of ghosts coming closer, but in order that it might not come too close, always another drink; he was having a hell of a good time. He began to think he saw some of his mistakes clearly. He had them all figured out. He even imagined himself expunging them by some heroic sacrifice, that would not only justify him to Garry and Mr. Kalowsky, but would, in a fantastic sense, free them. Free them? It would free everyone—all the patients, all the parents, all the Ruths, it would free mankind; ah—he would strike his blow for the right.

Ennobled, he went to the washroom where he finished his bottle. Glancing round for somewhere to put it he noticed an obscene sketch of a girl chalked on the wall. For some reason, suddenly enraged, he hurled the bottle against this drawing, and in the instant he drew back to escape the fragments of glass, it seemed to him that he had flung that bottle against all the indecency, the cruelty, the hideousness, the filth and injustice in the world. At the same time an atrocious vision of Garry flashed across his consciousness, and an atrocious fear. 'It was only a little scratch,' he had said.

It was dark, the darkness was full of vibrations. That terrible old woman he had seen posting the letter was it she who was with him at the bottom of some mine?

Returning to the saloon he picked out a secluded place to sit, where they brought his whisky.

But feeling he was being watched, even there, he moved later, drink in hand, to the very obscurest corner of the bar, where, curled up like an embryo, he could not be seen at all.

A Brief Bibliography of the Major Works

Ultramarine

Jonathan Cape, London, 1933
J. B. Lippincott Company, Philadelphia and New York, 1962
Jonathan Cape, 1963
McGraw-Hill paperback, New York, 1964
Four Square Book, paperback, 1965
Penguin Modern Classics, paperback, Baltimore, 1974

Under the Volcano

Reynal and Hitchcock, New York, 1947
Jonathan Cape, 1947
J. B. Lippincott Company, 1965
Joanthan Cape, 1967
Vintage Books, paperback, New York, 1967
Signet Books, paperback, New York, 1966
Penguin Modern Classics, paperback, 1962, '63, '66, '68, '69

Hear Us O Lord From Heaven Thy Dwelling Place

J. B. Lippincott Company, 1961
Jonathan Cape, 1962
Keystone Books, paperback, New York, 1963
Capricorn Books, paperback, New York, 1969

Selected Poems of Malcolm Lowry

City Lights Books, San Francisco, 1962

Selected Letters of Malcolm Lowry

J. B. Lippincott Company, 1965
Jonathan Cape, 1967
Capricorn Books, paperback, 1969

Dark As the Grave Wherein My Friend Is Laid

> The New American Library, New York, 1968
> Jonathan Cape, 1969
> Meridian Books, paperback, New York, 1969
> Penguin Modern Classics, paperback, 1972

October Ferry to Gabriola

> World Publishing Company, New York, 1970
> Jonathan Cape, 1971
> Plume Books, paperback, New York, 1971